Shorthorns in the 20th Century UK and Ireland

JOHN WOOD-ROBERTS

Shorthorns in the 20th Century UK and Ireland

JOHN WOOD-ROBERTS

Whittet Books

Frontispiece: Calrossie Triumphant

First published 2005
© 2005 by John Wood-Roberts
Whittet Books Ltd, Hill Farm, Stonham Road, Cotton, Stowmarket, Suffolk IP14 4RQ

www.whittetbooks.com
e mail: Annabel@whittet.dircon.co.uk

Cataloguing in Publication Data

A catalogue record for this title is available from the British Library.

ISBN 1 873580 70 3

Foreword by
HRH The Princess Royal

The Royal Family has been involved with the Shorthorn since about 1803 and the reign of King George III, and later had herds at Sandringham, Windsor and in the Duchy of Cornwall. My ancestors have been both Patrons and exhibitors since these early beginnings. Now as both Patron of the Shorthorn Society and a breeder member, I welcome this book titled *Shorthorns in the Twentieth Century*; the breed has had a unique history following its establishment in the early 1800s and the publication in 1822 of the World's first Herd Book. The breed evolved because of its capabilities and dominant genes which enabled it to adapt to all climates and systems; excellent feet and legs and productive longevity ensured the Shorthorn's rise to fame and fashion, but it was possibly these last points which also led to its near downfall as the breeders started to favour the South American market with its short legged, short coupled cattle.

The breed is also unique in that it is dual purpose, lending itself to beef or dairy; however this fact also presented problems as the two types were often mixed until Coates Herd Book provided two sectors enabling new and experienced breeders to select the right genes for their own purposes.

These breeders were determined to bring the Shorthorn back to prominence, as well as being determined not to lose the invaluable genes established throughout its history. This book gives brief outlines of some of the principal herds and explains what steps breeders took to ensure both the beef and dairy sectors made the necessary adjustments to their stock, which literally ensured the breed came back from the brink of extinction. Included in this history are graphs and tables vividly showing the rapidity of the breed's rise and fall and various derivations within the breed. Finally the book also provides an abbreviated history of the period leading up to the last century for the benefit of students and newcomers to the breed. I am sure you will enjoy reading it.

ACKNOWLEDGMENTS

I wish to record my grateful thanks to those who contributed towards the costs of publishing this history of the breed as well as their enthusiasm for the project. In particular I would pay tribute to the late James Biggar for his tremendous encouragement and information, as it was largely due to him that that I approached the project in the first place as he considered we owed it to the breed. I am particularly indebted to: Dr Austen Mescall, a past President of the Society and Past Chief Inspector of the Eire Department of Agriculture for his help and information in respect of that Department's involvement with their Improvement Scheme and his interest in that project; also to Diana and Donald McGillivray, Roger Osborne and George A. Dent as well as all those who responded to my requests for detail of the past.

To Frank Milnes and Sue Walters of the Shorthorn Cattle Society for their support and indulgence with my frequent visits to research through the records and publications. My main regret has been the impossibility of recording all those connected with the breed and apologise to each and every one of them as all have contributed to this breed's remarkable history.

To Valerie Porter, authoress of many books on agricultural and country matters, for her guidance and advice for this book.

To Annabel Whittet, the publisher, for her patience and help with my approach to the subject.

Every effort has been made to ensure the accuracy of the content but it is possible that mistakes will be detected for which I apologise. The views expressed in this book are my own interpretation and not necessarily those of the Society.

All illustrations are reproduced with kind permission of The Shorthorn Society.

Contents

1. Setting the Scene

Much has been written about Shorthorns over the years but no one to date has pulled this breed's history together during the 20th century. It is an incredible story as well as being a record and it is my sincere hope that readers will enjoy the following pages; at the same time I hope that people will recognise the warning and example of how a successful breed can also very nearly sink to oblivion before the industry recognises the problems.

Breeders of all stock are artists. All of us are born with a variety of talents or gifts and those of us who are able to interpret these are fortunate indeed. Stockbreeders are blessed with the gift of being able to assess the ability of two animals to 'nick' and produce progeny who will improve in conformation or productivity. This God-given ability is unusual and complex in itself but it isn't enough. The breeder has to be a prophet and optimist as well.

A major aspect of breeding is fashion and in agriculture this is highly influenced by commercial demands; these demands are in turn highly influenced by politics, over which the farmer has little or no sway.

As well as this, for the farmer who is breeding horses or cattle, these species normally only have one progeny per head so the endeavour is that much harder than for those breeding pigs, sheep or dogs which have multiple progeny and a shorter gestation. As well as this is the small matter of foreseeing how the thousands of genes will sort themselves out!

In a cattle-breeder's average working life he or she will probably only achieve say six generations; more likely three or four if one accepts the added gender ratio, therefore the dice is so heavily loaded we wonder why anyone even considers this profession!

Remember our forebears took on the challenge without the modern aides of electricity, tractors and a panoply of equipment, road transport, and more recently artificial insemination and gene identification. Their achievements were Herculean and even today this lottery is an incredible challenge and no doubt that is why it is a life's work. We can only surmise what might have been had our ancestors had the same advantages.

So we start by raising our hats in admiration of their achievements but unfortunately in a record of this type, time and space prevent the mention of all those who contributed so much or so many cattle; I apologise for their omission; but the Shorthorn is the subject we have all worked with. I will endeavour to detail its amazing development and history, both good and bad, admittedly with the benefit of hindsight. The history illustrates that if the problems can be identified the road back is possible (if long).

Arguably more progress in agriculture has been made in the twentieth century than ever before, although much of it has sadly been due to the two world wars and is a by-product of industrialization. The previous century and history of the breed has been covered in detail by such experts as James Sinclair in his excellent *History Of The Shorthorn Breed* published in 1907 but new breeders and researchers will find a very abridged history in chapter 2 and this will also set the scene for the rest of the story.

Other authors on specialist aspects have been Wing-Commander T.B. Marson, who wrote the *Scotch Shorthorn*, a detailed report of the Beef Shorthorn herds in Britain at around 1946. Another worthy publication titled *History Of Dairy Shorthorn Cattle (Vinton*, London, 1907) was written by George T. Burrows, the well known editor of the *Livestock Journal*, and other agricultural papers; this covered the dairy herds in some detail around 1950 and before.

At the start of the twentieth century the breed was demonstrating its superiority throughout the world due partly to genetics and partly to the public relations endeavours of the breeders. As an example of the latter, consider the wonderful efforts undertaken in the publicising of the Ketton or Durham Ox. There being at that time little road transport, this beast was carried in a specially constructed cart drawn by four, sometimes six horses. The ox was purchased for £250 by Mr John Day in May 1801 in Rotherham, who travelled, sometimes with his wife in the cart as well as the ox! From the north they travelled the country as far south as Wellington in Somerset and also through Scotland; however on a further trip, after six years on the road and two hundred venues, the ox suffered a dislocated hip while at Oxford in February 1807 and had to be put down.

Consider also the renowned Thomas Bates who in 1839 travelled by driving his cattle by road to a steamer then down to a canal barge and by road again to the first Royal Show held at Oxford and then home after winning the championship. He repeated this again in 1840 to Cambridge.

The pursuit of excellence in cattle-breeding as in other species is fraught with setbacks and disappointments; as well as being a prophet, the breeder must be an optimist. Despite the huge advances in livestock improvement techniques, nothing is predictable and this increases the challenge; like does not necessarily produce like, but the current aids substantially increase the chances. Throughout the following pages the pitfalls will be evident as well as the successes and it is hoped that readers will be able to recognize the problems that can so quickly bring about the catastrophic fall from supremacy; once lost, it can take a long time to regain this, and some never do. Organisations such as the Rare Breeds Survival Trust are testimony to the pitfalls as at the time of writing they have some 40 breeds of four-legged species on their lists.

It can be argued that there were too many breeds, many of which were localised, but each and every one of them has invaluable gene combinations that could be of future value in a given set of circumstances. This was particularly what set the scene for the Shorthorn that spread worldwide from a very small area of Britain.

Throughout the following pages, time and time again it will be noticed that success or disappointment will be brought about by the efforts of breeders, but also by happenings outside their control: it might be disease, politics, economic forces, sometimes natural conditions. Such factors make up the challenge that has occupied our forebears so much and what makes the history so fascinating.

2. Early Days

Here I give a brief insight for new breeders and to set the scene, so that readers can understand the stage the breed had reached at the start of the twentieth century and some of the reasons, good and bad, for its development. For those wishing to research more deeply into the period the *History Of Shorthorns* by James Sinclair can provide much information. Much of the early development is conjecture, owing to obvious lack of documentation but it is fairly certain that until Roman occupation the cattle of Britain were of Bos Longifrons Type: small, vari-coloured animals. Successive invasions by European peoples – Romans, Saxons, Danes and Normans – will have brought with them cattle of the Bos Urus type for food, draught and wealth. These were larger and gradually the smaller type would have been driven westwards but in the process there would have been some blending.

The interlopers obviously landed mainly on the eastern coasts but it is an intriguing thought that unwittingly the almost modern concept of breeds and types would have started as settlers confined their stock with barricades and within hills and valleys. Gradually as populations expanded they would also have selected for a variety of traits as well as survival: food, draught, weapons and tallow for heat and light being foremost and where there was adequate grazing the larger beast will have prevailed. As the island became more stable following the Scottish Union, so the population gradually settled and expanded and pressures for improvement increased. In the late 1600s and early 1700s livestock improvement really started but was still handicapped by the problem of providing winter food for the stock; once this was overcome the way was clear for progress as until then it was mainly the smaller cattle that tended to be more thrifty and survived.

The type known appropriately as the Longhorn was the first to attract attention with, even then, excellent qualities: good for draught, able to withstand the rigours of winter and the ability rapidly to put on large reserves of fat and meat. However in the fertile areas of the north-east around Darlington and down to Holderness there was a favoured type known as the Shorthorn, to differentiate from the longhorn; known locally as the Teeswater. This type was of large frame and strong bone and had the added incentive of a good milk yield. Nearby were the Holderness cattle with similar traits but which had benefited from an input of imported blood from Dutch cattle, known then as Hollanders from East Friesland. The two types, which were living in close proximity, were blended to form what at that time were known as Durhams but which later assumed Shorthorn as the breed's name rather than type.

It is possible that this may be the basic reason for the two types of Shorthorn that then developed although this is very much conjecture, but again more of this later.

One of the authorities at that time was a George Culley whose *Observations Of Livestock* was published in 1785; he referred to 'short horned or Dutch cattle which differed from others by the shortness of their horns and were wider and thicker and gave more milk than them as well.' He also referred to importations from Holland despite the fact that Charles II had, following the Black Death when 70,000 people died in London between 1664 and 1665, prohibited the importation of cattle from Holland. In 1666 the Murrain, or Red Water as I believe it is now known, and Rinderpest (Cattle Plague) was rife in Europe and was and is the most destructive scourge that affects cattle. Nowadays it is mainly confined to Asia and Africa. But it killed 200,000 cattle in Holland alone in 1745. We also know now that it does not affect man. We also know that the plague or bubonic plague or black death is caused by rats and dirt, but in those days there may well have been some confusion.

The prohibition of imports at that time will also have been difficult to police! But they evidently continued albeit in limited form as several other commentators at that time referred to Dutch cattle influences.

Another reliable source at that time, W. Marshall, in his *General Treatise On Cattle,* published in 1805, referred to the superior and larger cattle in Britain that were in Northumberland, Durham and Holderness known as Durhams, Teeswaters and Holderness cattle.

As we read this it is very important to recognize that in the 16th and 17th centuries there were many others who set out to improve their stock; otherwise the Collings, Booths, Bates and later Cruickshank would not have been able to find the base stock to work with. It is also true that Shorthorns were about in the region in some numbers as although records were scarce in that period it is said that the Dukes of Northumberland among others had bred Shorthorns since 1500. Many names such as Maynard, Millbank, Jolly, Allcock, Pennman and others were mentioned as sources of stock.

Robert Bakewell and in and in breeding

Robert Bakewell of Dishley, Leicestershire, who had a few Shorthorns, but mainly Longhorns and also Leicester sheep and Shire horses, was a man who took an incredible interest in his stock, their physiology and breeding especially considering that at that time such care and ideas were largely frowned upon. Born in 1725 and living till 1795, he set about proving his theories, saying his main aims were to provide meat for the growing population masses which were increasing with great rapidity.

He was the initiator of progeny testing as we know it today, as he kept meticulous records and hired his bulls out all over the country recording the growth and weights of their progeny under differing soil, climate and management regimes. He dissected carcasses that had been reared in differing circumstances but he was principally concerned with, and will be better known for, his stock-breeding policies that were radical and frowned on by many. People disapproved ethically of his teaching and his ideas on line breeding: 'in and in' breeding it was called at that time, where son is mated to mother, father to daughter and related sons and daughters, etc, so that a type or characteristic would become fixed.

It is established today that the downsides of such inbreeding practices can be depression in size and fertility, lack of vigour or of course the unintended fixing of faults or deficiencies. The skill in such policies depends on selecting stock as near to perfection as possible to start with and carrying out a ruthless culling policy. It is a very fine line which some are loath to follow.

Nevertheless his fame and his success spread around the world as did his stock, but it is also true to say that shortly after his death the Longhorn breed declined almost to oblivion. It was not able to compete with the improved Shorthorn in milk or meat production and could not mature so quickly; some considered these to be the fault of his policies. But they have long since proved their success in all types of stock and systems – provided they are properly managed. At the height of his fame, in 1783, he was visited by the Colling brothers, who were so impressed by what they saw they followed his lead with the Teeswater stock on their farms at Ketton and Barmpton outside Darlington.

Thomas Bates

Around this time Thomas Bates (1776-1849) also came on the scene. Bates was an extraordinary man who originally wanted to go into the Church but was dissuaded by his father. By 18 he had acquired his own farm after having been head of his school; at 35 he decided to go to Edinburgh University to study moral philosophy, natural philosophy, natural history and agricultural chemistry, at the same time maintaining his farm and his Shorthorns and in fact expanding, as he bought 1,000 acres at Kirklevington, North Yorkshire. He had also visited Bakewell and determined to follow his breeding policies and to apply them to improving the dairy qualities of the breed. He was very friendly, confident but outspoken and a master of his subjects; he also kept meticulous records of yields, food consumption and weight gains.

Much of his correspondence and principles are recorded by Cadwallader John Bates whose great uncle was Thomas Bates, in his book *Thomas Bates And The Kirklevington Shorthorns* and includes the paper submitted by the latter to the Board of Agriculture in 1807 promoting the need for the evaluation of cattle and the various breeds.

Bakewell and Bates, both of whom earned world respect for their stock, set the trends in record-keeping, so essential in breeding and breed improvement. Both being well connected and educated, despite their dissenters, they were also masters of what we know today as public relations. They were listened to. Their methods also appealed to a great many 'breeders', in the true sense of the word, who were intrigued and convinced that these methods were the way forward. So it was that the Colling brothers, the Booth family and Amos Cruikshank took up the challenge and the breed was formed.

The expansion in population and the growth of urban areas brought about by industrialisation led to an increased demand for food, fuel and clothing. There was competition between landowners, yeomen and those with new-found wealth as well as between villages, and at the same time exports were increasing and people were re-settling. Cattle played a considerable part in this, and inevitably competition and fashions were created. For example park owners and others were favouring white cattle as developed at Chillingham, Chartley, Dynevor and elsewhere, which resulted in the throwback red calves being killed. This fashion or colour prejudice occurred markedly much later, in the development of the black-and-white Friesian when red calves were also disposed of for many years, so far as registered stock was concerned. Competitions were held among breeders and villages for the largest and fattest cattle; with some adjustments, these still continue today!

With the expansion of the cattle industry, the need for bulls increased; they tended to be jointly owned by several farmers, or there were even village bulls. As demand increased for meat and milk production from both individual animals and systems, farmers tended to specialise in one or the other according to inclination, market or farm suitability or business pressures; the debate on dual purpose or specialisation was one that would run for many years.

In the sixteenth and seventeenth centuries there was a huge majority who kept dual-purpose cattle as they were in small units; but with expansion the units grew in size and specialisation crept in for ease of management and a host of other reasons. One of these was the problem of ascertaining with certainty how cattle breed true, as such is the complexity of breeding that maximum success would be hard to achieve in both beef and dairy disciplines and it was inevitable that one or the other must suffer as one or the other prevailed.

It became obvious, largely as a result of the work of Bakewell and others, that specialisation in one aspect or the other was easier; so it was that Bates, the Colling brothers, the Booth Family and Cruikshank set out to breed differing types.

The Colling brothers

Thankfully Robert Colling (1749-1820) and his brother Charles (1750-1836), the Booths and Cruikshank (1808-1895) all insisted that their cattle must have respectable milk yields, whereas previously they were for meat, or they were culled relentlessly.

Robert and Charles Colling farmed independently just outside Darlington at Ketton and Barmpton respectively; after a visit to Bakewell, they were so impressed that they decided to follow his breeding policies. They were gifted with the skills of true breeders, and the success of their work did much to break down the prejudices against 'in and in' breeding. Their initial selections were made from Teeswater/Durham cattle; Robert selected a bull which he noticed on his travels and purchased for the princely sum of £8. This was Hubback and he was mated to four specially selected cows – Cherry, Duchess, Lady Maynard and Daisy – who were reckoned to be the finest available at that time. It was these that put the Collings on their road to fame and started many 'tribes,' as they were called at that time. These animals proved so pre-potent and with refinement (more typey) in their progeny which was supported by many records of the time. Many others

Duchess

followed: the strangely named Foljambe (probably after the farming family of the time), Bolingbroke, Favourite and Comet, to name but a few.

Thomas Bates had decided to follow the teaching of Bakewell even more closely than the Collings and in fact bred even closer as he bred from his choices; one of these was Duchess, who proved such an excellent milker and was founder of his Duchess tribe which was to become famous in Britain, America and elsewhere, bringing the breed to the attention of the world. Bates succeeded in sweeping the board at the first Royal Show in 1839 at Oxford with four animals: the Matchem heifer, two from the Duchess tribe and the famed bull, Duke of Northumberland. This bull traced back to Comet and Favourite, who appears twelve times in the pedigree, he was so closely bred! Other tribes established were Oxford, Waterloo, Wild Eyes and Foggathorpes. Other contemporaries with Bates stock, the Bells, set up Barringtons, Acombes, Darlington and Cragg families.

The Booths

Born a little later than Bates and the Colling brothers, Thomas Booth and then his sons, John and Richard, made a huge impact on the breed, using their skills to select for beefing qualities but with milking capacity. Thomas farmed at Killerby and later at Warlaby. John farmed Killerby, and Richard ran Studley and Warlaby. They were succeeded by John's sons, John and Thomas Christopher. Thomas Christopher farmed Warlaby. The full *History of Killerby, Studely and Warlaby Shorthorns* by William Carr was published in 1867. One can be forgiven for a little confusion!

Thomas, having an unerring eye for stock-breeding, passed this gift to his sons and grandsons; in laying the foundations for his stock he bought judiciously from Robert Colling a strongly built bull, 'Twin Brother of Ben'. He had a concentration of Hubback blood and of another bull, Suworrow, who was bred back again to Hubback and also to Favourite. He also bought skilfully from Darlington Market, the source of so many good animals, five heifers which turned out to be the sources of his top families: Bright Eyes, Ariadne, Blossom and Red Rose. On another buying expedition he bought one which started the Strawberry tribe, the origin of Medora who produced six daughters and all seven came away with prizes from an Otley show. Others from that time went on to breed the Moss Rose, Farewell and Broughton lines.

Richard Booth started on his own at Studley with stock purchased from his father in 1814 with Bright Eyes and her two daughters Agnes and Ariadne from whom he produced the very famous cow Anna by Pilot who, with Julius Caesar, was one of his most successful sires.

Commander-in-Chief

At the time of his marriage son John took over Killerby and Thomas moved to Warlaby in 1819 at a bad time for the breed as a number of breeders had lost interest in breeding. With the coming of the 1st Great Yorkshire Show in 1838 interest was renewed in the region and the Booths were hugely successful in the show ring, although Thomas had died in 1835. Two cows, Necklace and Bracelet, twins, won 35 Championships and prizes, and from 1846 the Booths were supreme in the show rings; some of their bulls were outstanding in the breed for their prowess and their progeny: Windsor was shown 10 times and won 9 championships. Leonard, Crown Prince and Commander-in-Chief went down in history. The latter pedigree contains 12 allocations in the fifth generation to descendants of Pilot, and 8 in the pedigree to descendants of Leonard, demonstrating again the close 'in and in' breeding. Of the females, Charity, Cherry Blossom, Isabella and Hope Charity all bred very significant stock.

Necklace

Bracelet

Having briefly detailed the 'giants' of their time, we must not forget there were many others in this island and Ireland who were concentrating on improving their stock and as more and more joined in it became obvious that if they were to succeed, better records must be kept, other than those who kept their own which were reliant on memory, hearsay or possibly exaggeration and even on occasions, fraud!

The first herd book

As early as 1784 people like George Culley, in his *Observations On Livestock,* commented on various breeders such as John Maynard of Eryhome, Colling Bros, William Wetherall, John Wright of Catterick, as well as Bakewell and other breeders. He included such statements as 'their cows giving 36 quarts of milk per day and 48 Firkins (a firkin =9 gallons) of butter being made from 12 cows' when by comparison the more usual average quantity was 3 firkins per cow in a season and 24 quarts of milk in a day, which gives an indication of the progress being made. He also commented on the Dutch importations. It was indeed Culley, a mutual friend of Bakewell and the Collings, who persuaded the latter to visit the former and by so doing probably changed history.

Some influential breeders were concerned about records, considering that they must be accurate and in 1812 a meeting was called to discuss the situation, attended by Sir Vane Tempest, Jonas Whittaker, the Collings, the Booths, William Wetherall, Thomas Bates, Col. Trotter, John Wright, George Coates and others. It was agreed that George Coates, a Shorthorn and Leicester sheep breeder, who had kept similar records to those of Culley, should carry out the work. Sir Vane Tempest agreed to finance the project but sadly died soon after, so the work was shelved.

The Thoroughbred industry had set up a register in 1791 run by James Wetherby, but it was mainly concerned at that time with performance and identity records, rather than the breeding of the stock. Eight years later Col. Trotter again pressed the matter but again there was a delay owing to the death of Robert Colling who had, with Jonas Whittaker, agreed to advance the funds with subscriptions being sought to reimburse them.

In 1822 Mr Whittaker agreed to fund the Herd Book on condition it was printed in Otley, Yorkshire, and, with the assistance of Mr Paley, to help George Coates and later Coates's son prepare it. Thomas Bates had, in the intervening years, gathered copious detail from fellow breeders and the first herd book in the world was published.

Mr Strafford took it on after five volumes, with Mr Thornton helping him, and they published twenty volumes to the end of 1872 when the Shorthorn Society took it over.

Simultaneous to the improvement drive in England, the Shorthorn was being used by many in Scotland. William Robertson of Ladykirk and General Simpson of Fife were recorded as those using English bulls, having bought stock from the Collings; among them were a daughter of Maynard's cow Young Strawberry and Mary, a daughter of Favourite, and also Lame Bull. They had also hired a number of bulls, among whom were North Star and Young Phoenix and Wellington, both sons of Comet.

John Rennie of, East Lothian, whose Phantassie herd was established in 1822, was an admirer of Robertson's cattle and was a promoter of the Edinburgh Show. He exhibited both his own stock extensively and also Robertson's cattle with great success and also held regular sales, selling stock to their tenants at advantageous prices. One of the people interested in these was Capt. Barclay of Ury in northern Scotland; he was a well known prizefighter and an extraordinary man of his time, whose activities publicised both himself and his Shorthorns. He drove his coach from London to Aberdeen without leaving the box for a bet of £1,000 and similarly he walked 1,000 miles in 1,000 hours for a further £1,000! But he was also dedicated to his cattle and sold stock all over England and Ireland. In 1838 he held his first sale of Shorthorns when his noted sire Monarch by Mason's Monarch made a huge impact and 80 head made over £3,000. His second and last sale was not so good financially but his stock, sold all over Scotland, proved wonderful investments for its purchasers. One of those purchasers was Amos Cruikshank (1808-1895) for his Sittyton herd, and the bull Billy 315 went on to produce sixty head in the herd which descended from him.

Amos Cruikshank

Amos and his brother Anthony, who owned a hosiery and glove business in Aberdeen, were partners and although Amos was the breeder Anthony evidently provided the financial expertise and no doubt much of the funding as he was also a banker with many financial interests

Amos was a true breeder but he didn't show much interest in pedigree, in the sense that he preferred to rely more on his 'eye' and not be swayed by fashion; like many significant and successful breeders he was single which he claimed 'left him more time to concentrate on his cattle'! He was in fine company in this as in that era Bakewell, Richard Booth, Robert Colling, Bates and William Torr, of whom more later, were all bachelors. Amos was also a devout Quaker and again many successful breeders have been of this faith.

Like the Booths, the Cruikshanks took great care to ensure that, as well as being of the beef type, their cattle must be excellent milkers and many breeders thereafter had good reason to be thankful of this as it was, and is, one of the excellent points of the breed.

By 1855 the Cruikshanks' herd had grown to 300 head as they expanded, although it was reduced in later years to around 120. Violet, Venus, Broadhooks, Nonpareils, Butterfly, Orange Blossom, Clipper, Victoria, Brawith Buds, Duchess of Gloucester, Secret and others were all families originated by Cruikshank. He bought cattle from several sources and it was his skill and determination in blending the various bloodlines which created a type and gave him his reputation; in this he was like Bates and Bakewell in that he created a type which did so much for the breed and its furtherance. Obviously in a herd of this size he used many sires that after 1860 came from his own herd, probably the best known was Champion of England (this is the name of the bull) and he subsequently used sons, grandsons and even great grandsons of this great sire. Field Marshall by Gauntlet was another great sire that was later owned by William Duthie who then loaned him to stand in Her Majesty Queen Victoria's herd.

No doubt as Amos was a retiring man, contacts of Anthony had, following the incredible success of this herd, arranged for all spare animals to be sold to the USA and Canada, so few were sold in Britain except to his regular buyers.

Such was the Cruikshank's success that around the time of Amos's retirement due to ill health in 1889 negotiations were 'in train' for the whole herd to be exported to Argentina. But there was a financial crisis in Buenos Aires so, although a few went, the majority remained in Britain. Eventually Mr W. Duthie bought 38; Mr Deane Willis purchased 33 and 4 went to Mr C. Tindall, all of which did wonders for the breed as they were spread around the country. Amos Cruickshank died in

Field Marshal

1895, having had an enormous influence on Shorthorns all over the world, due to his success and the size of his herd. This can be seen by the fact that between 1842-1889 1,912 animals were sold from this herd at a total of around £68,000, not a huge figure today but vast in those days indicating a ready and steady demand.

It is an extraordinary fact that so much of Shorthorn history and outstanding breeders came from this region (Aberdeenshire) of Scotland; another breeder, William Marr, took on the tenancy of Uppermill, near Tarves, currently farmed by the Durnos, in 1833, and so this is probably the longest any farm has continually and successfully bred Shorthorns.

Spending spree

While all this was happening in Scotland some major events were occurring in the rest of the world in the cattle sector. Fashion was again taking hold; 'pedigree', now reasonably established, was partly to blame in that people in America and elsewhere were scrambling to obtain Bates breeding; a number had misinterpreted the 'in and in' policy and had bought and bred by pedigree alone, resulting in animals being small, shelly (weedy, with flat sides and no spring of rib), and having fertility problems demonstrating the futility of following the fashion without the skills of breeding. Bates himself as well as other observers of the time commented on this decline and there was widespread criticism of the policy but still the quest for Bates breeding

Comet

continued with sales rising to unbelievable heights, perhaps spurred on by the sale of Comet, bred by Charles Colling in 1810 for 1,000 guineas, by the syndicate of four: Col. Trotter, John Charge, John Wright and William Wetherall.

The most noted of the sales was the New York Mills sale in 1873 when Charles S. Campbell sold 109 head of almost entirely Bates breeding for £ 80,061 and a number were bought to return to England. Over 1,000 people attended and the top price was reached for 8th Duchess of Geneva who made 8,120 guineas and then the 10th Duchess of Geneva went for 7,000 guineas. The 1st Duchess of Geneva had sold at 1,000 guineas and this helped to raise the average for 93 females to £791 8s. , with males selling on average £403 16s. Fifteen Dukes and Duchesses averaged £3,680 and 9 Oxfords averaged £826, but other tribes averaged £205 which further emphasised the craze.

When you compare these prices with those obtained twenty years before when Bates died in 1850, you can see how fashion had influenced things: at Bates's dispersal, in bad times, 4-5,000 people from all over the world attended it. Very much lower prices were obtained. Cattle went mainly to English buyers and 68 head averaged only £60, a vast difference. The Duchess family again topped the sale, selling at 200 guineas for Duchess 59, and Grand Duke 204 guineas and this family averaged £116; other lines averaged much less: Oxfords made £68, Waterloo £59, Cambridge Rose £49, Wild Eyes £48, Foggathorpes £49, these prices vastly different from the New York Mills sale.

In 1810 Charles Colling's herd at Ketton of 47 head had sold an average of £152 including Comet. The females averaged £140 to a top of £410 for Lily, a daughter of Comet, and Countess for £400: both bought by Major B Rudd.

Robert Colling had dispersed in 1818 and the 61 head averaged £128, females averaging £111 and males £128.

John Booth at Killerby had a poor sale in 1886 when 57 head averaged £97 of which 39 females averaged £103 and 18 males averaged £83.

The best sale of this period was in 1875 when a portion of the Earl of Dunsmore herd in Stirlingshire sold 39 females, mainly of Bates lines, averaging £576 and 9 bulls averaged £ 992 of which two were Duchess bulls. Duke of Connaught fetched 4,500 guineas and the 3rd Duke of Hillhurst 3,000 guineas; of the females there were 5 which fetched over 1,000 guineas to a top of 1,950 guineas for Red Rose of the Isles purchased by the Earl Bective, MP at Underley. He had an excellent Bates breeding herd and had an excellent reduction of Bates breeding the year before paying some very high prices in the New York Mills sale and had held regular reduction sales. Sadly he died in 1893.

Bates and Bakewell and others had certainly created interest throughout the land and they had also gained the eyes and ears of the aristocracy who were keen to be involved in this investment opportunity. Lord Althorpe, or Earl Spencer, as he was better known, was reputed to have far more interest in his Wiseton herd than his politics; others included Sir Vane Tempest at Wynyard and the Earls of Dunsmore and Bective and the 7th Duke of Devonshire with his herd at Holker. Here he and his steward George Drewry followed Bates lines with great success, his first sale averaging good prices but the next in 1871 averaged £240 for 43 animals only to be exceeded in 1874 when 8 Oxfords sold at an average of £588 and yet again in 1878 when 30 averaged £664 and 9 Oxfords averaged £1,636 with Baroness Oxford making £2,660 and Grand Duchess realised £2,100 to Australia; three others made over £1,600 each. Then of course the Royal herds and Lord Lovat (about whom there will be more later), were only some of the major breeders of the day and their enthusiasm spread.

Another landmark at this time was the import of 32 head in 1877 from the Hon. M.H. Cochrane in Canada, when things were depressed over there. They raised £16,325 and an average of £510, selling at Bowness, Windermere, when the 3rd Duchess of Hillhurst sold for 4,100 guineas to Lord Loder but the 5th Duchess made 4,300 guineas at 20 months of age and a fortnight later, five of the Grand Duchess Line sold for £1,733 each.

These buying sprees almost 'burst the bubble' and one wonders what prices the Bates, Cruikshanks and others would have realised had they sold at this time. It is quite similar to famous artists and their work. The prices reached indicated again the huge interest but in a way they may have been a reaction to the bad years when agriculture was in the doldrums around 1851 when Shorthorns averaged £19 in 22 sales and again in 1879 when beef was 4 pence a pound. Farmers, then as now, battled against the recessions of 1873 and 1880 as well as coping with the major outbreaks of foot and mouth disease, of which there were serious ones in 1839, 1864 and 1883. Nevertheless the demand for meat and milk continued. Town dairies with their 'flying' herds (those which milked their cows and then sold them and bought another in their place) were being established, so the motivation to expand and improve continued.

The *Field Magazine* in the editorial in its first issue in 1853 stated 'prospects for agriculture are good and the bad days are past. The consumption of meat is increasing at rate scarcely known and if wheat does not yield 22 bushels the sooner it is turned to grass the better and farmers who once sold wheat will sell meat and Northern Europe will have crossed their pointed, long legged cows with our Shorthorns'!

The problem of the high prices was that they were out of the reach of the tenant farmers so they made do with other stock and were disappointed, they also bought poor cheaper sires. This had a deleterious effect, as did errors in management, all of which meant that the breed suffered a decline and as mentioned there was a flagrant disregard for import regulations which resulted in the importation of foot and mouth disease but also cattle plague, causing huge losses of stock. To a degree the control of these was influenced by Shorthorn breeders. Earl Spencer, Sir Nigel Kingscote, The Duke of Richmond and T. C. Booth and others achieved an act in Parliament in 1876 that restricted entry more effectively. This was the forerunner of the Disease of Animal Act in 1892, which was subsequently to be amended on many occasions.

The Sittyton cattle exportation and others to Canada and USA, and more especially the trade to South America, did much to restore confidence and interest in the breed but it was the latter that made and subsequently almost broke the breed from the beef point of view.

Another great breeder of this time was Mr William Torr of Aylesby, Great Grimsby, who admired the Booth herd and also the Bates bloodlines. The great man considered Torr to have a very poor eye, probably because Mr Torr, who was a much sought-after judge, had made decisions against him in the show ring, about which he was passionate. His home policies were more than vindicated, after his death, when his dispersal sale attracted huge crowds, said to be 3,000, and high prices. T.C. Booth, with whom Torr had exchanged bulls, was a major purchaser, taking 12 animals at an average of 945 guineas including the top price 2,100 guineas for Bright Empress. Cattle were also purchased by buyers from the USA, Australia, New Zealand and Ireland as well as all parts of England: 84 lots averaged £510. This emphasises that, although major dispersals are sad as they are the end of a lifetime's work, the plus side is that the good bloodlines go far and wide to found or improve other herds.

One could spend a great deal more time on this period, as it was then that the breed was forging its place in history, but this is not the purpose of this publication. Even during this time there was debate on the advisability of emphasising meat or milking capability, and also the habit of over fitting stock for shows (getting the stock too fat). The argument against emphasis on milk or meat was that the breed would lose its reputation for all-round capability; at this time Bates and others were very conscious of the variability of individual animals' abilities to convert food either to milk or meat better than others, in a similar way to the variability abilities of transmitting of their genes to their calves. Shorthorns have an outstanding ability to transmit their genes to improve the milking or beefing ability of other cattle in all climates and conditions, so this factor is very relevant. It was evident to all and sundry that the Shorthorn had special strengths in its ability to be so adaptable to any management system as well as having an outstanding temperament.

At this time of agricultural and industrial expansion stock-breeders, in the main, recognised the benefits of the herd book although it is true there were sceptics and a huge number who kept the breed but didn't subscribe. There is a similarly large number today for a wide number of reasons and in the very early days one of those was that the records were found to be wrong, which was inevitable with the wide sources of information gathered by Coates and his son. They must have had a huge task collecting and collating and correcting their initial records but a start had to be made somewhere and early credit must be given to all those involved, especially when one realises that most of the gathering was done initially on horseback!

Pedigree is no guarantee of success as there are many other factors that come into the equation. A pedigree is a record of all known parents and from this one can build up a knowledge of transmitting ability in a given situation and hopefully build an improvement in one or several commercial qualities, but this is in no way certain, the downside is of course that undesirable traits can also be transmitted. Furthermore one may find a propensity for a line to be more productive in breeding suitable females or males. However the value of such records was generally recognised and the other breeds and species soon followed: Herefords in 1846, Angus at first combined with Galloway in 1882 but the latter opened their own in 1877 the same year as the Ayrshires. The Kennel club had been running their register since 1873.

The Shorthorn Society of Great Britain

Some Shorthorn breeders were feeling that their herd book should not be in private hands and a circular was issued in 1872 to the effect that there had been allegations of fraudulent pedigrees and calling a meeting in London for July 1872, following which there was much discussion until on July 1st 1874 the Shorthorn Society of Great Britain and Ireland was formed. The Earl of Dunmore, Lord Skelmerdale, Lord Penryn, Col. Kingscote, the Rev. Storer, H. Chanders-Pole-Gell and T. C. Booth were appointed as the Committee and shortly after this Messrs C. Howard, R. Chaloner, H. Aylmer and E. Bowley were added with Mr Harward becoming temporary Honorary Secretary.

They were to form a company for the purchase of the herd book at a price of £5,000 from Mr Strafford and 'form a managing committee or council, for the purpose for the collecting and publishing accurate information as to the pedigrees and sale of Shorthorns, and for promoting the general interests of Shorthorn Breeders.'

The Committee met at Sir Nigel Kingscote's house on July 2nd when the Society was formally recommended and on the day following, the 7th Duke of Devonshire was elected the first President. The company was incorporated on June 15th, 1875, and Mr H. J. Hine was appointed the first Secretary in 1874. A list of Secretaries and Presidents can be found in Appendix IV. The condition of entry in Coates's herd book was agreed to be: 'No bull is eligible for insertion in the herd book unless it has 5 crosses and no cow unless it has 4 crosses of Shorthorn Blood which are or which were eligible to be inserted in the herd book.'

There was an earlier mention of the Royal herds and it was in fact George III in 1803 who started the herd at Windsor and later Sandringham; thanks to him, his successors and their managers, the breed spread to other nobility at home and overseas, increasing the popularity throughout Europe.

From very early times Longhorns and Shorthorns were taken to such large land masses as Australia, New Zealand, Africa, Argentina, Canada and the USA but there were few official records kept; France started their official book in 1855, Germany 1871 and the USA in 1882. However there are reliable records showing pedigree cattle exported to Argentina in 1848 of which the famous bull Tarquin was the start and such was the rapidity of increase of stock in that country that a

Ketton Ox (or Durham Ox), born 1796, bred by C. Colling.

census in 1895 in Argentina showed that out of a total population of cattle of 22 million of all breeds, 64,000 were pure Shorthorns and a further 2.5 million were 'Graded' animals (had been bred to pedigree standard by use of pedigree sires on non-pedigree dams); it is to Argentina that the breed owes both its rise and its fall, as will be seen in future pages.

Anyone wishing to research the fascinating data on the period will find a number of books listed, as well as those already mentioned, in the appendix but it is this century which is the object of this book.

3. The Early 20th Century

The previous chapter gave an all too brief summary of the very early development of the Shorthorn and its meteoric rise (considering the time scale) to fame. It is now time to move into the 20th century; of course many spanned the two periods, or the effects of their work did, hence the reason for looking back a bit.

One of the restraining factors had been the problems of imported disease which decimated herds, but once the controls had been initiated progress was made. Irrespective of these problems, the breed still forged forward. A major boost was the trade with Argentina, a country with a superb climate and the natural fertility of the huge 'pampas', as the plains are known. These benefits could have enabled the country to feed the world, had it not been for revolutions in the region and the seemingly endless political and financial problems which unfortunately seem to apply even today.

The grasslands with their very accessible water table were crying out to be developed at this time and the cattle required were those rising to quick maturity and of a blocky type; thus the short-legged fashion was created.

Early exports to Argentina were largely from Spain and were mainly the Lidea breed which, although fierce, were also very hardy animals; there were also Campo, Pasiega and Tudana breeds of cattle; stock was also imported from nearby Brazil, Chile and Peru with their progeny being used mainly for their hides with their carcasses being literally left to rot or be eaten by prairie dogs or other carnivores. The Shorthorn was bought in for the purpose of improving these breeds, with the result that the Shorthorn soon took over the market. This new outlet for Britain and Ireland was most exciting and productive for our breed. At this time records were very sketchy until such time as the Shorthorn Society started issuing export certificates in 1882; but news of their success was spreading across the world to all corners although some areas required differing types, with Australia, for example, requiring a beast which could cope with the rigours of long distances between water sources and therefore needing an animal with longer legs and excellent feet.

It was not just Argentina that was seeking the shorter-legged type; in France a bull from Hugh Aylmer was reported by several sources as, 'magnificent and rarely has a more massive animal been seen on such short legs.' Another fashion trait.

In fact more animals were transported from Britain and Ireland to Australia than went to Argentina during the period 1868-90.

The first recorded animal imported to Argentina was the bull known as Tarquin in 1848; then many others followed but it was not until 1889 that they published their own herd book and insisted that 'any imported Shorthorns must have the last registered sire and dam ... been born in or before 1850' but in a large number it was a problem to verify, so the date was moved to 1845. As well as this, a huge number of pedigrees had been lost but the animals were undoubtedly pure bred. In the initial stages a number were purchased without the certainty of being of a certain bloodline and the trade really started to take off around 1878; at this time several Bates lines cattle were shipped in, only to find that they had problems with too much milk. The few Sittyton cattle that did arrive in 1888 really set the trade on 'fire'.

Other breeds were being imported and other countries were exporting to this area but in 1899 shorthorns from France brought foot and mouth to this region, and this caused a pause in the importations until around 1903 when the demand was extraordinary: 1,000 certificates were issued, which increased to 2,352 certificates in 1906. The tragedy was that foot and mouth has since been endemic in large areas of Argentina. The huge size of the estancias was mind boggling, 34,000 acres was commonplace for one farm and herds of as many as 20,000 head were already in evidence. Two important other assets of the breed made it very popular: the first was its docility, which made it easier to handle, and the second was its propensity for easy calving, so essential on the range and no less important today in any beef or dairy situation. This is no idle claim but backed up by countless statistics and is probably due to the physical make-up of the breed; both the Shorthorn and Longhorn have a calf-bed (the way the womb is set in the body structure) and pelvic structure which is conducive to easy calving, a fact backed up and more recently verified in extensive tests and measurements carried out at Cambridge University in the 1980s. A further fashion created was the marked preference for red or dark roan cattle as they were thought to be more resistant to the heat and sun; this too was disproved later in experiments, and it was found that the skin and hair texture were the deciding factors, as in the tests white animals were found to be just as resistant.

It is important to appreciate the amount of stock exported at that time and the speed with which it increased. From 1882-1906 **16,368** certificates were issued with cattle going to **24** different countries. From 1912-1928 **17,486,** certificates were issued to **44** countries during which time the Argentine was by far the largest recipient. In the first period they took 12,376; Canada came next with 1,785; USA followed with 672, Germany 400, Australia 143, France 345. In the second period the figures were Argentina 7,780, Canada 2,418, USA 2,165, Australia 1,864. From these it can clearly be seen that the USA influence was not so large as has been made out by some, although a number to that country went via Canada; *but* pause for a moment to consider that the exporters will in the main have chosen off 'the top of the pack' so we can imagine the considerable genetic loss to the breed in this country, even if it was a huge money-spinner.

Unsurprisingly breeders valued that market, but the downside was that, as the herd book was not divided into beef and dairy sections at that time, so the whole breed was affected in that it lost its valuable size of structure. Many farmers lost sight of, or were ignorant of, the particular bloodline capabilities and suitabilities that in the end resulted in a catastrophic decline in its popularity.

George Taylor

This decline took many years and thankfully many breeders maintained they should retain a policy of middle-of-the-road cattle type and it was from them that the recovery started to happen. Obviously the dairy side was also affected in that the smaller animals lost production potential but again it took a long time for this to become a major problem; I started and ended the previous chapter with the exploits of the beef side, as it was in this production sector that fantastic progress was being made. The dairy side was in decline, not due at this point to the size factor but because of the Bates breeding 'phobia'. It was catastrophic in its effect as everyone, or nearly everyone, craved these bloodlines, principally the Duchess tribe; huge prices were charged for them and many farmers could not afford the good cattle and so bought cheaper, poorer ones. Also many bought on pedigree alone, irrespective of the animal or its capability; most had not acquired the management skills with in-breeding and line breeding; the result was poor, shelly cattle with poor yields and the breed lost ground to the extent that many decried Bates systems. Thankfully there were some who kept their feet on the ground.

Remember also that dual-purpose was still the vogue and in principle the Shorthorn was 'tailor made' for this principle.

Forgive the almost pun, but it was a tailor who almost saved the breed at that time: a breeder named George Taylor! He farmed originally in Somerset but moved to **Cranford**, Middlesex, and built a herd of around 200 head, using Cruikshank and Booth breeding, integrated with the Bates lines and choosing the more milky strains of the former. He managed to restore his cattle's constitutions. So the Cranford cattle gained huge respect with a number of animals yielding 1,100 –1,300 gallons per lactation. One of a group of females purchased by Lord Rothschild was a particularly successful cow, Darlington Cranford 5th, which had been a very successful show cow; she also yielded 10,174 lb average over 10 years and bred no less than three famous sires, Foundation Stone, Conjuror and Dreadnought. George Taylor's most successful sire was the bull Beau Sabreur which bred him many excellent animals.

Another successful breeder of similar thinking and success was Sir Charles Knightley at Fawsley in Northampton who gave the breed the Furbelow, Primrose Walnut and other families; one of his best known and successful sires was the great Earl of Dublin of the Princess tribe. A major purchaser from Taylor, Lord Rothschild was another very successful breeder with huge success at shows and dairy shows and very methodically kept records. Yet another breeder of the time was C. R.W. Adeane at Babraham whose herd was managed first by F. N. Webb, followed by Jonas Webb. Then there was Owen Webb who founded Streetly and who was followed by J. D. Webb so the family was very significant in the breed for some time to come. In fact Jonas senior had bought one of the Dodona tribe developed by Earl Spencer for £80 from which no fewer than 189 descendants followed. Another very far-seeing and successful family was the Strattons, first recorded in 1837, some of whom are still farming today. Richard Stratton farming in Wiltshire purchased a bull Phoenix from Warwickshire which went back as far as the legendary Comet and Favourite; he put him to a selection of cattle purchased by eye and a dynasty was born. One of his first progeny was outstanding, a Moss Rose whose progeny developed and bred a family which won them over £10,000 in prize money alone. Like his predecessors, the Bates and the Booths, he had the gift of foresight in his selection and policy.

Red Duke, by a son of Bates's Duke of Northumberland, was evidently his most successful sire. He was the sire of 3 Smithfield gold medal winners and the herd went from strength to strength until his death in 1878 when his herd was divided between his sons, J. Stratton and Richard, who both went on to huge success in the show ring, exhibiting both dairy and beef strains and indeed with exports all over the world. It is no coincidence that these names were both prominent and market leaders and Richard Stratton Jnr was in many ways blessed as a prophet as well, since he foresaw the requirements in terms of type that farmers would need. Fortuitously he was elected President of the Shorthorn Society in 1895 and one of his many quotes was, 'The Dairymen of this country should be the best in the world and have numerous customers for pure Shorthorns and if the foreigners fail us, as they will do some Day, where will the outlet for our bulls be?' How right he was.

In 1897 he wrote, 'Whether the Shorthorn of former days was more remarkable for milking or beef producing qualities may be doubtful

——there had been a tendency on the part of modern Shorthorn breeders to pay less attention to the milking properties in favour of the beef producing and the quick feeding propensities of their stock and the modern show yard system of feeding breeding animals brought only the quick feeders to the fore,' he went on 'bulls bred from these non-milkers were often sold at public auction to dairymen who had never even set eyes on the dam and disappointment at the degeneration of his dairy stock followed, so much so that they purchased bulls of non pedigree stock of good milking character.' So strongly did he feel that in 1901, after years of expressing concern over the promotion of the breed, in company with George Taylor and John Thornton, he raised a fund to support prizes at shows for those showing excellent dairy properties. Eventually in 1905 the Dairy Shorthorn Association was founded with a committee fittingly comprising Lord Rothschild, Richard Stratton, Sir Oswald Mosley, the Earl of Crewe, George Taylor, F. N. Webb, J. P. Cross, C.R.W. Adeane, R. Carr, agent for Lord Rothschild, C.A. Scott-Murray and another very significant name, R .W. Hobbs.

This association did not get off to a fantastic start as by 1907 the total prizes only amounted to £100, but a start had been made. The association appointed judges and even published and promoted milk records. A section of these contained a list of cows qualified by their records to breed bulls. They also produced a Year Book, later to be of some substance, and also some promotional material. The members were slow to join at first but increased steadily so that in later years the Year Book grew and grew, later carrying details of herds and their records and indeed was the first attempt at official recording; it was this organization that started promoting the grading-up of stock (the process of breeding up to pedigree status by the use of pedigree sires on non-pedigree dams). In order to give some idea of recording costs at the time: it was two shillings and six pence for each cow inspection, with a minimum of 20 shillings, and a further half crown (2s 6d) if the record was required to be published in the Year Book.

The association's aim was 'the promotion of the Dairy Shorthorn' and even in those early days they sponsored milking trials at eight shows.

George Taylor used to sell his stock by regular auctions and set a precedent at this time by always cataloguing the milk records of those on offer; as a result he not only created a following, but also his cattle went on to start or improve many excellent herds of the time. Although he did not show much, many of his customers spread around the country had show winners from his breeding.

He also raised the profile of the breed and average prices rose. In his reduction sale of 1911 there were 32 animals whose yields averaged

10,032lb and the 75 head averaged £74. In 1912, following his death, there were 189 animals in the catalogue and 126 of these had their records tabulated to within 7 days of the sale. There were 90 buyers and the 166 females' average was £106, with bulls averaging £76, therefore the total average was £104.

Another of those first DSA board members was Robert Hobbs whose father Charles had founded the Kelmscott Herd in 1878 and spanned the twentieth century, starting with mainly non-pedigree cattle and graded up from a choice selection that he put to a large, skilfully selected selection of bulls. Around the start of the century the herd was one of the largest, having over 100 milkers, and they supplied, like many others, a London dairy. At that time there was much co-operation with another well known Gloucestershire breeder, William Arkell, and another influential Dairy Shorthorn family, the Garnes. The Hobbs had a number of very successful families and probably one of the best of these was the Primulas which by 1909 had resulted in 70 retained females; the latest, Primula 70, won Hobbs his first Royal Show Championship. Such was the quality of this herd that they produced twelve Royal Show Champions; one bull family, Kelmscott Juggler, and his son, Kelmscott Acrobat, and two grandsons, Kelmscott Conjurer 2nd and Kelmscott Conjurer 36th, were all Royal Champions. At the 1921 London Dairy Show, 4 of the first 6 places in a class of 32 in milk heifers were Kelmscott bred. This herd was a major influence on the National Dairy Herd as they held a number of reduction sales.

The aforementioned Garne family herds started as early as 1825 and also had a large influence in the 1800s and on into the 1900s as George Garne went to Churchill Heath, about which more later. It was this family also that did much to further the Cotswold Sheep and it is interesting but not perhaps a surprise that so many Shorthorn breeders should have also been influential in the sheep breeds.

I mentioned earlier what a huge influence George Taylor had on the breed, with his stock and breeding featuring in pedigrees for many years; in fact a survey was done in 1944 which showed how many of the top dairy herds had stock going back to Cranford breeding.

William Duthie

A similar herd on the beef side was **Collynie,** started by William Duthie Snr in 1856, and then taken on by William Duthie Jnr, no doubt helped by the purchase of the part of the Sittyton Herd (38). He had also earlier purchased the famous bull Field Marshall from Cruikshank, as this bull did two stints in the herd at varying times. Duthie also used a son of his, Mario, among others who seemed to 'click' (the genes went well together). Hindered by an incident of foot and mouth in his early days, he characteristically dealt with this by totally isolating both himself and the affected animals so that it did not go any further, he also dealt later with a severe outbreak of that scourge, contagious abortion, in the herd with a ruthless slaughter policy. Neither of these problems deterred him from his successes.

Many Collynie cattle went all over the world, particularly to Ireland, Argentina, and the USA, as well as Britain. Not surprisingly in such a large herd he also used sires from his neighbour's herd, Uppermill, as well as buying several high-price females which he meticulously sought from the top sources to add to his superb breeding herd. This paid off so effectively that Collynie sires were in nearly all the top herds for many years to come.

One of the best he bred was Collynie Ringleader, who sired more winners in the shows and Smithfield than any other bull at the time; in fact at one Smithfield all the 1st prize animals in six classes were sired by him. Collynie King Lavender was purchased as a calf in 1919 by Peter Cazalet for £5,300 guineas, the highest price ever sold from the herd. The long-standing sire in the herd, whom Duthie considered his best, was Scottish Archer, who was used for nine years. Yet another major sire was Knight of Collynie by Collynie Commodore, used for seven years, who sired many famous offspring including the Durno's Mesmerist and Millhills Bright Star. There were of course a number of sires used but one other worthy of inclusion was Balcairn White Eagle who, as well as producing many top class sires, sired Collynie Royal Leader, assessed by many the best sire of his time when in the Callrossie herd. The sire used so successfully in the Will's herd was Collynie Royal Regent, purchased for £4,200. Duthie was in the practice of holding annual sales; with astonishing success he raised huge interest and got the top price mentioned by P.Cazalet and achieved consistently rising averages.

Wm Duthie died aged 91: another single man, despite his charms! Shorthorn breeding seems to involve not only cattle having very long productive lives, but their owners as well! Wm Duthie certainly lived up to his nickname Shorthorn King.

The Collynie herd numbered over 200 but it must not be assumed that it was only the larger herds that enjoyed success: one of the great herds of the time to influence the breed was the **Naemoor** herd which had around 40 head and although we don't hear this prefix mentioned often now, some very influential sires were bred by the Moubray family. This herd was dispersed on several occasion, because of deaths, etc. The last time was in 1961 when bought by the Hon. Mrs Irene Dewhurst of Dungarthill who probably saved it from going overseas as several of the prominent herds at the time had done. It was founded originally in 1885, which is why it is mentioned here. It is extraordinary how many principal sires can be traced back to this prefix. Commenting on

Collynie Royal Leader

this herd, J. T. McLaren wrote, 'It is an article of faith among breeders that the stock bull is half the herd and some people think a good herdsman is the other half which does not leave much scope for the females of the herd'! How right he was – the herdsmen/stockmen had/have a huge influence in successful herds even if many cannot afford them today. McLaren was making the point that herds are fortunate if they can find and produce prepotent sires. In this case he was referring firstly to the skills of James Forsyth, a famed stockman of his day, but also to the two sires that in his opinion 'made' the herd and so influenced many others: Edgecote Masterpiece and Garbity Field Marshal, both being of the Mabel families (from McWilliam). Masterpiece had been sold previously to go to Russia at £2,000 but failed his tests so was purchased by Mr Moubray for £450, so bad luck can be turned!

In two successive years of Perth sales more than $^1/_3$ of the total sum realised was for 67 sires that were progeny of 5 sires bred by Naemoor and the average of these was above £440 per head. Again in his article J.T. Mclaren made a very pertinent observation when referring to the magnificent bull, Naemoor Jasper, who could be traced back to Masterpiece, purchased and very successfully used in the MacGillivray Brothers' herds: ' If some of these potent sires had not fallen into the hands of distinguished breeders they would not have had the chance to be mated with some of the very best females and thereby left an indelible mark on the breed. ' So very true.

4. What is the Shorthorn Breed?

At this stage of the book it will be evident to many that there have been incidents, breeders and cattle that have been omitted; sadly this is inevitable as even in the early days of the century there were so many involved and all have contributed to the breed's history. In the '40s and '50s numbers rose to over 6,000 herds and 25,000 registrations plus the 20,000 grading up as well as the non-members.

My hope has been to record more of a story and a record rather than a breed directory in which herds were documented on an A to Z basis. Furthermore I have been loath to split beef from dairy herds, as prior to the '50s they were not detailed as separate registers. Dual purpose was the intent, although you may find Scotch (although this breed type was known as the Scotch Shorthorn, as the types became more defined it became colloquially known as the Beef Shorthorn and the latter description became the title) or dairy grouped; neither route is intended to confer superiority as they have all contributed, so I decided to 'pick and mix' and of course this affects personalities as well. One breeder said, 'Personalities and characters are always in the previous generation' and in many cases I agree with this view; having in this case the benefit of hindsight makes it easier. But some of our generation are certainly characters!

Principal, chronological events are in the main also listed in Appendix IV for ease of reference, as are Presidents and Secretaries.

Types
In the early development as well as throughout history there have been types within the breed created by location, fashion, adaptability or circumstance. The **Lincoln Red** was perhaps the first of these. This type grew in the middle eastern counties among those who favoured the rich red colour in preference to the others and it developed as a very hardy, dual purpose strain to be known as the Lincoln Red Shorthorn which gave very creditable yields, was a good size, and left an excellent carcass.

In 1895 they established a herd book and this continued until 1935 when they re-amalgamated with the Shorthorn Society, with their own section in the herd book and their own representatives on council. This lasted until 1943 when they departed on their own way again, dropping the word Shorthorn from their title, and developed steadily into the beef breed they are today with their own history.

Some others followed and formed their own associations, such as the **Northern Dairy Shorthorn** in **1946** to be re-amalgamated in **1965** and the **Whitebred** in **1962**: both are covered below.

As the Shorthorn breed was developing, others were evolving also and the principal of these was the Friesian, of which a number were imported over the years and eventually formed their own society, first named **The British Holstein Society** in **1909**, later changed in 1914 to the British Holstein Friesian Society, and again in 1919 to the **British Friesian Society**. Like others, they started with a few dedicated supporters. By 1911 they had 50 members but by 1921 they had 1,600; as with the Shorthorns, Friesians then mushroomed as can be seen by the various tables in the Irish and A I statistics later (see p. 61), increases bought about by fashion and circumstances.

Another major organisation was started at this time: the **National Farmers Union** in **1908**.

Northern Dairy Shorthorn Association

As early as 1933 Shorthorn breeders in the north of England were perturbed that the type of cattle that suited the area and had been bred for a number of years was either being ignored or abused as other breeders sought higher production or a differing type. Furthermore many were being crossed with other breeds. They were also worried that the Shorthorn Society was attempting to raise both milk and butterfat standards in order to compete with other breeds, mainly the incoming Friesian. They considered that to push their type to the current targets being suggested would be uneconomic in their circumstances; also to increase their size or number would cause management problems as the majority had hill flocks of sheep and these would be deprived of all important in-bye land in the spring. The breeders, who in the main were on higher poorer land with late springs, considered that if targets were set that would inevitably mean that some would attempt to achieve them by feeding more concentrates, this would force them to compete uneconomically with south country breeders.

Many of the dales type had been bought into the south and in the easier conditions they had enormously increased yields.

Milk production was becoming a top priority owing to the war but town dairies were closing down due to the improvement of transport, and to increase the total output value many in the dales turned to producing butter or cheese with particular specialities such as Cotherstone, Coverdale, Swaledale and Wensleydale.

So it was, after several years' discussion, they held a meeting in Penrith in **January 1944** at which it was agreed to found **The Northern**

Dairy Shorthorn Breeders Association (NDS) and this was incorporated in the October.

The dales men are a close knit community and they initially formed 25 areas delineated as: Allendale, Alston, Bentham, Barnard Castle, Caldbeck, Carlisle, Cockermouth, Darlington, Eskdale, Hawes, Kendal, Kirkby Stephen, Kirkbride, Kendal, Keswick, Leyburn, Masham, Penrith, Richmond, Sedburgh, Settle, Shotley, Skipton, Weardale and Whitehaven. In 1961 these were modified to 8 regional associations encompassing the 6 northern counties. Each branch had appointed inspectors varying from 3 to 33 depending on the size of branch; 116 in all were appointed. These men selected a huge base of some 10,000 or 11,000 females and around 1,000 males, all being given a number and the tattoo ND. All breeders were given prefixes and designation letters.

The reorganisation of areas in 1961 created Northumberland and Durham, West Riding, North Riding, Cumberland, West Cumberland, Kendal, Kirkby Stephen, Teesdale.

The rules became that in their selections both parents *must* have passed an inspection, then their progeny were eligible but the dam must have yielded 500 gallons with her 1st calf, 600 gallons 2nd calf, 700 gallons 3rd calf, all in 315 days (later changed to 305 days) and this had to be certified by a milk recording officer. These were put in a supplementary register. Good progress was made as in 1945 there were 257 qualified which averaged 7,526lb and this had risen by 1949 to 493 females averaging 8,308lb.

Their first President was N. Field of Lartington Hall, Barnard Castle. He remained in this office till his death in 1958. There were three Vice-Presidents: A.L. Kidd of Penrith, G .W. Dent of Kirkby Stephen and E. Blythe of Penrith. They were exceptionally fortunate in their President as he was very well known in a number of fields and a first-class sportsman. He was a keen yachtsman and cricketer, he played golf for England, was a North Riding councillor, and chairman of magistrates as well as being able to find the time to be a racehorse owner! He also had a herd of NDS.

The association got off to a good start and such was the enthusiasm that by 1946 there were 1,498 members. In 1947 they recorded 1,560 members with 12,171 registrations. The herd book had one unusual feature: the facility of including the height above sea level in their entry, but not many seemed to have taken this up although when quoting yields it was often used.

In 1947 following the death of their first Secretary, H. J. Shute, Mary Forcett was appointed to this post; at the same time she coped with the Blue Faced Leicester Society, and remained with the NDS Association till it rejoined the Shorthorn Society and during NDS finalization of negotiations.

They printed their NDS Review for member information and publicity from 1950 until they re-amalgamated with the Shorthorn Society in 1965. The review was an excellent production for a comparatively small organisation.

They closed their herd book in 1948 and finalized this in 1950; only progeny whose ancestry could be traced back to the first seven volumes for males and six volumes for females were accepted for entry from 1951 and at the same time they raised the fees to 7/6 for females and £1 for males.

Like other breeds and breeders in the early stages of the practice there was suspicion with regard to the advisability of A I. There are still some who do not support it. The association had accepted A I registrations from 1947. The centres were buying bulls and the council of NDS was adamant that only proven bulls should be allowed at these centres. In 1950 the society had not been in existence long enough to provide several such sires so there was a temporary hold up in this scheme, but by 1961 there were three bulls at centres.

Whether the selection process was biased in respect of colour is impossible to say but NDS cattle were predominantly roan then red with a few whites; a further aspect of the selection process may well have had a bearing on conformation as it was noticeable that the roan cattle were in a majority for quality of conformation.

The association held up to about 12 sales a year at venues such as Barnard Castle, Penrith, Leyburn, Kendal, Sedbergh and Kirkby Stephen and there was usually a good representation as there was at shows where there were NDS specialised classes for this Dales type section of the breed.

In the NDS classification of records by the MMB for 1955-56 they started to list them, first in 1956, 192 herds were recorded with averages

1956	7,774 lb for cows	6180 lb for heifers	@ 3.5%
1957	7,799 lb"	6,423 lb"	@ 3.6%
1958	7,828 lb "	6,559 lb"	@ 3.69%
1959	7,776 lb "	6,208 lb"	@ 3.69%
1959/60	7,901 lb "	6,481 lb"	@ 3.59%
1960/61	7,960 lb "	6,655 lb"	@ 3.61%

There were many excellent yields: cows like Kilne Hall Eva 3rd gave 16,860lb @ 3.19% in 1957.

The record for NDS cows was West Field Tiny with 21,119lb with her 8th calf in 1955/56 and Longburgh Kate held the lifetime yield with 169,150 lb in 10 lactations.

The highest herd average was in 1958 when W. Greenhow of Pittington, Durham, averaged 10,931lb for cows and 8,546lb for heifers.

Elmtree Sunlight: a typical Northern Dairy animal.

Those whose cattle were kept at heights under 1,000ft were J.F. Herdman of Alston with 9,745lb with 31 cows and between 1,000-2,000 ft was 9,745 lb with 15 cows.

In 1956 Mr. E. J. Robinson of Farleton's herd was showing a three year average of 10,673lb with 18 animals.

In 1960 Mr B. Walling's herd at Kendal averaged 10,141lb @ 4.39 % but with only 7 animals.

In 1961 Mr P. Milburn's Herd at Renick, Penrith, averaged 10,645lb@ 3.75% but with only 12 animals.

In 1962 Mr Greenhow's herd average was 10,501lb at 3.6 % with 11 cows.

L. Hutchinson and Son of Bishops Auckland won the Silcock Cup for the best NDS herd for 4 years with an average for 34 cows of 10,603lb at 3.38% and 7649lb for 22 heifers.

Rather than pushing for high yields, most breeders stressed the productive longevity of their cattle, a benefit of all Shorthorn types, and one excellent example of this was Redgate Tulip in the herd of E. L. Hutchinson and Sons; she gave 12,770lb in twelve lactations with a top yield of 13,029lb.

Many northern shows allocated classes for NDS which were well supported; the Royal Show had separate classes for a time. With good attendance at shows (e.g. 90 entries for Westmorland show in 1953) and publicity stands, as well as the *Breeder's guide*(the NDS review), there was quite a bit of publicity. The most beneficial events were the field days and one of the highest attendances, with 400 present, was at Mr G. W. Dent's farm at Wharton Hall, Kirkby Stephen, where he was running some 200 NDS and 800 Swaledales which were another of his great interests. The Dent families have all been very much involved with the NDS cattle and G .W. Dent has been more involved than most, having been President in 1959 and Vice President from when the association started. It was largely his thinking that brought about the association at which he seldom missed a meeting during its history.

He had a number of show winners and one of his greatest successes was when Brook Jennifer was Supreme Champion at the Great Yorkshire in 1953 when the NDS were first given their own classes, also at one time there were 29 bulls of his breeding in as many NDS herds.

So far as NDS were concerned they were able to have over 250 bulls licensed by 1958 so the word was spreading. A number of breeders also featured the dual purpose capability, rearing their steers on for beef as butchers stated that these cattle yielded meat of high quality and the killing out percentage was very favourable, for example with bullocks finishing out at around 9-11 cwt out of cows giving 8,260lb; another group reached 14 cwt 3 quarters at two and a half years of age which were purchased by the Ministry of Agriculture for, as they put it, '1,100 meals'! Another group out-wintered at the famous Cockle Park on silage alone, graded special, they were reared at 1,000 feet by Hugh Handley from Ravenstonedale, sired by a bull from a dam giving 17,190lb with her 4th calf. This group had a few at A+ (a grading category) and 59% killing out.

In 1954 two NDS females were Champion winners at the Scottish Dairy show: Manor Brenda, bred by Messrs Coward from Winton was Reserve Champion ' Shorthorn on Type'; she was beaten by supreme Champion Maggie from the herd of F. Brunskill of Appleby. The following show Maggie was supreme Champion all breeds at the event and in 1956 she was Royal Show Champion.

The association was slimming down; in 1952, the membership stood at 1,320 and in 1955 it was 1,003. Registrations of animals were 5,085 and if one considers that this figure should be added to the Shorthorn Society registrations of around 24,000 plus 11,000 grade stock, then the numbers of the breed were considerable. Many of the NDS members at that time would not have registered their stock with the principal Society so this was a considerable help to the breed.

Although NDS cattle were small in numbers, they exported to New Zealand, Africa and Australia; but around this time the tide was beginning to turn and Friesians were continuing to increase, despite the fact that a spokesman from that society was the *only* one to abstain from approving payment for milk on quality, saying '60% of sales are attributed to use with tea, coffee, or catering'! One recalls that at that time that breed was low in butterfat yields. The British Friesian Cattle Society was founded in 1909 and by 1911 they had 50 members. This

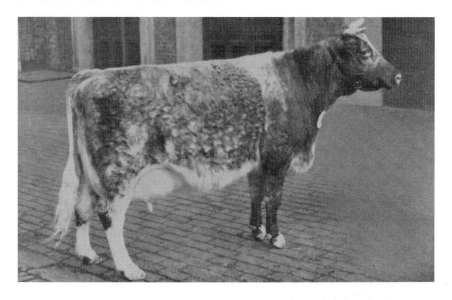

Maggie: all-breed Champion at 1955 Scottish Dairy Show.

had increased after a hiccup in imports, to 1,600 by 1921. They were on the march!

By 1959 a decline was very noticeable in the Shorthorn herd and this also applied to NDS despite the breed performing better on solids-not-fat than both the Ayrshire, which had had a flutter of popularity owing to it being further into accredited status, and the Friesian. Many reasons were given at the time: the dual purpose attitude meant lower yields; the post war payment system; the race for higher yields; the claim that too much attention was given to minor aspects such as horn shape; size, the tendency for Shorthorns to lose size, and so on. Whatever the cause the decline was ongoing.

The NDS was beginning to feel the draught economically and there was discussion on the subject of closer relationship with the Shorthorn Society as by 1960 they were down to 497 members and 1,856 registrations with 225 added in the Supplementary Register. By 1964 the membership had fallen to 302. There were talks about joint show classes with a joint stand and members were encouraged to attend one another's field days. A joint sale was planned in Penrith. Added to this, because of A I, there was a huge decline in the demand for bulls and this of course affected both societies, but the problem for most of these hill farms was the pressure of sheep competition and lack of suitable buildings so they were unable to intensify further and incomes continued to drop. Many dales farms were left derelict as hill farmers were having a very difficult time.

The association was suffering from severe financial cramp and as well as moves to work more closely with the Shorthorn Society by having a joint sale, the President of NDS was invited to special meetings about a merger in 1963. Inevitably negotiations continued in an effort to suit both organisations until in **1965 agreement was reached** with protective clauses:

• Existing members of NDS would gain membership of the Shorthorn Society free of entry fee

• NDS calves could go into Coates's book with ND incorporated in their registration and progeny of NDS females would be so designated for three generations but if these were mated to a Coates's registered bull the progeny would be denoted ND for two generations with bulls denoted for three generations.

• The two journals would be incorporated from 1965 so the last issue of NDS Breeder's Review would be the December 1964 issue. Also the NDS herd book would end.

• NDS would have up to three members on the SS council. The rest of the arrangements were financial and not relevant in this context but both organisations were adamant that this move would ensure the best interests of both the breeders and the breed.

It was also unique and fitting that one of the founder members was G.W. Dent and the final 'caretaker' on the Shorthorn council, to represent the members of NDS and their affairs, was his son, G.A. Dent.

The demise of such an organisation is always sad for those concerned but in this case it was not the fault of the members. More, it was caused by government policies and their consequences, also changing fashions. Many well known names continued with their type, such as Messrs. Birkett, Nicholson, Dent, Metcalf, Craig, Hutchinson, Sledge and many others who had done so much to further their cause; some had already got dual membership as they were adding other types but of the same breed.

Finally it is probably appropriate that I record the Presidents here as they also worked so hard for the organisation, which they headed: 1944-57 N. Field; 1958-59 A.L.Kidd; 1959-60 G.W. Dent; 1960-61 T. Addison; 1961-62 W. Rawling; 1962-63 J. R. Peart; 1963-64 W. Coulthard; 1964-65 A. Harker.

Whitebred Shorthorns

As in the north-east, where the Shorthorn evolved, the north-west region developed very successful derivations to suit their market and their climate. One of these types was what was known as the Cumberland White as distinct or derived from the Cumberland Shorthorn which was the type that played so much in the forming of the breed in Ireland. The Cumberland White also played a very important role in that part of the country for a different reason in that when joined with the hardy Galloway cow their progeny was the 'Blue-Grey' which made a name for itself as a fast maturing beast, so valued by feeders of beef cattle and in the early days Ireland was famed for producing these of great quality by the boat load!

The actual origin of this specialist type is somewhat obscure and it is this that serves as a reminder of the overwhelming importance of a breed's capability to withstand the test of time. It is known that it aroused interest in the border country over 100 years ago and one of the pioneers was David Hall of Larriston, Newcastleton, Roxborough, who, along with Andrew Park of Stelshaw, Bailey, Cumberland, sold Blue-Grey suckled calves in Newcastleton suckled calf sales in Roxburghshire, way back in the late 19th century, very successfully and consistently. Newcastleton is still the home of the Blue-Grey with sales held every October.

Breeders can remember the early 1900s when there were only five forward but as sales increased breeders would bring along the occasional Whitebred bull to follow the stores into the ring.

As entries improved, a decision was taken to sell the white cattle immediately following the Blue-Grey sale but even this arrangement failed to cope with escalating entries, which continued to increase as the popularity and demand for these cattle soared. The situation eventually got out of hand, so a specific day was allocated for the sale of Whitebred cattle.

It became increasingly obvious that this cross was producing fast-maturing store cattle and that these qualities could be developed in existing breeds of hill cattle.

It was in order to preserve its identity that **the Whitebred Shorthorn Association was formed**. At a meeting at the Greenhead Hotel. Greenhead, Northumberland, on **December 16th, 1961**, it was decided to consider the formation of a breed society and a working party was set up under the chairmanship of T. R .Johnson; this was followed on March 12th by a meeting of almost 200 interested breeders. There was an overwhelming vote to set up the association again with Mr Johnson as Chairman, J. Kilpatrick vice chairman, E. Stokoe secretary, with Sir Fergus Graham KBE as President. His Grace the Duke of Buccleugh,KT, GCCO, Lord Henly, Major J.E. Joicey, the Earl of Lonsdale and J. R. Blackett-Ord were all elected vice-presidents.

After the business was concluded Mr John Thornborrow, the Penrith auctioneer, stated he had been requested to attend the Shorthorn Society meeting. He intimated that the society was aware that an association was premeditated and it would be prepared to give all possible assistance if this occurred.

However the chairman in his reply stated that a similar association

A view of Northern Dairy cattle at Penrith sales.

had been contemplated some years ago and, although the Society had been contacted at that time, no interest had been shown so he considered that it was unlikely any advance would be made!

Like the Northern Dairy Shorthorn Association, a panel of inspectors was appointed to select the foundation stock, mainly in Cumberland, Northumberland, Dumfriesshire and Roxburghshire.

Cattle were inspected from 134 herds and 2,310 males and 506 females were entered in their first herd book and in 1966 the herd book was closed to foundation animals after volume 4.

Mr Eric Stokes remained as Secretary till May 22nd, 1978, when Rosie Mitcheson (née Little) took over, having served as assistant secretary for two years; she is still holding that position.

Mr John Kirkpatrick was association auctioneer until 1981 when Mr David Thomlinson took over and was joined by Mr John Wharton from 2002.

Sales continued to be held at Newcastleton and Bellingham in Northumberland until 1966 but the official Whitebred Shorthorn Sales were moved to Carlisle. Spring and autumn sales continue to be held there. One of the most successful sales was in 1971 when some records were broken. Supreme and male Champion Murtholm Investment, bred by I.S. Henderson, fetched 1,080 guineas, selling to R.B. Hope of Lockerbie; the reserve Champion Spittal Rover at 14 months of age, bred by Major Joicey, sold for 1,000 guineas to Brisbane Glen Estates.

Really good prices at that time. Definitely a good day as 204 bulls averaged 466 guineas and 85 females averaged 143 guineas.

The association continues to have some members who have interests with both the Whitebred and Shorthorn organisations.

Polled Shorthorns

Although the early work on polling was almost entirely done in the United States, the bloodlines used came from England. The term 'poll' or 'polled' means an animal without horns; where this is not entirely successful the term 'scurred' is used, indicating the animal has still got a rudimentary stubby indication of a horn which is not attached to the skull. This scurred factor is determined by another gene that manifests itself in polled cattle. If cattle are naturally polled, this is due to genes; this sometimes occurs naturally in a strain or in a breed such as Aberdeen Angus or the Red Poll where both are universally polled. The horn can also be removed very early in life by heat or chemical. The gene that determines the presence of horns is recessive to that which creates a polled and if it has a pair of recessive genes, it will be horned. Just to complicate things: if the genes are mixed, some progeny will be polled and some horned but sometimes the process is incomplete and so scurs appear. 'Homozygous' is when there are two like type pairs of genes and heterozygous are those where there are two mixed pairs. The naturally polled Shorthorns were originally known as Polled Durhams. One line can be traced back to a Gwynne of the Princess tribe, one of the oldest lines, going back to Medora by Horatio; another is descended from White Rose, an English bred cow by Publicola born in 1823, and the third was from Young Phyllis, bred by the Duke of Carlisle in 1831. These were all pure Shorthorn. Then there was a second type which were from American 'Muley' cows crossed to pure Shorthorn bulls.

In 1881 Dr William Crane from Idaho got interested in the possible benefits of polled cattle (ease of handling) and several people expressed a similar interest; Salem Clawson also could see the potential. J.H. Miller of Indiana joined in this a slow process of grading up from Durhams and these became known as Single Standard Polled Durhams. However, these were not pure-breds but were grade animals put to a pedigree shorthorn bull; consequently there were many animals discarded as having horns, or were bulls and could not be kept. In 1888 Capt. Miller from Ellmore heard of a Shorthorn herd in Minneapolis which was small but polled; after negotiation he bought twin animals born in 1881, Mollie Gwynne and Nellie Gwynne. He also bought a bull, King of Kine. All of these were out of a scurred cow, Oakwood Gwynne 4th, and also two yearling heifers .The twins were by 7th Duke of Hillhurst and the bull was sired by Bright Eyes Duke; all were registered in the

American Book, were hornless and were considered 'mutants', known later as 'sports'. So these were pure Shorthorn and this section became the basis for double standard polled Durhams. King of Kine was mated to his half-sister Nellie Gwynne and the result was history as they say. The calf Ottawa Duke, born in March 1890, was polled, eventually turning out to be a prolific sire with 54 sons and 75 daughters; he had been used in several herds in Michigan, Ohio and Kentucky. All his progeny were polled. There was another 'star': a bull Young Hamilton, born 1890, and his half-sister Mary Loudon, both bred exceedingly well.

The American Polled Durham Breeders association was set up in 1890 with their first herd book. It contained 185 bulls and 319 females.

These cattle traced back to Medora, White Rose and Young Phyllis, all imported cows, to whom nearly all today's cattle can be traced back. There were also two significant 'sports', Rose's Red Rover, born 1889, tracing back to Adelaide another imported cow, and Orphan Girl 1886, who traced back to Elizabeth, yet another imported animal by Memnonan.

By the time 10 herd books had been published 60,082 pedigrees had been included. The stipulation from the first was that stock must be 'at least one year old and hornless and have at least 75% shorthorn and the remainder must be from old Mulley strains'. In 1896 the rules were changed so that *only* progeny of recorded Durhams or registered Shorthorns could be recorded in the polled book and also that polled 'sports' should not be recorded, although it still allowed the progeny of a Shorthorn 'sport' and a recorded polled Durham.

Interest was spreading and very shortly 95% of those applying were double standard and this upset several and puzzled others as there were effectively all double standard Durhams which were Shorthorn but could not be called Shorthorns, so in 1919 the title was changed to Polled Shorthorns. It was also a problem publishing a separate herd book and not having one book including *all* Shorthorns so eventually it was agreed that they should be taken into the herd book with an X in front of their registration, so the original registry was discontinued in 1923.

Very soon 10% of all registrations in their book were polled and by 1948 there were some 51 cows with over 10,000lb milk and 39 had over 400lb of butterfat. Several high yields are to be found.

Pearl was the top at that time at 15,077lb with 642.4lb of fat and Emily set a double record of 14,038lb at 525lb fat followed by 13,734lb and 494lb.

Successes came in the beef section as well when in 1920 a polled steer won the carcass competition at the international show and was placed 4th over all breeds. At 26 months he weighed 1,280lb and dressed out at 64.92%.

In the UK interest was being shown by Mr H.B. Stirling of Allenbank, Edrom, Scotland. In 1932 he had been breeding his cattle to a Shorthorn of unknown breeding which was naturally polled; his sire was called Donald and one of the females he was mated to was a cow named Polly from Merse Biddy Broadhooks, who lived and bred till she was 16. Also in 1938 Mr Duthie Webster imported some in-calf pedigree heifers, a bull Red Star resulted from this import which went to Mr Stirling and in fact on the death of Mr Webster the remainder of his imports also went to the same herd in 1944. To this time no other polls were in this country, so Mr Stirling at Allenbank had to go it alone, but to add to his problems the Shorthorn Society were not accepting poll registrations! In 1948 a group of breeders commissioned Mr Harding of Anoka Farms, Illinois, to buy some suitable poll animals and his eventual consignment was of 2 bulls and 14 heifers, which went onto several, established breeders: Mr D. Stewart at Millhills, Sir James Denby Roberts, Bart. at Strath Allen and Messrs. W.B. and A.D. Robertson of Scotston.

Because of the Shorthorn Society's reluctance to register, these gentlemen and W. Stirling, R. A. ,L. Duncan of Auchterarder and J. B. F Coutts of Crieff formed the First Herd Book Membership of the **Poll Shorthorn Society of Great Britain in 1950**. The book emulated the Coates's Herd Book in its conditions and was strictly overseen. There was a prefix register and animals would carry P in their registration if they were polled or H if any came with horns; however scurred stock were also classified P.

Their secretary and office was with a firm of solicitors, Stevenson and Marshall, at 41 East Port. Dunfermline. The first directors were W.B. Robertson, Sir James Denby Roberts and D.M. Stewart. There was steady growth of interested breeders, including such illustrious names as Cecil Moores of Oldmelldrum, Capt. MacGillivray of Calrossie, Watt Taylor of Philorth, W. Young of Milnathort, Mary Furness of Otteringham, Pentecost of Cropwell and Gordon Blackstock at that time at Bapton, to name but a few.

By 1962 the Beef Shorthorn Society recognised the interest and influence in polled stock and the two organisations amalgamated and the situation today is that just over half the registrations are polled and an even greater percentage have polled breeding in their make up; but strangely the dairy sector in the UK has hardly used the polling blood lines.

Consider also that it was not until 1952 that *dehorned* females were allowed to be entered in show classes. It was not until 1960 that *dehorned* bulls could be exhibited.

Types evolved from the Shorthorn

LINCOLN RED

The Lincoln Red was originally the Lincoln Red Shorthorn in Coates's Herd Book and gradually by selection in the eastern counties developed as a dual purpose type, able to stand the rigours of the exposed conditions in that area. They formed their own society in 1896 'To secure uniformity of type and colour.' The first herd book registered 203 bulls and 917 females.

Then in 1935 they joined up again with the Shorthorn Society, so their next inclusions are in Vol. 82, 1936. They also had two representative members on the Shorthorn council.

It is believed the Lincoln Red Society was the first society to beef record.

The milking aspect has been somewhat forgotten today but those that followed this discipline got some quite respectable records with many herds averaging 3,500-4,500kg and individual records were as high as Kite Brook Rosemary of Chivers, giving 117,804lb with 9 calvings and Castle Acre Violet for W. Everington that gave two successive yields of 19,076lb and 18,131lb.

The breed was also used in the formation of the Pankota Red, which was 80% Lincoln Red Shorthorn and 20% in the Hungarian Pied.

Another home breed, the **Beefbilde**, founded by E. Penticost, had 55% Lincoln Red Shorthorn, 35% Poll Beef Shorthorn and 10% Aberdeen Angus.

In **1943** the Lincoln Red Society broke away again from the Shorthorn Society and in 1960 they dropped the word Shorthorn from their title. In 1977 they adopted a controlled development scheme. They were never a very large population but they have succeeded in making their mark with many achievements; however their history does not belong in this publication.

This section would not be complete without overseas shorthorn types which developed from British blood lines originally and also later had influences over here.

WEEBOLLABOLLA FROM AUSTRALIA

In 1848 the Weebollabolla cattle station was purchased from John Lee of New South Wales by Hall Brothers who had come out from England in the 1930s and were descended from Thomas Hall who had bred 'Tripes', the dam of the Princess family, the first family recorded in Coates.

In 1868 during one of Australia's periodical droughts the Hall brothers moved their stock to Weebolla, but in 1873 A.G.F. Munro, who had also emigrated from Scotland in 1868, purchased the station from the Halls with 500 cattle and a very numerous flock of sheep. He formed a family partnership including his brother W. R. Munro.

In 1902 they purchased a further stud up at Gooniwindi; during this period A.G.F. Munro had purchased many bulls from Britain. Among these in 1901 he imported Bovril and later Grand Duke of Ruddington from Mills of Ruddington; in 1908 King Jubilant and the following year Lord Weston. In 1909 he bought more locally, Grand Chat from Victoria, who was Grand champion in the Melbourne Royal Show.

By 1909 the partnership herd was 3,000 strong and after 1953 no bulls were used from outside the herd as there was such a wide gene pool.

Wallace Munro had a policy of breeding cattle for maximum profit; to do this they needed to be big and able provide the most weight to be sold at any age. He insisted on them having wide high pin bones and good wide hips also to have bulk and able to give quality milk to nourish their calves well. Furthermore he believed, regardless of fashion, in ensuring a common uniform type throughout. Cattle were stocked in small (by their standards) paddocks with two and a half percent bull coverage and they reckoned to brand 90% each year. A further consideration was capital investment; he reckoned in 1972 on $50 of land in the poor areas and up to $600 on the good or river land.

In the days of World War I when the Stud Breeders' Association was formed, Munro strongly disagreed with the policies of the organisation and would not register but he founded a herd of polled cattle at Boonal Boggabilla which was kept completely separate. In 1934 small cattle were also the fashion but R. F. Munro refused to go down that route in his area and his persistence was justified. Poll bulls were gradually introduced and they joined the poll society and one can tell the influence of these cattle firstly by their spread but also by their regular customers: 1,600 bulls were sold in Queensland, 415 to Alexandria Down alone, and the greatest number sold in one season was 603 bulls. They also exported overseas to Canada, South Africa and the Solomon Islands. In 1962 W. F. Munro took over on the death of his father.

In 1968 the herd set up a non-registered record with an average of $1,116 for 146 bulls; the top was $2,600 for a three-year-old poll weighing 1969lb. His sale was to celebrate 100 years of Weebollabolla shorthorns and the first lot sold for $2,000 for a four-year-old weighing 2,335lb. A Miss Golden had such confidence she purchased eight bulls for $6,300; another quantity buyer was the Manaroo Station which finished the remarkable day with five for an average of $1,300. In 1983 at their sale over 240 bulls went with a top price of $ 8,100. Ten poll bulls averaged $2,765, 14 unregistered horned bulls averaged $2,321, 37 unregistered bulls sold to average $1,659; 75 horned bulls averaged $1,405; with the

Ronnie Henderson with Weebollabolla Royal Commission

pound worth 1.62 Australian dollars, the sale average was £1,030. Sale averages at that time were impressive:

1972	144	avg $1, 660	1973	154	avg $3,492
1974	133	avg$1,180	1975	137	avg $1,134
1976	137	avg$801	1977	145	avg $665
1978	144	avg $1,154	1979	145	avg $1935
1980	136	avg $1,368	1981	146	avg $1,732
1982	118	avg $1,551			

Such was the satisfaction and loyalty that one northern territory company bought 3,000 bulls from this company over 14 years and over 16,000 bulls were sold from the Munro company since its inception to 1971.

Their most recent sale demonstrated continued demand and loyalty to this special type: 118 bulls sold to average $4,653 with a top of $14,000, made up of 36 registered polls, averaging $5,014, 55: polls $4,127,27; horned $5,241. The volume buyers were Stockport Pastoral who took 10 bulls at $3,300 average and Woods of Boggabilla who took 5 bulls at average of $3,700. (The conversion then was 2.4$ to the £1)

With such figures one can recognise the reputation of this type and it was why Weebollabolla Royal Commission was one of the first to be bought over to Britain to help correct the size problem. In working condition, he weighed 2,634lb at eight years of age. Bought in by the Henderson brothers, he sired many prizewinners and fine daughters as well as grand Champion and junior Champion at Perth.

ILLAWARRA FROM AUSTRALIA

Supposedly originally a dual-purpose breed, but for a long time it has really been developed as a dairy animal, with its own society since 1930. This derivation came about almost by accident as the Shorthorn breeders in the Illawarra area of Australia were running out of suitable bloodlines to improve their herds and there was not much in the district to appeal to them; there were other breeds with bulls producing good stock at that time – Ayrshire, Lincoln Red and Devon were involved and were winning awards at local shows, so catching the eye of breeders in the locality of Kiama, Sidney, Albion Park and elsewhere who were seeking to better their results. Not too much was recorded at that time but bulls such as the Duke of Argyll and Major and Dunlop were used with success; these were predominately Ayrshire owned by a keen improver, Evans of Dapto, who also had an excellent show winner and dominant sire, Robin Hood, who won consistently at Kiama and Sydney.

All these were dark red or red and white: the 'Durhams' (as Shorthorns were known) in those days, although big framed, were with long teats and untidy udders which this infusion of breeding succeeded in improving, so much so that cattle like Honeycomb and Honeycomb Lady were continuous show Champions against all breeds at a number of shows. In 1910 the Illawarra Milking Shorthorns Society was formed and almost at the same time the Milking Shorthorn of Australia Association was also formed; unfortunately friction developed between the two over the use of the title Shorthorn that was being used by the

New Park Queenie 21st. An excellent example of the Illawarra breed. She measures 56 inches at the shoulder and gave 16,180 lb @ 3.9% 1st lactation and 18,155 lb @ 3.7% 2nd lactation.

Illawarras despite the fact that the Sidney show recognised the two types. The Illawarra Shorthorn Association, as it then became, was having considerable success with animals such as 'Gold', bred by J.W. Cole of Jimberoo (5 times Champion at Kiama), whose sire was milking Shorthorn type Comet and others such as Flower of Mayfield and Fussy 2nd with successful sires such as Earl of Beconsfield and Warrior being used. Eventually, as mentioned, the Illawarra type became fixed with predominantly roan colours until about 1910 and then the rich red, with the familiar pronounced wedge shape they have today, predominated. They dropped the word Shorthorn. One of the best known Illawarras was Melba 15th of Darbalara who created a world record when weighing over one ton, giving 1941.1lb of fat in 365 days.

Illawarras have been exported all over the world to New Zealand, South Africa, Canada, USA, India, Parkistan, Korea, Thailand, the Philippines and Europe.

The society continues to thrive and by 1998 they had 350 members and recorded 16,500 Illawarras.

MANDALONG

This is another type in Australia and is in fact quite similar to the Weebollabolla in that it was developed in one area, Mandalong, near Sidney *but* it is a blend developed from Shorthorn, Charolais, Chianina, Brahman and Australian British White.

5. Irish Shorthorns

Ireland has always had a great reputation for high quality cattle and the Shorthorn has played a major part in this. Owing to the separation of the country in 1922 following the treaty of 1921 and with a separate government in Dublin, I decided to cover much of the detail the whole island in a section on its own. The breed has been more prominent in the south in recent years, as will be seen, because of the differing type that it favours. Early records are not clear but the first recorded introduction of Shorthorns was by Sir Vane Tempest of Co. Durham, who sent some 'Teeswaters ' to his estates in the north at Glenarm in 1812 and these were 'of the Shorthorn breed from Collings'. It is fairly certain that there were also other importations previous to this of the Cumberland type as they were in close proximity to Ireland. In 1812 it was recorded that there were '10 Shorthorns at Ballinasloe from Sir Thomas Newcommen, the Rev. Dean Burke, John Trench and W G Adamson'. In 1816 Mr Luke White of County Dublin purchased Agamemnon 9th by Pilot from Richard Booth, then at Studley, who was a very influential sire with a huge reputation.

In 1818 Sir Robert Bateson of Belvoir Park, Belfast, established a very successful herd with the idea of improving what he termed, 'the Indigenous cattle which are small, light and various'. This presumably excepted the Kerry breed which was already established but somewhat localised in the area of the south west of Ireland. The Longhorn had been used successfully as in England and there were several well known herds throughout Ireland at the time but they became supplanted by the Shorthorn doing its work as 'the Great Improver' as it had now become known.

The country had a very substantial export trade and even in the 16th century as many as 100,000 live cattle were shipped to Britain. By 1906 their total exports were £46 million of which £9 million, or $1/5$ was attributed to cattle. Such was their fame that as early as 1815 shipments were sent to the USA.

The trade then, as later, was for beef cattle but as the economy changed as the dual purpose demand increased and the Irish farmer decided that in general the type required was that bred by Booth and the Collings. It was not until the time of the Irish depression that some decided to swing to Bates dairy type with quite large herds like Kirker of House, Belfast, being set up. It was established that dual purpose herds were quite capable of good yields, with records, as will be seen later, of 800 -1,000 gallons.

In the early days the type stamped on Irish cattle was consistent with the type of farming carried on in large parts of the country: largely grass based so milk production was very seasonal. The Shorthorn had, and has, an amazing ability to recover from the rigours of winter having foggage (long mature grass still on the stalk, to be grazed) or hay diet and with the coming of spring grass quickly assume a completely new look!

After the Irish land act of 1881 Irish farms were in general small tenanted family units and in those days many were on subsistence levels although there were a few with larger units like Bertram Barton in Kildare with 175/200, Major Craddock in Tipperary with 120 and the Duke of Northumberland with 200.

Consistent exporters at the time from the mainland were Christopher Mason of Chilton in Durham whose eventual dispersal had a huge influence on Irish cattle breeding, and Lord Althorpe, whose Wiseton herd was in fact a major purchaser at this sale sending many cattle over through the years with several influential sires from excellent families.

Regular importers with quality herds themselves were Robert Holmes of Athlone and Robert La Touche of Kildare, both of whom favoured the Booth type; they also bought from Cruickshank whose influence had so quickly spread around the world including Ireland and the amazing figure of 1,912 cattle were sold from this one herd for export.

Irish breeding was obviously considerably set back by, first, the potato famine of 1845 where so many people died and which had been preceded by a national outbreak of what was described as cattle lung distemper in 1842 with huge losses. Comparatively soon after both came the depression of 1879 and for a time in the severe financial climate, pedigrees were allowed to lapse. But after a time, in the recovery period, the breed was expanded with more breeders and bloodlines, which can be illustrated by comparative breeder statistics with 57 registered breeders in 1867; 182 in 1902. It went up to 578 in all Ireland by 1957. But all was not bleak and in 1870, Joseph Meadows of County Wexford was the first Irish owner to win the English Royal Show with a bull, Bolivar, which was bred by W.S. Marr; in fact this animal succeeded in winning a first at three successive Royals as well as countless other shows.

Progress was not only in the south as men like H. Richardson of Fermanagh and Sir John Leslie in County Monaghan founded some notable and long lasting families. The Earl of Caledon from Co.Tyrone bred one of the most famous bulls to go to the Argentine for the highest price at that time – named Farrier and sold to Senior Leonardo Pereyra. Among many influential and successful sires in Ireland from this herd was Sign Of Riches, purchased from W.S. Marr at Uppermill. He had won both the Highland and Dublin Royals and was in fact sire of the above Farrier. In later years the Earl's daughter-in-law, the Hon. Mrs H.C. Alexander, had a very famous herd with the prefix Domville following Bates lines. Other influential herds at this time were those owned by the Lyles at Donaghmore, whose herd was founded in 1857, Walter Crawford of Tullyhogue, County Tyrone, and Tom Conelly, which were founded on Cruikshank and Duthie lines. Conversely A. Kirker of Belfast had a large herd along Bates lines, as did Rev. Moutray in County Tyrone although he introduced Booth breeding later.

This brief coverage of the early years would not be complete without mention of the herd from the Midlands of Louth where Lord Rathdonnel's select herd was founded, before being transferred to Co. Carlow. Founded in the late 1880s, this herd produced Anchor and Arthur, two very influential sires of Medora breeding. The former won 1st prizes at Dublin, the Highland and the English Royal, a very rare feat. The Gypsy families came from his adviser Richard Chaloner, who was arguably one of the greatest influences in the early days, from Meath. A consistent winner at both Dublin and Belfast, he too preferred Booth lines and selected this type from a number of herds in England, Scotland and Ireland. He hired his sires out to his neighbours who he considered would benefit. Chaloner's fame spread and buyers even came from USA and elsewhere so it was partly this that made him decide to sell his herd in 1860. It was such a success that he decided to start again with heifers from Mr Torr of Aylesby and Warlaby bulls from the Booths and others. In 1869, possibly spurred on by his previous success, he decided to sell this herd as well! Yet again it was a success so, lo and behold, he started again winning hosts of prizes with his resulting stock and cashed in again in 1878. This time he retained a strain, however this time he was beaten by the 'Grim Reaper' and passed away 1879.

In Ireland as in England and Scotland the breeders were so numerous it is not possible to mention all in such a brief outline of the period before the century but again it would not be right to move on without a mention of J. G. Wood, or Grove as he later became, by deed poll. He was a tremendous enthusiast for the Booth families, securing a number of their cows and using several of their bulls at Castlegrove in Co. Donegal. There he had great success breeding cattle of quality which were in much demand.

During the latter part of the century the continuing fashionable demand for Booth encouraged men like Talbot-Crosbie in Kerry at Ardfelt Abbey and Nathaniel Barton of Kildare who both bought and sold stock in England and Scotland securing cattle from Uppermill, Sittyton, Aylesby, Warlaby, Althorpe and Bapton, to name but a few sources.

One of the points continually made at this time was not only the fleshing and early maturing of the Scottish Shorthorn but also its milking ability being able to 'produce an average of 24 quarts a day and still provide stylish frames Thickly Fleshed'. With these capabilities they were like their Scottish contemporaries and were exported to USA, Argentina, France, Germany, Australia and Canada; but also like their Scottish contemporaries there was already a tendency to lose size.

Even during the time after the depression, around 1879, the Royal Dublin Society (known here after as the RDS), the oldest Society of its kind, having been established in 1731, was assisting administer public funds and livestock in particular, with schemes for breed improvement by bull selection and premiums at shows. This was largely brought about because of the effects of the depression when pedigrees lapsed and also farmers were inclined to save by the use of 'scrub bulls' in their efforts to economize. Both the Government and the RDS were extremely conscious of the need to retain their trade for top quality stores which would be lost if something were not done. With the coming of the 20th century and expansion, coupled with the need for extra income sources, there was a swing to produce milk to supply the city areas and the creameries but at the time this was more noticeable in the north where there was a tendency to find more of the Bates type.

In the south this trend was tempered by a tendency to retain a prominence of the Booth types and their local adaptation to this was to be the unique type which in later years was so sought after by the Americans to improve their cattle and meet their changing trade. They sought the large framed milky animal producing a good calf.

In **1901** the Irish Department of Agriculture, called the Department, was formed. At this time the Shorthorn was the dominant breed by far and had been since the late 19th century and continued till the middle of the 20th century; however the Department was worried by the quality of the store cattle being produced. The Department gradually took over the livestock improvement schemes also selecting bulls at shows and sales for use by the small tenant farmers who had not been able to afford such sires.

The Department also drew up schemes for premium bulls to go, at a fixed fee and special terms, to areas of poor land in the west. These were often selected at the bull sales in Dublin and this event attracted huge crowds. Similar sales developed in Belfast but without the same government support structures. Nevertheless it was at Belfast where they held what was to be known as the biggest sale ever held in all Ireland in **1908** with over 500 entries.

In **1907** the Association of Irish Shorthorn Breeders was formed to 'promote and improve the Shorthorn' and was in effect the first of the regional associations. They began with this position of comparative

Shorthorns and Kerrys at Tipperary market, 1910.

strength with the breed being so prominent and proceeded to a catastrophic fall from grace. The cause was a chain of events which is described below.

The pertinent facts were spread over quite a period and consequently were harder to follow at the time; with hindsight all is glaringly obvious.

The breed in Ireland was formed mainly on the Booth type and developed to suit the climate, conditions and situation; this had produced a large-framed milky animal which produced a very good surplus calf – in itself a vital contributor to profitability especially while there was a demand for 'baby beef '. All the while the milk price was very low and it was not till the 1950s that the price of milk exceeded one shilling (5 new pence) a gallon. Thus for a long period the surplus calf was a relatively large portion of the producer's income. It will be seen that the relative prices profoundly influenced breeding policy and ultimately the fortunes of the breed. The underlying causes of the decline that occurred from the late '50s and early '60s went much further back.

The demand for smaller beef joints increased in the '30s and to achieve this and maximise income, the farmers in the majority used the early maturing Scottish bulls on their cows. In this genetic case it tended to reduce the milking ability and reduce adult cow size but of course the cattle were still Shorthorn. The Department attempted to remedy the situation by introducing English dairy strains from such sources as the famous Reading sales but these in the main were smaller and lighter-boned than the Irish types; this had the effect of reducing both size and quality of the resulting calf, in fact it did little to bring back the milk yields sufficiently. It is fascinating and infuriating that sometimes genetics just do what is not expected, a fact which will later be demonstrated in another context.

At the end of the World War II the trade in live cattle for fattening gained momentum and the crossing of Shorthorns with Hereford and Angus became popular; this increased prices but decreased the Shorthorn base herd and furthermore the females went, in many cases, into the commercial milking herd, further reducing the milk yield. It must also be borne in mind that the Hereford or Angus cross were colour marked (calves were white-faced or black). There was much debate about this at the time as Shorthorn breeders, while having to admit this was so, contended that fatteners should know a good potential beef store. To a degree they had a point but a number of dairy farmers would at one stage buy stores for finishing and would be influenced by the colour mark to identify the cross. Added to this the fatteners paid a very high price for the 'blue-grey' heifers to be used as beef dams.

Down in Eire there were still several influential herds, as will be mentioned, which maintained their faith in the Bates type and continued to breed quality dairy stock with excellent yields; there was no separation in the herd book so the uninformed might well use a beefing type sire inadvertently. In the south-west of Eire in Co.Clare and Limerick there were several small farms that were, or had been, pedigree or even in some cases not used any Scottish beef or English dairy bulls and some of these were destined to gain tremendous attention in the not too distant future.

Like other countries, Ireland introduced a scheme for the eradication of bovine tuberculosis and their scheme gathered momentum in the 1950s; but there was quite a problem in this respect as many milking herds were slaughtered. The predominance of the national milking herd being Shorthorn, this had a devastating effect just at a time when milk prices were climbing and making an increasing contribution to the farmers' incomes. Replacements were urgently required, thus creating a fantastic opening for the up and coming Friesian breed.

By then the A I service could provide good quality dual purpose Friesian bulls, their progeny, although from Shorthorns, came looking like Friesians. Again the lack of colour marking had its effect as, although the stock was in most cases 50% Shorthorn, the Friesian got the credit when in reality it was probably the Shorthorn improver genes that had ensured the quality of the stock.

The increased milk yield of the Friesian continued the impetus and again this received a boost when Eire entered the Common Market as this coincided with a significant increase in the milk price. However almost at the same time there was an increase in milk production through the introduction of the Holstein strain; however, the Holstein was no good for beef and therefore the surplus calves fetched a dramatically low price.

Towards the end of the 1960s the Department, alerted by beef producers, recognised that the decline in the Shorthorn breed was a 'bad thing'; so they introduced a Government-sponsored cattle study group which eventually reported in **1968.** The outcome of this was a state-sponsored scheme run in full co-operation with the Shorthorn Cattle Society of Great Britain and Ireland and also the breeders, with the aim of re-establishing the Shorthorn as a major breed and influence. The scheme sought to identify and then propagate the type of the breed best suited to their national economic circumstances. Department officials and a panel of breeders carried out selection of stock jointly. Financial incentives were given for the retention and propagation of selected animals and all these were allocated a separate section in the herd book. Selection was rigid and out of every 10 females inspected only about one was approved; bulls were even more selectively chosen. Only 375 were selected in the first two years. However from 1970-76 the figures were considerably increased with 26,000 inspected and 1,250 selected. Of these 915 actively participated and there were also 25 bulls.

The tables below show the population changes in the south:

| Premium Bulls | 1960 Shorthorn | 436 | Friesian | 7 |
| | 1970 Shorthorn | 63 | Friesian | 84 |

A I	1950 Shorthorn	38.7%	Friesian	4%
	1962 Shorthorn	29%	Friesian	28%
	1970 Shorthorn	9.4%	Friesian	36%

| Populations | 1960 Shorthorns 993,000 | Friesians 78,000 |
| | 1970 Shorthorns 683,720 | Friesians 791,877 |

The Department is to be congratulated for its action and support. Would that the British Government could be so sympathetic to our agricultural problems. The breed and breeders must be grateful to the wisdom of the Department, the Minister of Agriculture of the day, Neil Blaney, together with his many officials. Particularly men like Dr Austin Mescal who took such an interest in the scheme and the breed; he later accepted the Presidency of the Shorthorn Society following his retirement from the Department; also his able assistant Jim Flanagan who succeeded him and men like Joe O'Cane. In more recent times, around 1992, the milk price was 'stagnant' and profitability of milk dropped; the increasingly Holstein national herd had irregular breeding, a short herd life and unwanted calves. The increase in Shorthorn awareness was evident with its ability to produce quality milk efficiently, breed regularly and last through many lactations with an essentially productive longevity, it was once more in the commercial producer's eye.

European proposals also increased the demand for calves of substance and quality and the picture is now improving; furthermore the ability of the Irish Shorthorn, like its Scottish and English counterparts, is increasingly recognised. Its mothering ability, coupled with its ability to produce the type of beef required, and the greatly improved milking ability of the dairy type, means there is renewed interest. Trade at the beginning of the new century is buoyant.

No one can deny that much of the problem, emphasised as it was by the mixing of the 'strands,' resulted in cattle in Ireland that, as elsewhere, were not suited to their trade. *But* what is also evident is that almost too late the problems were recognised. With the support of the Eire Department and with the full co-operation of the breeders the re-creation of, in this case, the Irish type was re-established and it was this type that created the overseas interest once more.

Going back to the 1970s an American buyer, who came in fact to see Irish Simmentals, glimpsed the Irish Shorthorn in the south-west ; this was the start of, firstly, the renewal of interest but also the renewal of a lucrative export trade. As at the time it was the smaller herds that had most of this type, it was they who gained most of the benefit.

Cattle have been exported to a number of countries but mainly the USA where this particular breeding has had a huge effect; they were searching for an answer to their problems of loss of bone and size at the time. Indeed the interest spread around the world. The scheme encountered two problems: firstly, in Eire this type was scarce and also the bloodlines were narrow. Secondly, the endless increase in milk price at that time did not encourage a type that laid emphasis on the value of the calf. As ever, times change, the pendulum is swinging and the other factor emphasised is that the type of cattle produced is never 'all things for all men' in all countries or markets. There are often huge variables and circumstances can bring about a particular demand; hence the huge value in the past of semen banks and organisations like the Rare Breeds Survival Trust, also gene banks and DNA; time will no doubt bring other problems but the huge variety of types within the Shorthorn means the breed will have the answer.

To return to breeding through the period: all over Ireland, as elsewhere, Shorthorn herds were being founded and making their contribution to the expansion of the breed but inevitably some will have left more of a mark or influence. In fact by **1938** there were over 1,000 Shorthorn herds in Ireland, but most of them were non-pedigree. A few of the principal herds (as well as those already mentioned) from the North were the Crawford brothers, W. R. and T. J., of Tullyhogue, who were great influencers of the breed. T. J. bought the bull Baron of Tullyhogue in 1897 after he had won at Belfast, promptly sold him to the Argentine and the resultant publicity 'awoke' the breeders, both north and south and also bought British exporters to both Belfast and to the Royal Dublin Society (RDS) bull sales.

This snowballed, and Irish buyers went to English and Scottish sales to purchase bulls that they could use and emulate the Crawford success. The Cookstown Show was establishing itself also as the venue for the top bulls of the year and in the boom of 1919 Windmill Golden Crest sold at 3,000 guineas, Inverchin Ballechin made 1,250 guineas and Fernhill Mariner sold at 1,000 guineas. The Inverchin bull had earlier been bought at Perth for 350 guineas.

Unfortunately the generated interest was very largely squashed in the autumn slump of 1919 but by the end of this the Argentine trade had swung the fashion to short-legged bulls and this was the start of the rot, coupled with the slump when only the top sold, so the slump increased. The main results of this were: (1) The loss of size, (2) The loss of milk, (3) The loss of substance. It was not until the 1950s that the long road back was on the horizon.

There was still confusion in respect of the Scotch or dairy type issue as Tom Lyons MP, at that time President of the Ulster Shorthorn breeders Association, recalled in 1947: 'There are anomalies, as in 1921 the supreme Champion at RDS was recorded as a roan dairy Bull and every sire in his pedigree was Scotch (beef) Shorthorn, the same applied to the reserve supreme.'

Another set of brothers, the Perrys of Killane and Fourtowns, created lines which bought some success to the dairy type from English lines, but still the Irish quest for increased size was dominant. One of the oldest herds in Ireland is that of the Lambe Brothers at Ballytrain, Castleblaney, Co. Monaghan; they had run a non-pedigree herd for over 100 years and only decided to go pedigree in 1970 as many did during the Irish Improvement Scheme.

One of the characters of the breed was the Taoiseach, W. T. Cosgrove; also, in a different way, Father, later Cannon, Michael Connolly of Bondoran, Co. Donegal, who had only a small herd but won many awards at shows, both north and south. There were several members of the clergy with Shorthorn interests: Bishop McNeely of Raphoe, also the Cictercions of Mount St Joseph and Cannon Quinn of Ballynote to name but a few.

Ireland was also full of brother and family partnerships, such as B. C. and R.A. Williams of Clough Jordan and the very influential Wrights of Kildare whose herd, Kilkea, had been started in 1896. R.K. Wright farmed with his son Edward and **Pumplestown** nearby was farmed by J.F. Wright, brother to R.K. Both had considerable success in the show ring and with their exports. The herds had consistent inputs of Calrossie and Collynie breeding. The group Championships at the RDS in the years between 1936-48 were won consistently by Kilkea- or Pumplestown-bred animals and in 1948 5 out of the 40 entries were bred at Kilkea, 14 Kilkea bulls were shown and again all gained rosettes including the Championship and reserve Champion.

In the years 1938-40 Kilkea won the Championships and reserve Championships at the RDS for the best bulls in Ireland. In 1949 Kilkea won the handsome Phoenix cup for the best yearling bull outright, having won it three times. Edward Wright was the youngest judge ever to officiate at the Royal show in England and he also judged at Perth in 1949.

Pumplestown was equally successful for J.F. Wright as Pumplestown Rover by Calrossie Royal Sovereign sired the supreme, two-year-old, and junior Champions and four first prizes at Palermo show shortly after going to the Argentine. He had already sired the Champion at Montevideo, Uruguay. Pumplestown Golden Miller, purchased by

Magheramorne Masterkey

Hugh Maude for the record price of 1,000 guineas in 1947, won RDS championships on three separate occasions. The RDS was a good hunting ground for the herd as it won two female Champions, two reserve Champions, the male supreme and male reserve up to 1949. Possibly their main export success was the consignment of eleven to Canada. Wright's bulls Pumplestown Goshawk and Battleship were probably his best known.

Another very consistent breeder and winner was Major H.C. Robinson of **Magheramorne,** Co. Antrim, who took the Champion of all Ireland award with Magheramorne Masterkey sired by Cruggleton Rock, who had taken the Championships at Belfast and/or Dublin for three successive years; this herd had also supplied the Champion female at Dublin and Belfast with Glenanne Clipper 19th. In fact 8 exhibits had taken 7 firsts, one third and all the championships, a truly remarkable performance.

Herds like the last few were often in front in the show line up of their dairy colleagues but many of those and others were also concerned not only by this anomaly but by the loss of size on the dairy side and many were saying they did not maintain their milking ability, despite this being disproved as many produced proven yields of 1,000 gallons. The problem of the undivided herd book and lack of individual bloodline understanding was largely to blame, added to the fact that there was a tendency towards reducing size also causing lowering of yield; but at the time this talk was overdone.

A further breeder who preferred Scottish lines was R. Gallagher, of Cappaghmore; *but* he insisted that all his females must qualify for the dairy register. He had many show and milking trial successes and a similar Scottish enthusiast was James King of Clougher, Ballymea, who had a small select herd.

Influential families in the north as far as the breed is concerned were the Bests of the Cairn, Aghalee, Co. Antrim: W. E. Best and then his son R.D. Best, who was President of the Shorthorn Society (1966-7) as well as being connected with the Royal Ulster show society and chairman of a number of organisations. They were followers of the Scottish type but were very concerned about the loss of size, which was occurring and they sought to maintain size in their cattle. Much of this stock went back to an influential sire Sunrise who was also a successful show winner.

Bates type followers included Sir Gilbert Greenall, later Lord Daresbury, with the **Loubagh** prefix, who had been one of the fortunate buyers from Taylor of Cranford, Middlesex, and Lord Rothschild of Tring, Herts; but when he died in 1938 a number of these went back to England to Sir Henry White-Smith. One of the earlier successful herds was the Moffat family of Ballylyl and Co. Wexford, who ran about 50 head and were noted sellers of these bloodlines.

One of the larger units was that of John Byrne of Wallstown Castle, Co. Cork, with around 170 head, specialising in milk production and having regular sales consignments of bulls in the Cork sales but also selling privately.

During all this period the swing followed the fashion trend: the cattle tended to lose scale and size and obviously in Ireland particularly in the south this had an effect on the very important store trade as well as yields. These factors, coupled with the idea of A I and the start of the black and white trend, it took its toll.

There were several misgivings on ethical grounds both in Ireland and in the UK concerning the A I concept: if it took off it would decimate the bull trade, so there were commercial misgivings as well. Logic finally won and by the 1960s there were 14 Shorthorn bulls in the north, 70 in the south as well as the other breeds of beef and dairy cattle in both regions; although there were still reservations in the many small herd owners, they swung over to A I but the bull sales at the RDS and Belfast and other centres continued with bulls subject to strict inspection and for approval for licence and some for A I.

At this point it may be appropriate to refer to the two main centres for sales and shows as well as education and agricultural excellence: the RDS site and the Balmoral, Royal Ulster, site. They also became great social centres with the consequent incredible atmosphere. Sadly in recent times the RDS has been forced to give up the cattle sales and

Deerpark Leader.

agricultural shows as traffic congestion problems made it virtually impossible for exhibitors and visitors. So no longer are the assignations below the famous clock! But the summer horse show continues, so all is not lost! The spring show has been re-located out of the city; atmosphere and scale are lost but the work for agriculture continues.

In modern times the peripatetic ploughing match continues, an international event that everyone should visit at least once in their life as one of those unique experiences. It has massive livestock and machinery exhibits in an entirely different way and if you are there it feels as if the whole world is there too! I digress.

The aim of the A I facility was to enable both the commercial man and the pedigree breeder to access better genetics and create an improved national herd; but it also meant that the demand for bulls dropped like a stone resulting in a huge loss of income for those in that sector of the industry. On the plus side the value in breeding terms could be much better analysed across a number of bloodlines with modern techniques; yields and conformations could be very closely monitored. One of the principal supporters from the initial days of the improvement scheme was Dermot Cahill of South Eastern Cattle breeders who had implicit faith in the future of the type of Shorthorn and gave tremendous help with the A I development.

With this facility, coupled with the Department's Improvement Scheme, the Irish cattle situation was revolutionised.

As well as a lack of Shorthorns, the coming of the black and whites combined with the introduction of the Continental beef breeds at almost the same time further hit the breed. It was already out-marketed, so the hoped for turn around was slower than it would otherwise have been. Those concerned in the Department were quite right in their assumptions that there were other very useful genes 'out there' which had not been tapped and these turned out to be largely in the south-west. With the introduction of the scheme many herds were physically inspected and those who were in many cases almost unknown offered their stock. Small herds whose owners were content with their own Irish type and had used few if any of the outside sires came forward. They were in several cases born 'stockbreeders' who could identify suitable genes. The most outstanding and exciting of these were the **Highfield** and **Deerpark** owners. Naturally there were others but it was mainly these two herds that literally hit the beef world; they proved to be almost a fairy story.

First **Deerpark**: the Quane family, two brothers, Ned and Michael, both single men, and their sister farmed in a very quiet area but had a well known pig unit and a stud of Irish Draught horses as well as their milking herd. The latter went back to 1919, when the brothers attended Kilfinane Fair and took a shine to an attractive heifer which was to become the founder of their famous Scarlet family. Their herd was officially recorded for milk and butterfat by the Cow Testing Association.

This Scarlet family bred a bull who was used by the Quanes and their neighbours, as was the custom; so it was that this bull's daughters were often top of the other herds in this Association with yields of 4% fat being commonplace and milk yields well over 1,000 gallons, some of which records I saw personally. Their cows, about 25 of them, were kept in the shadow of the Galtee mountains and always out, calved with the spring grass and were in fact fed little else with only hay or foggage in the winter and of course hand milked until 1972. In 1942 they found another 'huge' female at the Mitchelstown fair. They stressed that they never used Scottish bulls and used one of the Department bulls once only and swore never to do so again! In many ways the brothers disagreed with the Department. They did not start registering until the start of the Irish Improvement Scheme so attention was not focused on them until their first bull at the RDS bull sales topped the sale at 1,700 guineas. This was the now world famous Deerpark Leader 4th. They sold two others at Cork and Limerick and each topped the sales.

Other families were: Tulip, which produced Deerpark Leader 5th, Kildysart from the O'Gradys of Limerick, Strawberry, and Cocked Horn developed from other heifers bought at Irish fairs. Remembering the

Highfield Improver

cattle only received grass the weight figures of their cattle illustrate the incentive to use this breeding at the time, with cows weighing 1,200-1,600lb and bulls 2,400-3,000lb. Their 12-month of age figures were 1,200lb for males and 900lb for females. Word spread through the cattle world and one Dick Judy from USA thought he should take a look and promptly signed a 3-year contract to buy all calves. Ned died but at the time of writing Michael, in his 90s, alert and unchanged in his character, is still with us.

Another herd of similar type was the **Highfield** herd of Matthew and John Malloney, another single man (both single men) but like the Quanes so hospitable that many gatherings were held in their parlours! Later John seemed to take over more of the running of the farm and his office was somewhat unusual with most of it in his lorry and some even in his fridge! This herd, like Deerpark, was kept out day and night and was only fed hay at calving time. The two herds worked very closely together with bloodlines being exchanged. They both took part in the Department's Beef Recording Scheme and the cattle from this herd recorded regular weight gains of 2.92lb per day for heifers and 2.52 per day for steers in figures produced in 1978.

It was from this herd that Highfield Rathcannon created a world record at a sale in Illinois USA in **1978** when a $^2/_3$ share of him was sold at $48,000; the sale averages were $5,297 for females with a top of

$9,200 and males to $23,925 average in what was almost all Deerpark and Highfield breeding although there were some from Ballingarrane and Shannon; in total 52 had an average of $1,555 or £904. One of the other successes of this event was that Saltertown Pirate, bred by J. Purvis, had sired 11 of those in the sale and they averaged £1,115. Basically all cattle from these and some others went first to USA and from there all around the world, going to the U S A at a time when it was looking to correct several problems, thus ensuring that they could get back in 'the frame'; it resulted in a complete revival of their Shorthorn fortunes.

This situation is a classic argument for genetic diversity and conservation and further justification for such organisations as The Rare Breed Survival Trust if such was needed. In the recent horrors of the foot and mouth disease outbreak in 2001 one of the greatest stockbreeders of our time, James Biggar, lost his life's work and, having travelled the world over the years, he decided even at 90 years of age, almost before the horrific smoke had cleared, that his family's herd future should be by the import of embryos from what cattle he and his son Donald considered would fill his vision of the future needs. They came from Canada and some three generations back they traced back to an infusion of these Deerpark and Highfield bloodlines.

In the period before, during and after the Improvement Scheme many other breeders all over Ireland were continuing their principal aims of quality and maintenance of successful dairy units: one of those was the Partnership of Major and Mrs Hastings of **Friarstown**, Limerick, whose herd was a great influence in this sector. One of their most notable animals, Friarstown Fidelma, gave the highest yield of all breeds at the RDS in their trials and another, Friarstown Collie, won the McCarthy cup in three years: 1943-44 and 46. The animals of this partnership were renowned for having consistently high yields and they also attracted high prices; their bull Friarstown Royal Guard sold at the RDS bull sale in 1959 for 1,000 guineas. The highest price for 10 years, he had an English sire, Earlsoham Safeguard, purchased by the Department in Reading sales for 1,600 guineas. Not content with this, in 1960 they created an Irish record with Friarstown Wild Seraph who was sold to Ballyclough A I station for 3,000 guineas. Islip Wild Baritone sired him. While on the subject of records it was in 1953 that Mr James Mulligan of Banbridge Northern Ireland set up a yield record for Ireland with his cow Netherton Kirklevington Lass 13th who was purchased as a yearling from J. Horn, yielding 20,870lb @ 3.6% fat in 315 days in her 4th lactation; another of his animals also won supreme Champion beef at the RDS in 1952.

Another long established herd was **Ballingarrane,** started by W. F. Watson in 1919, who previously had bred Angus, later carried on by his widow Mrs Bagwell and in turn by her son Col. S. J. Watson, a great character who later became one of the Shorthorn Society's Presidents (1982-84), about whom more in another context.

This herd developed many families sought after by dairymen and became famed throughout Ireland: Cressida, Lilac, Belle, Daisy, Ringlet, Duchess, Barrington and Jennie Dean. Ashgrove, Loobagh and Carragh were the Irish herd bloodlines from which these successful families sprang. The first of many sires was Ashgrove Marquis followed by Loobagh Ranger and Duke 51st; then followed an English sire, Kelmscott Solus, from Robert Hobbs, Redrice Rose Prince and several from the Thornby herd, Lord Foggathorpe 15th, County 5th, Wild King 11th, and then Hoveton Thorndale Baron who had considerable Irish herds bloodlines in his breeding.

Many British lines were involved, tracing right back to Comet and Favourite, of which they were justifiably proud but again many back to Booth lines as well as Bates and more recently to the renowned Histon Dairy Premier. Several of Ballingarrane breeding were brought to the mainland, principally by Lord Monck who showed them with great success against all breeds; in fact Ballingarrane Cressida 9th was top price at his dispersal sale at 580 guineas and B. Jennie Dean won the Southern Area Gold Cup in 1953 with a yield of 14,759lb at 3.64% for Mr Bentall.

The herd was mainly shown at the RDS and Cork shows winning many Championships at both as well as milking trials with Ballingarrane Foggathorpe 2nd against all breeds at the RDS in 1939. One of their best known bulls was Ballingarrane Belgold in the 1980s who won three successive Championships at RDS and many others. They had shown less regularly in earlier years, but Bellingarrane Cressida 9th won over all breeds in 1948. Col. S. Watson died in late 1999 almost at the close of the century and the herd was taken on by his son John Watson, who had already found fame in another sphere as a team member of the Irish Equestrian Olympic Team. The herd was managed for very many years by one of Ireland's best known cattlemen, George Fennel, who over the years had many friendly combats in the ring with one of his greatest friends outside it, the other nationally renowned herd manager, John Farrell. He was a character of great integrity and much skill. He managed for the Hon. Mrs H.C. Alexander and later for Mrs P. Fegan.

The former lady owned the **Domville** herd and previously been involved with the Loughinstown herd which had many old connections such as Mignon Daisy a 100,000lb cow with over 52 first and second awards, also the sires Loughinstown Imperial, Imperial Charm and Imperial 2nd, all of which won the RDS Championship in seven years and all were directly related in three generations. The herd had been extremely successful winning countless awards, a few of which are

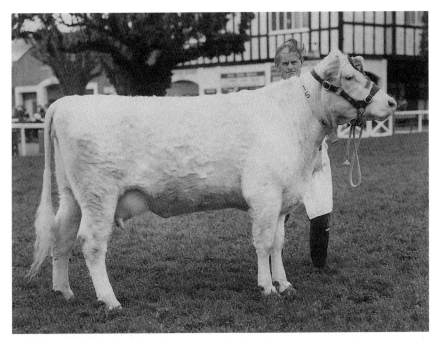

John Farrell with Moyglare Lilac 2nd.

listed here: Imperial was also Champion at the Royal Ulster in 1956; in 1957 Imperial Charm also won 4 show Championships and one interbreed Championship. He also won in 1958 and 1959 at Dublin and his son Imperial 2nd won both the RDS and Ulster Championships in 1962. His dam Mignon Daisy 2nd also won over 50 awards.

Mrs Fegan's **Moyglare** herd, which was started in 1974, saw the continuation in some ways as in 1975, when the Domville herd was sold, Mrs Fegan, wife of a famous surgeon, acquired a number of her cattle and John Farrell! The herd, based at Maynooth, which had already got off to a storming start, continued the winning streak with championships at countless events. Mrs Fegan had purchased Deerpark Leader 12th from the Quanes and then got impressed by a visit to Ballingarrane and purchased a number of females. Their initial outing to RDS in 1976 bought them 13 awards including the female Championship and the next year they took both male and female Championships. They certainly were not just ornaments as the herd average at this time was 11,361lb @ 4.10%; with yields to 17,000lb. This herd really enjoyed remarkable success over a short period at this time. Their stock was obviously admired on the mainland as Moyglare President sold in Perth in 1978 for 1,400 guineas. Partially owing to John Farrell's ill health, combined with other circumstances, the herd was sold in 1982 with cows selling to 870 guineas and calves to 500 guineas all over Ireland.

It was rewarding that one of the Farrell daughters, Carmel Kelly, whose father had shown at over 40 Dublin shows and won over 22 Championships and 120 classes, was able to carry on the family traditions and skills with a small herd in Co. Carlow, the **Ricketstown** herd, as well as becoming regional Secretary to their Association.

While mentioning associations I must mention Jim Norton, who as Secretary to the Irish Association for around 40 years worked so hard for the breed through such a difficult time. There are of course many who take on this role throughout the Society, for which the breed must be forever grateful as most carry out this sort of work in an honorary capacity but to deal with a troubled political situation as well as the ups and downs of the trade needs a special talent. Jim, who was a very outspoken man at times and made a few enemies, had a passion for the breed; in fact he kept a small herd himself by the beautiful lake at Blessington and enjoyed much success with his cattle, the best known being Tournant Sir James and Kinaghmore Roy, both RDS Champions. The latter had the highest weight gain of all breeds – 3.9 lb per day – being $13\,^3/_4$ cwt at 13 months. He also exhibited at Smithfield show in London with other stock and set a record in 1979 when he bought Kimble Rose 68th for £2,000 from Jim Collins of Cleckheaton, Yorks, after she won the 1977 Royal Championship and reserve supreme at the Great Yorkshire. Jim Norton also ensured that Shorthorns were at the National Stud, run at that time by Michael Osborne; they were the store cattle who grazed their magnificent pastures with the priceless Thoroughbreds, and Michael always said they were a huge asset towards keeping the mares and foals docile. He later got Shorthorns into Sheikh Mohamed's famous stud at Kildare for the same purpose. Jim Norton was such a busy man, as, apart from his farming, he regularly broadcast and was the farming correspondent for the *Irish Independent*, which enjoyed a large circulation, as well as having, like most Irish, interests in horse breeding. Through these and his many committees he enjoyed so many contacts throughout the land few were allowed to forget the breed!

While these herds and personalities were excelling in the south there were many successes in the north with superb quality cattle selected by renewed interest from the Perry Family and the **Caufield** herd of the brothers Sam and Joe Kelly based largely on English lines like Iford, Stourhead and Aldenham but also from herds like Friarstown and Taringa, also Clarke of Co. Cork. Their breeding skills ensured a consistent type that was very successful in the show ring. Later they used a number of A I sires and then went with Twells and Maxton blood which included the bull Maxton Centurian who proved so successful he was to go into A I on a national basis. Their winning continued with awards at many shows but sadly Sam suffered a severe

Hadnock Lucy Ringlet 11th, sold to Sir Gilbert Greenall for 1,000 guineas in 1915. A nice heifer but this fine type did not help the Irish type.

stroke and, after a long illness, died.

Great friends and competitors of theirs were Ken Workman and his family with the **Whitefields** herd; their stock, based on similar lines, often won at events around the country and had great success with Twells breeding as well as carefully selected local lines. Other more recent herds in the north are the small but select herd of Tom Glenny, a businessman doing stirling work in publicising the breed, as is Stephen Girvan from Dromore, Co.Down, who has been rapidly expanding his herd.

Back in the south and just over the border, the Carter families have combined a busy guest house with a dairy-like herd at Knocknaea. Close to them are the McKeons, Doney and Maura at Sligo who, as well as running a business, seem to find time to organise a show and a choice herd of quality Shorthorns with the **Carrowhubback** prefix, with bloodlines based on English herds. Among their trophies are RDS Championships. So many people and herds have contributed much to further the breed: names like Bill Mulligan, with over 65 RDS attendances, the Brosnans of Killarney, the O'Connors of Rathmore, the McArthys of Skibbereen. The late Bert Cole, who with his great friend and character Bill Cairnes of the famous **Moatfield** prefix, was a council member and travelled to the mainland for meetings. The latter, despite great suffering after losing both his legs still remained incredibly cheerful, with a never-ending fund of stories! They and their friends, some mentioned earlier, have seen the improving demand for Shorthorns that is gathering pace.

Others, like the late Kevin Culhane of **Castletroy**, Limerick, did much to further and promote the breed during the low time, although he had previously had a well known Friesian herd for many years. He had a strong belief and faith in the Shorthorn's abilities and worked with people like the Quanes and Malloneys to help them market their stock; he had the contacts and the expertise that they neither had nor wanted to bother with! He was helped by men like Paddy O'Callaghan of Limerick with the **Kilfrush** prefix who also had a Hereford unit as well as running a bank! When Kevin Culhane was forced to sell his herd owing to ill health, the crowds and the new herds founded demonstrated both the respect in which he was held but also the great revival in interest which was just starting to be evident.

This chapter, apart from giving an insight into the most influential herds over the period, shows what was done with the support of the imaginative Government scheme in the south and the full support of the breeders through the country; how the island's problem, in providing marketable stores, etc, and that of the breed was corrected; but that those who require a differing type for their purpose can all exist together and progress.

As the century ends there are many new breeders coming up with very promising stock and it will be in their hands to 'pick up the ball and run'. They have a great chance with tremendous prospects but they have a huge responsibility to all those who went before. The future and the past have faced each generation and each has to adapt his stock to meet the demands and the trends of the day but all owe a debt to the endeavours and the genes established by their forefathers.

6. The Breed Gets Organized

Over the recent two centuries it seems that it has been the beef aligned herds that have attracted the high prices and the international publicity more than the dairy, possibly due to the fact that at the beginning, around the time of Collings, the accent was on beef; but dairy herds have far outnumbered beef. Certainly since the very early period the controversy and discussion regarding the dual-purpose aspect has continued and for a time the size of beast was also a problem.

With the huge trade overseas, particularly to South America, breeders quite naturally turned to that market and went for those strains that were shorter on the leg. Accompanying this there was much talk that the milk yield suffered, with accusations that beef cattle could not even support their calves; much effort and paper was used to disprove the point. Evidently this was also a problem overseas as early in the 1900s there were papers and records being published from Canada hoping to counteract these accusations by showing that their cattle of the beef strains had yields of 10,859lb and 427lb of fat quite commonly and from Scotland where they were recording yields of 10,120lb with 400lb of fat.

Of course if you were dual purpose this was fine at the time but if you were beef-orientated, this type of yield could cause you problems unless you were multi-suckling. But if you were after milk, you just wanted more. These came at the time when the Friesian was just starting to appear. It was larger and required more maintenance but it gave more milk; initially it did not give such a quality carcass, even though the Holstein influence had not yet occurred. The debates continued with the Scotch Beef Shorthorn men, as they had become known, seeking the short-legged strains; even the dairymen slowly followed suit, despite their wish to maintain a Bates type fineness and they continued to press the concept of dual-purpose for many years. They rightly stressed the breed's productive longevity, its adaptability to both climate and management, its easy calving ability, and also – what was very important at that time – the ability to produce a decent carcass either from their surplus calves or from the dairy cows at the end of their working lives. They also stressed, I feel wrongly, that with these qualities the farmer did not need to compete with the 'specialist' milk breeds, as they referred to them. The market was changing and as things turned out they certainly did, but this was as yet quite a time off; the breed still had such a hold, far from decreasing at this time, expansion continued with a vengeance. The concept of a fat cull cow being able to pay for its young replacement continued with the huge demand, particularly in the future war years, for home-produced beef. This aspect also covered, or masked, the problem of the breed losing its size.

Exports continued to rise to a peak around 1920 when 2,589 Shorthorns left for other shores (44 different countries); of these 1,230 were to Argentina and other South American countries. The return to exports is possibly the moment to return to the beef type as they were primarily involved. To go further would be to miss or delay possibly the greatest story of any breed – the Uppermill history, despite the fact that it is still going on!

This was, as can be expected, an era when a number of herds started: the **Histon** herd of that great family, the Chivers of Cambridge; the **Hastoe** herd of the Timberlakes; the **Reborn Naemoor** herd for the Moubray family; the expanded **Millhills** unit, the **Aldie** herd of Finlay MacGillivray; **Orfold** of the Luckins; **Iford** of the Robinsons; **Calrossie** of Capt. J. MacGillivray, **Upsall** of the Turton family, **Parton** of the Hewsons, and many more that will crop up constantly in the following pages. This was also the time when the **Eaton** herd went pedigree, although founded much earlier.

In 1904 the Society decided that the exclusive names for herds would be an excellent ideal, not necessarily for making money for the Society as the fee was and is very reasonable, but to identify breeders and their policies and their stock by a **prefix** or **affix** and indeed it has enabled herds around the world to maintain their individuality and trade mark. This was also followed by an exclusive three-letter combination for the particular herd's earmark. It is the Durnos of **Uppermill**, or Hobbs of **Kelmscott** and Thomas of **Drisgol**.

So much happened in this time with, for example, the first milking machine being developed in 1903. Again this was a slow starter as by 1918 only 1,000 were using it; even by 1938 only 50% were milking by machine.

Uppermill

It has already been mentioned the Aberdeen area was the centre of much breed history, particularly the Tarves district, so much so that a 600-page book *The Aberdeenshire Shorthorn* by Isabella Bruce was published in 1923.

Nearby Tarves is Methlick and it was here that the Duthie's **Collynie** herd was situated; in 1923, when William died, he left the herd to his nephew, Duthie Webster, who had also acquired some fame. Duthie Webster and his predecessors had held joint sales with Uppermill with great success; it was at one of these, in 1919, that several things happened. On this occasion the event was shared by the dispersal of Robert Bruce's **Heatherwick** herd, which had been established for over 100 years, the oldest in the country at that time; their average was £32, which serves to illustrate the esteem which was held for Collynie when their consignment on the same day averaged £1,400.8 shillings for 24, with a top of £5,535. This for Collynie King Lavender which was sold to a south country buyer from Fairlawne, Tonbridge, R. Peter Cazalet. At this event Duthie Webster was concerned that a particular bull was wrong for the herd of the person bidding and stopped the sale to tell him so! I only remember one similar incident in 1990 when Gilbert Withers at the dispersal of his famous Gateshayes herd stopped the sale momentarily saying that people were paying him too much! At the 1919 sale the Uppermill herd had an average of £921 for 9 heifer calves with a top of 2,000 guineas.

Sharing these joint sales for over 47 years was **Uppermill**, which was tenanted first in 1833 by W.S. Marr, then by his son, also W.S., until 1904 at the dispersal sale when 113 cattle averaged £156 5s 4d. The annual joint sales continued until 1937.

At this sale in 1904 Mr Roger from the Argentine bought 17 lots, although some did not go as they failed their tests. One of these was the top-price animal, Bapton Favourite, sold for 1,200 guineas. They eventually returned to Collynie, as did some of the others that could not be shipped. Mr P. Clune bought several for Albert College, Ireland. Mr Duthie was a great supporter, and bought seven, one of which was Duchess of Gloucester at 160 guineas. She later bred him a calf of the same name who sold for 1,550 guineas! He also bought the 'massive' Missie 157 for 300 guineas. The highest priced female was Princess Royal 82 who fetched 400 guineas from Mr Roger and she did go to Argentina. Quite a day! Following this a cousin of W.S. Marr, John Marr, took on the tenancy of Uppermill bringing with him a herd already started at Cairnbrogie; all of which was dispersed on his death in 1914, with an average of £75 and a top of 1,000 guineas paid by Duthie Webster for a calf out of Lancaster Lady: so the circle went on.

In 1914 **James Durno,** who had been farming at Jackstown with a herd founded in 1882, took over the tenancy of Uppermill, moving his well established families like Blossom, Miss Ramsden, Broadhooks, Clara, Orange Blossom, Rosebud, Clara, Princess Royal, Violet, Secret, Goldie, Lavender, Charity Clippers among others, who were coupling at the time with Mesmerist from Collynie, a white sire who was so successful. In 1923 James Durno's son Dr James Durno took over in partnership with his brother Leslie, but in 1932 James took over full control. Dr Durno was a man of many parts. a businessman, like Duthie, he was involved with many organizations and Chairman of several,

Calrossie Christmas Carol

including the Royal Highland Agricultural Society, the North Eastern Agricultural Executive, Aberdeen Markets and the North Eastern Co-Operative Society, to name a few. He was also a very good employer, as was his daughter who followed him. As testimony to this his famous head cattleman, Sandy Forbes, was with him for over 25 years and the equally world-renowned Robbie Minty was his successor. He had been assistant since 1945, lived at Uppermill from 1938, serving well over 50 years. In fact at a presentation some years later when Mary Durno held an award ceremony, seven employees had served 290 years, and one of these was her secretary, Mrs Evelyn Gray, who served 31 years.

You will be saying, 'deviating again.' Yes. But you will agree that breeders would not have achieved half of what they did, or do now, without the dedication, care and very long hours, often under difficult conditions, of so many stockmen and women for which this breed and many others are noted.

Agriculture, like so many industries, has changed enormously. Before the milking machine one man was needed to milk 10-12 cows; now one man milks 130 or more in a modern parlour. In the days when large herds used to bring forward up to 30 bulls to a show and sale, the number of bulls per man to care for and train would be 10. Often the head stockman/herdsman would be responsible for the breeding policy and the records. Now the large demand for bulls is long gone. So are the men; thousands have left the land and since the last foot and mouth disaster and the milk price slide, 15,000 have gone, including 8,700 farmers. Some would say this was progress, others disaster. Whatever view you take, the stockmen/herdsmen and women are part of the history and one could write a book or certainly a chapter about them alone; so many have gone and now many owners cannot justify managers and stockmen and do it themselves, unless they have a sizeable unit.

In the early days the Uppermill estate ran to several thousand acres, employing up to 50 staff; recently it was cut to just under 800 acres. It also included a sizeable Friesian herd but it was the Uppermill Shorthorns that won world acclaim, being exported to many countries. The herd won every award possible including over 12 Perth Championships as well as Championships from at least 15 Royal Highland and some 16 Royal Shows, also winning supreme interbreed awards: and it is still going. Mary **Durno** took over on the death of her father in 1971 as sadly her two brothers had been killed, one in action, the other in a road accident. At this time the herd included about 100 cows. Despite the decline and disasters that were to befall the breed in her time, she never lost faith in the Beef Shorthorn, continuing to adapt the herd to the needs of the day and even taking some very controversial decisions when they were needed as will be seen. In 1983 she became Patron of the Beef Shorthorn Society, following requests from the members who recognised her work for the breed in so many fields.

Following her death in 1998 the estate was taken over by her nephew Stuart Durno so another chapter has opened in the affairs of Uppermill and hopefully it will see another 200 years of continuous Shorthorns.

Other noted sires at Uppermill have been Mesmerist, Glastulich Watchman, Collynie Bright Light, Collynie Crown Prince, Calrossie Sweepstake and Evening News, Millhills Clarion, Uppermill Metaphor, Saltoun Red Ensign, Beaufort Benbow, Westdrums Prince Maurice and Pablo and then Prince Ian and Wallace, Erimus Hansard, Cruggleton Benedictus, more recently Chapelton Xile, Banner Instant Royal, Newfield Colonel and Balmyle Warpath and all have huge achievements behind them. Quite a lot of this success is of course due to the female stock they cover, as in so many well known herds, and this herd has always been noted for the quality of its cows, with both bulls and females going all over the world including Argentina, Australia, Canada, South Africa, New Zealand and USA. Even in the early days their stock was at a large premium: in 1919 heifer calves were sold from Uppermill at 2,000 guineas and 1,450 guineas and the average for 9 heifer calves was £921. Possibly their best known females today come from the Lovely and the Queen of Rothes families but there is so much choice!

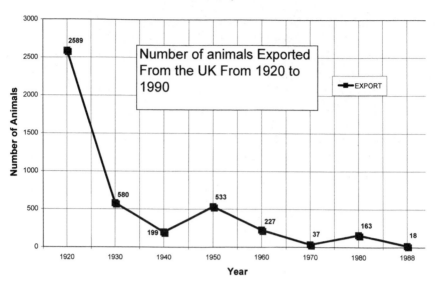

Animals Exported From UK

Number of animals Exported From the UK From 1920 to 1990

Albert James Marshall

Another one of the Shorthorn 'greats' was on the other side of the country: great in every sense, having been one of the largest herds in the UK. One of the foremost exporters and one of the greatest cattlemen of our time who had a huge influence on the breed, he also had very many friends and admirers of his skills as well as an outstanding reputation for fair play and straight dealing despite his thousands of deals and hundreds of stories of incidents concerning him.

Like Bates, Cruikshank and Duthie, he stood out as one of those responsible for the major developments in the breed not only here but all over the world: he was Albert James Marshall from Stranraer; though it would be better to say 'the Stranraer region', as he farmed over seven farms in the area between Luce Bay and Wigtown bay. At the height of his work his herd was 800 strong. He was also known worldwide for his stud of Clydesdales.

His father Matthew Marshall was one of the early exporters in 1890 who also had a first-class reputation. He sent Bertie, as he was known, to the Harrisons at Gainford, who will feature later, to learn his trade and also entrusted him as a young man of 18 to accompany cattle on their way to Argentina with all that it entailed. With this experience and training he acquired vision and expertise far beyond his years. He also was one of those men who are always 'top of the tree', or in front of the game; like Dick De Quincey, who came later, one could always be sure in whatever he engaged he would have what was needed at the time. His 'empire' also enabled him to have flexibility of type, with over a thousand head at some stage; in one three-year period he

Mr A.J. Marshall's Cruggleton Beverley

registered 1,026 head in Coates's Herd book (1925-28), comprising 486 females and 540 bulls, all registered by his long-serving secretary Miss McWinnie (for 31 years).

As one of the largest exporters, if not the largest, he bought from all the top herds of the day at top prices and in many cases he would use his purchases across some of his own herd before sending them around the world.

He had two prefixes, **Bridgetown** and **Cruggleton**: he said he used the second as he had run out of names for the first! Which quite possibly could be the case. The huge enterprise started with very small beginnings with the purchase of three calves from Col. Munro's sale in 1899 and some more from the Uppermill Marr Dispersal in 1904. Their first bull was thought to be Viceroy 2nd and then Royal Star from Lord Lovat. Viceroy was then sent to Argentina where he sold at the highest price of the time.

Marshall believed in showing both as an achievement and an excellent advertisement; he hardly ever exhibited females, though many who purchased them had great success. Like Uppermill he won virtually every possible award, among which were at least 11 Championships and 6 reserve Championships at the Royal including in 1932 when he took all the 3 Championships and the same number of Royal Highland Championships added to which he won 7 successive Championships at the Great Yorkshire.

The herd produced Champions at the RDS (Royal Dublin Show) three years in succession with different bulls. So many famous animals came from this herd it is impossible to list them all but many considered Bridgebank Paymaster, which won at the Royal three times, to be one of his best. He thought the ones that bred the best were Gainford Ringleader by Collynie Mandarno; his own Cruggleton Perfect, whose pedigree went back to the greatest in many breeders' eyes, Collynie Royal Leader, which he had purchased as a calf at a Collynie draft sale and later sold to Mrs Fletcher at Rosehaugh; later he went to Capt. MacGillivray; Ringleader went further back to Balcairn White Eagle who, as his name implies, was white. Bertie had a theory that a good stock bull always had a white ancestor within three generations of his pedigree and there had 'never been one with all red sires and dams all the way '!

The bloodlines spread around the world, exemplified by the fact that in 1926 Cruggleton Orpina was Grandchampion at the Rand Show, and in 1949-50 75% of all the winners at all the shows in South Africa were of Cruggleton breeding. In 1949 the three highest priced bulls at the Toronto Royal and the Toronto International Championship were of Cruggleton breeding.

Cruggleton Captivator, who had won junior Champion at the Highland and reserve Champion at the Royal Show and the Great Yorkshire, was sold at Palermo in Argentina for the then record of £6,250 to Senior Ceres, whose Santa Angela herd was over 50,000 head. Bertie Marshall also sold Cruggleton Commander at £2,500 and Cruggleton Borderer at £1,250, with the total consignment of 12 coming to an average of £1,030 when the other consignments averaged £790, which was double the previous year. In 1927 Bridgebank Bayardo was Champion at both the Royal Ulster and the Royal Dublin shows.

In 1945-6 he sold the top-price females in Perth for the then records of 1,600 guineas and 2,000 guineas. At a draft sale in 1948 he sold thirty animals to the USA, Canada and South Africa. In 1949 he achieved the Perth Supreme Championship with his bull Cruggleton Account and sold him to the Boots Westdrum herd for 7,000 guineas. In 1951 he had 28 bulls in Perth sales. They averaged £711 and included Cruggleton Raeside (£4,500) to Pitodrie, Cruggleton Paudelus to Australia and Cruggleton Balmoral to James Biggar.

When the Russians came over on a buying mission, half of their eventual purchase consignment was from Cruggleton.

At one time over twenty major herds in Britain had sires from this great herd, so great was their influence; in this case it was not fashion alone as his policy and skill had enabled him to provide whatever type the market required at any time. Here again mention should be made of his long-serving herdsmen Billy Maxwell and Jimmy Dickson, who went on to another famous name, Newhouse of Glamis.

The eventual sale following Bertie's death in 1952 was an event that stands out in Shorthorn history and will be reported elsewhere.

The Shorthorn Society

From the time when the society was incorporated in 1875 until the Dairy Shorthorn Association was established in 1905 with the main idea of supporting awards to shows and milk records, the Society was evolving, as was its Council and the variety of matters they had to deal with was extraordinary. For example, as early as 1888, they were requested by the then government to call a meeting with the various railway organisations around the British Isles to establish the correct dimensions and charges for trucks to transport livestock and appropriate fees for transportation. The eventual decision was that the cattle truck should be 16 feet x 8 feet with no inside fittings and that advisable charges would be 1 animal at 3 pence a mile, 2 at 5 pence, 3 at 7 pence and 4 at 9 pence. Whether or for how long this applied I don't know as not all decisions were implemented! Like the one in the early part of the century when, after long discussion, it was decided to publish the names of people who 'bent' the rules in the herd book or made fraudulent entries. This was a long time ago!

As the breed expanded so did the council, and the number of committees: at one stage they rose to 12 including sub-committees but in more recent years they were pared down to 5 or 6. Throughout one has to be thankful to all those dedicated people who serve either on a committee or more particularly as an officer. First and foremost the Society has had a very impressive list of Presidents. People who have acted in this capacity (see appendix) have given much, as the involvement and travel can be very time-consuming and expensive. The term for this office was originally one year but more recently in the '70s it changed to two years as it was considered that more could be achieved. Norman Lee served six years, throughout the war years, and did phenomenally good work in that time. Quite apart from the work, throughout these difficult times the Society raised over £34,000 for the Red Cross by sales and donations during his Presidency.

Many who served in this capacity had time-consuming work and illustrious positions in other fields so their involvement is even more appreciated.

All have been male except one, Mrs Anne Wheatley-Hubbard, whose original herd was in the Midlands at **Berkswell,** near Coventry, and her herd of this prefix was prominent in the dairy sector for many years. She was acknowledged as an extremely capable farmer and administrator whose herd was founded in 1926 by her father. She took over at nineteen when her father died. She produced one half of the Burke trophy team at the Royal Show in 1954 with her bull Berkswell Sharon Lad 3rd, who had a distinguished show career. As well as her cattle she ran the oldest herd of Tamworth pigs that still continues today at their home now in Boynton, Wiltshire. As well as her farming achievements with her husband, she served for many years on the Royal Agricultural Society Council and was Vice President in 1986 when Her Royal Highness Princess Anne was President. Mrs Wheatley-Hubbard was also on the council and eventually President of the Rare Breeds Survival Trust. She was also the first Lady Master of the Worshipful Company of Farmers and was therefore regarded as the foremost Lady Farmer in the land in her time with some justification. She died in 2003 and her son Thomas took over the reins on the estate. Her example is another affirmation of the saying, 'If you want a job done give it to a busy person.'

Council members have been and are selfless in their work for the breed and the Society, having many differing farms and experiences; their combined strengths are invaluable, some travelling long distances to represent their views and those of their regional members on the variety of subjects that arise.

Originally council members were elected regardless of their district but in 1918 council decided that members should be elected by geographic representation in order to give improved representation. It still applies today. As does the ability to co-opt people for specific skills to advise, etc.

The longest-serving council member was probably Richard Stratton who was referred to briefly earlier. He had been one of the principal instigators of the Society and a founder member, who in 1895 was elected its President. He was the person who pressed for the introduction of dairy classes at shows and also the prize funds, and succeeded. He was on the first council of the Dairy Shorthorn Association in 1906 and ran the famous **Duffryn** herd. He insisted it was maintained as truly dual-purpose and was an active member of the Smithfield Club, being on their council and Vice President in 1912 as well as winning Championships in 1874,1879 and 1882 with Supremes in 1878 and 1882 at the Smithfield show. He was a member of the RASE (Royal Agricultural Society of England) for over 70 years and a council member for many of these. He was the instigator of the control of the warble fly and was on several committees of local agricultural organisations until only a short time before his death at 94 in 1937. Again a selfless and busy man!

Secretaries of the Society have almost all been long-serving despite their stresses! E.J. Hine for 14 years; E.J. Powell for 32 years; V. H. Seymour for 15 years; Leonard Bull for 13 years (known as 'Beef Bull' and reported by Capt. MacGillivray while in Ireland to have been 'the best bull the society ever had'!). Arthur Furneaux, who had been Bull's assistant, was Secretary for 11 years; Arthur Greenhaugh 17 years; Keith V. Cousins just over 1 year, sadly suffering a fatal heart attack ; myself 20 years; M. Taggart 1 year and Frank Milnes to carry into the 21st Century.

Staff at the height were also long-serving and rose in number to 50 but this period was well before computers. The manual checking of the pedigrees and the herd books must have been very hard work. The staff was eventually considerably cut at each move of the Society offices.

The associations also had long-serving Secretaries, who did much sterling work, much of it voluntary, dependent on the size of the regions but they contributed so much to the furtherance of the breed and its supporters.

Several meaningful organisations had been founded before this, such as the **Smithfield Cattle and Sheep Society**, founded in **1798** with its first show at Woottons Stable Yard, Smithfield. It became the **Smithfield Club** in 1802 and after a time it had as the same Secretary as that of the Shorthorn Society, Henry Hine. He was with the Shorthorn Society for 1874-88, and was followed in the Smithfield Club by Edwin J. Powell, 1888-1924, followed by Leonard Bull, 1924-1948, so there was an association between them and the Shorthorn Society for 80 years; also many of its Presidents and committee members were members of our Society. The breed has exhibited throughout their history and in fact one of the early champions was the HRH Prince of Wales with a Shorthorn Steer and before him Her Royal Highness Queen Victoria with a home-bred heifer in 1890. The Royal Family has been a continuous supporter of this event over the years in many capacities. The association of Smithfield show with their administration ended only because of the incredible expansion of the breed around the mid '40s and the consequent workload.

The **Royal Association of British Dairy Farmers** was founded in 1876, with annual shows first in London then more recently based in Leamington Spa, Warwickshire, with the show moving to the Royal Showground, Stoneleigh, in about 1972. The breed has also always exhibited at their events with considerable success both in yields and conformation.

Just as there were outstanding and large Scottish herds, there were large dairy herds and one of the earliest of these, which continued at the top for many years, was the **Iford** herd on the downs of Sussex where the Robinsons, J. C. and H., farmed a unit approaching 3,000 acres at their peak. Their herd, founded in 1895, numbered 900-1,000, consisting of up to 250 milkers and their followers. The Robinsons worked very closely with Taylor of **Cranford** fame, exchanging bulls with one another, and mainly followed Bates lines. They were running at about 200 milkers producing for a contract of 6/700 gallons per day; they did not show except at dairy shows and in fact they were one of the first to fly cattle to events when they took cattle to the Glasgow Dairy Show where they were highly successful. Mr Robinson was firmly of the opinion 'that the show yard is the grave yard of the Dairy

Shorthorn'. Their stock was often at the top of the line with other breeders. They were always very progressive and were T T Tested in 1877. They were the first of the large herds to consistently achieve an average of 1,000 gallons and over and producing more 100,000lb cows than any other, one of the top of these was Iford Cactus 46th who yielded 149,309lb with 14 calves. Five generations of Cactus had six figure yields and by 1954 there had been 300 Lauras registered.

Their cattle attracted much overseas interest with stock going to USA, Canada, South Africa, Cyprus, Egypt, Denmark, Germany, Australia and New Zealand, all attracted by their heavy-yielding ability which had won them many dairy shows and made them gold cup winners in the UK; Iford Cambridge Duke was Champion at the Melbourne show in 1953. Iford Golden Rose, sold to J. W. Perry, was the top cow in Ireland in 1959. One of their most famous bulls was Iford Lawrence 4th who was among one of the leading bulls of his day and was sire of the world record holder Winton Gentle 2nd whose yields are mentioned elsewhere. He remained in the herd until he was twenty years old.

Closely associated was the **Northease** herd, founded near Lewes largely with stock from Iford by J. Harris Robinson (related to the ones at Iford) in 1874. The unit was smaller, with around 130 head and one of the stars here was Northease Royal Waterloo 2nd by Iford Lawrence 4th who bought about huge improvements in his progeny with his first ten unselected daughters averaging 8,024lb at 3.66% improving yields by 44% for milk. Although Harris disliked showing, he did exhibit at dairy events and in fact won at the London and Glasgow events in 1958 and 1959 winning the Championships at both with record achievements. Northease Cactus 24 created an all breed record giving 112lb @3.52% butterfat in fact she gave a total of 22742 lb @3.52 % in her total lactation. Northease Mary 5th created a breed record yielding 89lb @5.2%, Northease Mary 13th created a breed heifer yield of 77lb@4.04%. Later Northease Rose 27th created a double record giving 16857lb @3.99% with her first calf and then with her second she yielded 17533lb @3.93%.

One of the favourite sires was Northease Charming Lord 2nd whose first four daughters averaged 12,903lb at 3.61% with their first calves, a long way in front of the national averages. Much later, like Iford, this herd was an early entrant to the Experimental Programme Scheme and was immediately successful with Northease Citation Janette and Northease Citation Louisa being top of the breed Cow Genetic Index (CGI) indices with figures of 933 and 900 respectively. This herd was dispersed in 1990 after over 50 years Other sires such as Iford Lord 8th, Iford Lord Lavender were also successful and well chosen.

Another near neighbour at Billingshurst was Alfred Luckin, later followed by his son Edward, and it was Alfred who in 1899 also bought from George Taylor and started pedigree breeding with Bates and later Hastoe lines as a result, from a graded herd very successfully with the **Orfold** prefix, so much so that his famous cow Orfold Jessy 2nd won at the London Dairy Show three years in succession 1929/30/31 giving, at the last one 80.7lb milk at 4.69 %. From Taylor he purchased a Gentle and a Cherry, later buying Fortune 10. From Rothschild three excellent bulls were purchased over a period, Orchard Prince, Dukedom and Desmond 2. A series of good bulls followed, from Hastoe Grand Magnum, Regal Wildman, Grandeur 6th and Hinxhill Wildman and Barrington Royal 3rd to name a few, all tracing back to the Taylor breeding.

When showing was practised the herd was highly successful with constant friendly rivalry with the Hastoe and later Hinxhill herds, but he gave up most showing around the late 1960s. The herd was always fed on home-grown foods and kept strictly commercially at the same time. The herd average for 10 years was 1,000 gallons at 3.71% and during its time there were two early reductions, the first in 1925 and then 1930. In more modern times several joint sales were staged with the Orgreave herd as both were founded on similar lines but Orfold was dispersed in 1999.

Histon

Another large concern which started small was at **Histon**, Cambridge. The Chivers family, firstly John and William, started in 1810 with 14 acres and their enterprise grew apace as by 1860 they had 150 acres; by 1875 they had one large copper making jam and had 150 staff; in 1896 they built their first factory of 60,000 feet and had built up to 500 acres. Still they went on; by 1914 they had 4,000 acres and by 1918 they farmed 8,000 acres and had 3,000 staff; their Quaker principles ensured that they created an incredible community business with their own fire brigade, doctors, education facilities and chapels. They had their own health service long before the NHS, even with sick pay. The family measured their success by the number of staff they could employ so they also had their own canning plant and dairy as well their own bus service.

Their livestock was started to supply manure to their fruit and provide winter work for their many staff. They had horses for transport and working the land, which developed into one of the foremost Percheron studs. They had cattle for milk production and meat that developed into their famous Shorthorn, Lincoln Red and Jersey herds. Their fast-growing business included poultry flocks of Leghorns and Rhode Islands and also Large White Pigs, all on a very large scale so that one could buy anything from them from a ferret to a bull or draught

A great cow – Histon Waterloo Rose 24: winner of 2 Royal Shows.

horse with the business being advertised nationally. They were one of the first companies to practise mail order.

Many top famous Lincoln Red, Shorthorn and Jersey cattle came from these farms where the attitude to showing was very different to that of the Robinsons, probably because the names of Chivers and Histon were kept before both the agricultural and general public with their many successes. Their stock grew in numbers until they had 1,500 pigs, 250 Percherons, as well as over 1,300 head of cattle, of which 600 were Shorthorns in 4 herds, and 300 Jerseys. Their Shorthorn successes in the show rings by 1950 numbered 4,400 winners including one London Dairy Show Championship, one reserve Champion, 27 other Championships and 29 reserve Champions. All while producing 2,750 gallons per week.

Eventually they specialised in their Shorthorns and Jerseys and the Lincoln Reds activity died down. The former most successful lines were Wildeyes, Flora Gwynnes, Waterloo and Duchess families but they maintained most of the Bates lines. One could write a book on this business alone and indeed one booklet was by the company! So I will list a few of their outstanding triumphs. First and foremost must be **Histon Dairy Premier**, who was the highest rated bull of all breeds in the contemporary comparisons; at the age of 13 in 1959 he had 1,000 daughters of which 85 unselected daughters with their 1st calf yielded

Histon Dairy Premier

8,360lb at 3.69% butterfat-50 unselected daughters with their 2nd calves yielded 8,437lb at 3.63 %; 17 3rd calf daughters yielded 10,027lb at 3.66%. Not content with this in the Selby trials his beef progeny averaged 10cwt 70lb at 22 months and 10cwt 75lb at 26 months: the highest of all breeds.

His daughters showed an increase of 150 gallons' yield over their dams but his prepotency caused some problems as the small national herd meant he could not be fully used because it would restrict bloodlines and reduce genetic variation; even so by 1960 he and his pedigree were represented in almost 50% of the breed when it was numerically at its lowest ebb.

It was interesting to note that the Histon cattle traced, like many of the others that were so successful, directly back to the historic Cranford cattle mentioned earlier. The daughters of herd sire Deenwood Lord Oxford 12th, whose dam averaged 14,000 lb with her first three lactations, showed an increase of 89lb of butterfat in their first lactations.

One of the herd sires, Orma Barrington Premier, sired more Penrith Champions than any other up to his time. Another, Histon Foggathorpe Dairyman, had 31 qualified daughters including London Dairy Show and Royal Show winners in 1936, with supreme all breeds at both the Royal and Dairy shows.

Histon Premier Gwynne sold at 1,000 guineas in 1944, a very high price at the time, and his sister Histon Favourite Gwynne yielded 116,905lb by the age of 13 years of age; his dam H. Flora Gwynne yielded 145,000lb in 11 lactations with two and a half tons of butter.

Histon Kirklevington 7th was 1st in the trials and won the Cornwallis cup at the 1949 Royal Show averaging 13,500lb at 4.18% with 6 calves. Histon Musical Bouquet 8th was 1st at the Glasgow Dairy Show and reserve breed Champion in 1950 and 1951 and led the Shorthorn milk records in 1951 yielding 18370lb at 3.2% when 4,832 herds were recorded. Once again these are only a few of this illustrious herds' performances, run for so many years by J.Stanley Chivers who as well as managing the business during his long life, managed to find the time to serve on the Shorthorn Society council for many years, being one of those who were responsible for regularising the regional associations in 1946 and was President 1952-53.

Eaton

One of the first breeders to join the Dairy Shorthorn Association was the Duke of Westminster who had kept non-pedigree Shorthorns since 1850. He decided to change to this in 1915 and quickly established the **Eaton** herd as one of those to be reckoned with. He purchased his first two registered animals at the Lord Rothschild's dispersal and four at the Cranford sale and then his first sire, Thornby Lord Foggathorpe. The herd has always been efficiently managed and they have been recorded since 1886, making it probably one of the first in the world and even with the non-pedigree status they attained averages of 758 gallons on one farm and 636 gallons on another giving a mean average of around 640 gallons per cow of which they usually maintained about one hundred. Judicious purchases were made from several north country herds. One of these, Bare Charm, which won the Royal in 1920 was later re-sold to USA for £1,202; subsequent lots at this draft sale, which later became a regular feature of this herd, averaged £328 for 105 lots, a very high figure at the time. Another successful sire of the early days was Eaton Ruby Prince, a son of Bare Charm, whose progeny where both successful in the show ring and had very high butterfats. Reaseheath College, Cheshire, published some figures showing the improvement of his daughters' yields compared to their dams: the dams averaged 7,975lb while their daughters averaged 10,150lb. No mean achievement in those days.

An interesting sire was Eaton Rose King who was sold as a yearling to J.W. Wardle of Lawndale in Staffordshire and was so successful he was bought back with some of his progeny. His successes include siring thirteen winning progeny groups.

Penwortham Style and Diadem followed, the latter having Darlington Cran 5th 7 times in his pedigree and it included 6 London

Dairy Show winners. Until the herd curtailed showing over 3,500 prizes had been won.

The herd was also very successful with exports sending over seventy to all corners of the world.

The Eaton herd sires were well chosen and were sought from a variety of bloodlines and nearly all 'nicked' in well. Early cows had been purchased from the Hewsons of **Parton**, another old-established herd started around 1870 and still going today, which has exported to over a dozen countries. It produced Cumberland's first 2,000 gallon cow Golden Queen 2nd who gave 2,090 gallons with her 11th calf and 149,844lb with her aggregate yield to then. A bull from this herd, Parton Premier Dairyman, did excellent work at Eaton, his stock winning them a number of Championships.

Stock from this notably uniform herd also achieved several records. One in USA, when Illington Beauty sold for 210 guineas, yielded 18,252lb milk and 678lb of butterfat in a year. Another was in 1943 when Eaton Lord Foggathorpe was sold at Reading to F. Morris of the Groby herd in Leicestershire for 3,000 guineas when he was unable to be featured in the prize list as Eaton farm's manager H.P. Hamilton was judging. A year before this the herd had set the previous record for a dairy bull at society sales, 800 guineas for Eaton Diplomat who had won the Championship selling to P.E. Hill. Before this Eaton had also set the previous record! In 1937 Eaton Diadem sold for 250 guineas, then the record at show and sales since they were started eleven years before.

This herd's progress was curtailed twice by foot and mouth disease (1923 and 1967): on the first occasion they became quite famous as they isolated and nursed some back to near health, but on the second occasion they lost a third of the herd.

This Cheshire estate was known for long-term employment, first being run by John Crowe for many years and then by H. Packenham Hamilton for 43 years, who started his own select small herd with Eaton Telluria 7th. The herdsmen for the Eaton herd were successively from the Powley family. Another great record.

In 1948 the Duchess of Westminster set up a herd at Maynooth in Eire, the **Eatonstown** herd, which was started with a group of 35 Eaton heifers and the bull Eaton Imperial Foggathorpe. This herd was no less successful, winning Championships at the RDS, Cork and Reserve All Breeds Championship at Belfast. These long established herds have certainly left their mark on the breed but we need to look back again.

The early 20th century

The period around the beginning of the 20th century was a time of large expansion of both population and industry. There was also great demand for cattle overseas for them to improve their own stock and output so the export demand continued to increase and exports of the Shorthorn reached one of their peaks in 1906 with a total of 2,462, which was only exceeded after the Great War. It was a time when the Society decided that because of the number of registrations it would need to split the herd book into bulls and cows for ease of management: this was in 1911 when 5,496 bulls and 7,904 cows were registered from 1,900 members.

Price structures were interesting then with agricultural workers receiving 14 shillings a week or £36 4s. per annum. Milk was one shilling a gallon and wheat £11 per ton. Labour was plentiful for milking and stock work and there was, as yet, little mechanisation with nearly everything done with horses and by hand. The exports were, as stated, rapidly increasing and one of the breakthroughs during these days was the start of Shorthorns going to Russia, and more followed after the war which will be reported in more detail later. Much of the initial and follow-up work was due to Sir Richard Cooper Bart whose herd was founded in 1889 at Shenston Park near Lichfield where he ran some 120 head. His diplomatic contacts enabled this market to be opened up. He was a Vice President of Smithfield in 1911; a successor to the title of the same name is still connected with that organization today, having also been elected a Vice President in 1996.

Breeders and farmers were slowly coming round to the concept of milk recording and in 1914 the Ministry of Agriculture considered something more had to be done to improve the national herd performance, so they inaugurated milk recording. Yet again there was a very slow response, as only 6% of cows and 3% of herds were recorded by 1939, the practice only speeding up when the Milk Marketing Board took over the scheme, when it trebled in two years.

This was also a period when the Society shared its offices with other organizations although in most cases the administration was independent. The Hunter and Pony Society, the Shire Horse Society, the International Horse Show and the Smithfield Club all shared 12 Hanover Square. History was to repeat itself later.

It is also interesting to note that although the Perth sales started in 1865, it was not until 1915 that the Show Championships classes were included in the sales; again looking ahead, between 1915 to 1954 only 21 herds participated in the supreme Championship; between 1915 and 1941 only 11 herds shared the 26 supreme awards: Calrossie won 11, Cluny won 4, Millhills won 3, Redgorton, Naemore, Garbity, Inschfield, Garguston, Pitpointie, Coldoch, and Kirkton all won one. The sales were not in any way a closed shop! Many herds were involved both in competition and attempting to obtain interest for export because there was a huge difference in the prices obtained for export and that for UK or Irish use, as will be seen in tables quoted elsewhere.

Finding it quite a problem to know in which chapters to include the influential herds I decided to include the next two in this one as, although they were established very early on, like many others their contributions were spread over many decades.

Another Aberdeenshire herd **Cluny**, at Cluny Castle, Sauchen, was founded in 1864 by Captain John Gordon. The abbreviated history may be a little hard to follow as it was successively owned by four relatives and descendants and was prominent with them all. The initial herd was based on Booth types ; when Captain John Gordon died in 1878 his work was carried on by his widow Mrs Gordon later Lady Cathcart. Taking a great interest in the herd, she changed the policy in 1888 and introduced a number of other bloodlines. Following her death in 1933 she was succeeded by Mr Linzee Gordon and on his death by his daughter Mrs B.H. Claeson Gordon in 1937. The herd was highly successful with bulls such as Collynie Royal Pride, Radnor of Cluny, Glasstulich Sirdar, Callrossie Souvenir and Command, Chapleton Crusader, Cruggleton Godwin, Cluny Brave Knight and President of the Mint, and later Uppermill Grenadier and Ballechin Rodney to name several! The herd has also been fortunate both in the owners' interest and the successive managers' skills; some of these were Mr Conacherthen Charles Crombie followed by William Crassick and Fred McWilliams. Their combined skills ensured the many Championships at Perth and the principal shows, prizes and consequent exports to almost every country where there are Shorthorns.

The Crieff-based **Millhills** is another long-lasting prefix of great repute founded by Mr Duncan M. Stewart in 1897. Early female stock, also a bull Golden Gift, came from Marr at Uppermill; other stock came from Duthie of Collynie from whom Mr Stewart bought a regular input of stock bulls. The first of these was Captain of the Mint who bred a host of magnificent females and President of the Mint, mentioned above, who did a really first class job in the herd. The outstanding sire was Cup Bearer of Collynie: among his get (animals he sired) were 70 bull calves which sold to average 750 guineas, two of which were record breakers of their day, both were Perth Champions and one, Pride of Millhills, sold in 1918 for 3,100 guineas. The other, **Millhills Comet**, supreme Champion of the 1920 Perth sales, sold for 6,600 guineas, a record which stood for 25 years. Millhills made something of a specialism of winning Perth group Championships: they won in 1905,1914,1916,1918 and 1920.

Some years later, in 1941, at Perth the herd won Reserve Supreme Champion with Xerxes who sold for 600 guineas and the herd was also Reserve Group Champion with Xtra who was sold for 300 guineas and was exported to Argentina, being sold to Bernard Duggan of Sittyton, Argentina, for $86,000. A job well done! The herd also bred successful females and one of these bred Millhills Charming King who was bought by Bertie Marshall for 1,700 guineas and sold on again to the Duggans in Argentina were he excelled for many years: between 1932 and 1933 he sired 37 bulls which were shown at Palermo and every one was a prize winner and two were Champions.

Two later sires from Collynie were both out of Royal Leader cows and by Lawton President Roosevelt, a massive sire: the first, Ascreavie Democrat, left a number of quality females and the second was Kinsman, whose breeding traced back to Naemoor. He left progeny with both bone and size, vital to the breed at that time. Later, in 1944, Millhills sent the largest consignment of bulls ever to Perth totalling 22. Their average of £276 spoke for itself in these difficult times. The later sires were Calrossie Highland leader, again a Royal Leader descendant, followed by Banchory Metaphor and Bapton Balmoral. The Millhills unit was similar in a way to Marshall's in that it extended to quite a number of farms making up some 3,000 acres at one point and these were grazed by notable flocks of Blackface sheep and a hundred-strong fold of Highland cattle. The Millhills stockman, John Gordon, who had been with the family since 1899, died in 1954 after 44 years' service with two generations.

Those who have misgivings about judging the success of animals or herds on the prices attained or the prizes obtained often base their views on the fact that a prize given is only one man's opinion, in the main. This may be true in isolation, but where a herd or animal wins consistently I feel it is a true measure. Showing demonstrates one's stock to possibly interested buyers, furthermore it provides an excellent yardstick to the exhibitor to compare his animal with others of similar age. It is true however that fads and fashions can be an influence. Remember the importance put on horns and their shape. The animal at home can be a star but when it stands side by side with those of other breeders it may be seen that it is not quite the star one thought! Millhills and the other herds that have won so many awards and whose bulls or females have bred well in the herd that they have joined, must be considered to have contributed an invaluable asset to the breed.

The Millhills eventual sale was another milestone which will be discussed later. Tribute should be recorded here for Duncan Stewart, another like De Quincey who had so many successes in breeding no matter what stock he was involved with. In Duncan Stewart's case he bred winners in terriers, fighting cocks, racing pigeons, Percheron horses and Highland cattle where he served twice as their Society President. His knowledge of pedigrees was both photographic and detailed in that he could recall the plus or minus points of virtually every animal. He was often questioned regarding a choice of sire but the eventual progeny invariably proved him right and he was adamant on the need to breed larger cattle; he was equally adamant on the way forward being to increase the use of polled Shorthorns and was one of the first to go down this route. One of his other successes was the company of which he was chairman, Ben Challum Company, a hill farming enterprise of some 40,000 acres producing sheep and cattle which was held up as a model to be followed for its efficiency.

In summarizing this period from the Shorthorn perspective it is essential to recognize that those almost unbelievable prices obtained by the 'stars' from the individual herds, most of them large, bear no relationship to the average prices attained by the breed. If one starts at the time when pedigree was hardly spoken of, there is very little improvement until a long time later. In 1810 when Comet was the first 1,000 guinea bull it was incredible then, as it is still today. The rest of that sale had very credible prices: 29 cows averaged £140 and the 17 remaining averaged £112. The sale average came out at £151. In 1853 the average was £19 9 shillings over 22 sales.

By 1868 it had climbed to £35 7s. with 31 sales and in the boom time of 1874 £364 18s. with 61 sales. When we entered the new century in 1900 it had dropped back to £32 over 41 sales but it crept back up to £45 over 45 sales in 1904; however by 1904 it was back again to £41. A home sale like Collynie bull sales started at £123 for 29 and rose to £304 for 18 in 1874. A top for the period was an average of £410 for 17. Perth was also well up with £189 for 19 in 1899 but by 1914 it was a different picture with the average of £72 for 301 bulls. All this demonstrates further, if proof were needed, why the breeder aimed for the export market. Of course the buyers with their vast herds were able and willing to spread the cost and pay these high prices. On the negative side it meant that the tenant farmer, or even the not so well off owner in Britain or Ireland, could certainly not justify let alone afford what were possibly the best bulls, so huge potential was probably lost.

7. The Great War and After

The period covered by this chapter includes the Great War and therefore is one of great sadness for many families whose men went off to fight, many not returning. It was however a period of incredible progress in both agriculture and industry with farming in favour again. Food and milk had to be produced in large quantities from within these shores, livestock became more intensively managed and corn requirements were urgent. Mechanisation was accelerated and in 1917 Fordson produced the first of the mass produced tractors.

Horses were needed in numbers to go to the fronts; like the men they died in terrible numbers so the march to mechanisation was under pressure to speed up. The cattle industry became extremely important with the demand for more and more in order to feed both the army and those at home when imports were slowed down. This caused some controversies: large areas were designated by the Government to be compulsorily ploughed up for cereals or better grass, but the Shorthorn Society and the Dairy Shorthorn Association complained that if more cattle were to be produced there would be a problem whilst the grassland was being ploughed up and re-seeded; grassland being turned into cereals meant less grazing. Furthermore if suitable pastures were ploughed up they would not be able to be restored. The sheep section was thought to be all right as they were mainly produced in the uplands.

From the dairy sector point of view the large town dairies were drawing to a close for two reasons, the first being that with the hostilities the imported cows which were a major source of supply were not available and secondly the improvement and growth of road collection and rail distribution meant the end of city dairies. The obviously named Express Dairies came into their element and the 17-gallon churns became the principal initial method of handling. Imagine what the large cities must have been like prior to this. Around 1900 the Royal Commission reported that London alone had 300,000 horses and 50,000 cows. Consider the waste and methane problem! Also remember that London was much smaller than we know today!

From the beef point of view the demand also increased immensely; incredibly the pedigree export trade continued and far from being reduced it increased year on year. For example in 1914 the total figure of Shorthorn exports was 1,511, of which Argentina took 828, USA 62,

Canada 16, South Africa 442; later in 1918 the figures were a total of 1,875, of which Argentina 580, Canada 463, USA 478, South Africa 266. I understand very few, if any, shipments were lost. This demonstrated the enormous skill and dedication of both the Royal Navy and the Merchant Navy.

The war

Prior to the approach of the war years the Shorthorns and the Society were continuing to expand; the time when they and the Dairy Shorthorn Association were to amalgamate was still a long way off. Many herds were being established and others were being expanded and came into their own. The Friesian breeders had got together in 1909, forming what was titled **the British Holstein Society**. They were evidently not too happy with this as they changed it in 1914 to the British Holstein-Friesian Society; still unhappy, it was changed again in 1919 to **The British Friesian Society**, only to be changed again in a few years! They made a very speedy expansion, assisted by the cry for more and more milk, and were greatly helped by major special selected importations from Holland and South Africa.

The major Shorthorn landmark at the start of this period was connected with Lord Rothschild who had been a very generous supporter and initiator in the Dairy Shorthorn Association. In 1913 he held a reduction sale from his carefully selected choice herd which drew much attention from overseas, particularly South Africa, as well as at home: 57 cows averaged £86 and 10 bulls £107, an overall average of £91 14 shillings. In 1914 he died and the subsequent dispersal sale in June of 1915 brought another huge crowd of buyers and spectators; several noted herds were enlarged and others founded. The average for this event was for 166 cows £106 13s. and 13 bulls £76 14s. Names may well be monotonous but the buyers recorded here were associated with many herds which later justified their purchases. They included J. Chivers, J. and H. Robinson, E. Robson, G. B. Nelson, T. B. Silcock, Capt J. Buxton, Sir E. Mann, R. W. Hobbs, F. H. Perkins, The Duke of Wellington, R.W. Cooper and Capt. A.S. Wills, who was later considered to have gained the best bargain of the sale with his purchase of Drusus, an eight-month-old calf who topped the first sale at 280 guineas: his dam Dorothy yielded 15,951lb in her 10th lactation. Drusus's dominant genes, from the milk-producing ability aspect, created very high-yielding daughters for many years.

The sale produced a very level price range with two exceptions in the dispersal sale, Barrington Duchess 53rd selling at 950 guineas to R.L. Mond who purchased several for his new herd in Kent, and Apple Blossom for 650 guineas to Sir J. Thursby. These and the others contributed to making this sale memorable.

Milking Dairy Shorthorn cows in the ring at the RASE show, Reading, 1926.

1918 was also a time of notable additions and alterations in the society, the most significant was the introduction of the **Grading -Up Scheme**, a register to assist the many herds not yet pedigree to attain this status, whereby the approved the female progeny of an inspected and approved foundation dam could ultimately be entered in Coates's Herd Book, provided registered pedigree bulls were used on each generation in the female line from the original foundation dam. The parameters changed from time to time and one almost immediate addition was to make provision for bulls so the initial interpretation was, 'that once you had a foundation cow her progeny, if a heifer, is in due course mated to a pedigree sire, this continues until the right number of generations have been achieved (four in the case of a female and five in the case of a bull).' This scheme was extremely well received and a large number 'joined the fold' but it did take several years allowing for the gender balance to achieve full status; nevertheless many major herds started in this way. The first seventeen years saw an average of 3,707 registrations per year in this section alone.

The other change in 1918 was that council decided it would be more appropriate for council delegates to be elected so that geographic representation was achieved. One of their problems during the war was caused by the Government, which appropriated powers to commandeer a farmer's hay crop for fodder for horses at the front. Probably a needy step, but it caused a national outcry as farmers feared firstly that their best hay would be taken, also that their own stock would have insufficient, especially as they were being required to keep many more cattle and sheep. So many representations were sent to allow some district control.

Owing to the war several county shows were cancelled but '63 certificates were issued to Shorthorns which have yielded the stipulated quantity of milk when milked in the show ring.' The milking in the ring was a practice to demonstrate the quality of the udder when full and later when empty which was carried on until the early 1950s.

Hobbs

Sir Gilbert Greenall in his report of 1917 praised R.W. Hobbs, 'A true dairyman first and last but he realises the importance of maintaining dual purpose characteristics and although the object is to give a good yield they must also graze quickly into good bodies of beef when their milking days are over. No cow on earth will compare with the Dairy Shorthorn in this respect.' He went on to refer to problems with the American Shorthorn Breeders Association which had been insisting imports had to be able to trace their ancestry back into the first 50 volumes of Coates's Herd Book. This had been a thorn in the side of UK breeders and they requested that all animals registered in the book should be accepted. This was eventually agreed.

The dual-purpose discussion continued and some years later comment was received from a breeder that it would be better to specialise. 'Consider for a moment the comparison between the so-called dual purpose and dairy or beef. On the one hand you can concentrate on improving one or the other and on the other you have to recreate your stock. She cannot combine both beef and dairy virtues to combine maximum output of both. She has to be a compromise; she must have good teats and an well-attached udder. She must be able to put on weight; the very act of so doing will reduce her milk yield. Surely it must depend on your market, if we have to be self sufficient we do need dual-purpose capabilities in order to feed us but in the days of specialisation this does not apply. We have to encourage either beef or dairy production the former with limited fat production the latter with beef ability. Values must be one or the other.'

At the same time it was stressed by many farmers that they were reluctant to have all their eggs in one basket, a very reasonable viewpoint. The debate continued with the possibility of the breed going two distinct ways by a break, but such a move was discarded, again rightly, as it was agreed that although there were two distinct types there were also a number of types in between. However there was an article in *The Times* in 1925 saying that 'non pedigree owners were going away from the registered Shorthorns, not from desire but of necessity as they found that the yield of milk was discouraged by the use of sires that had no milking performance behind them.' This debate and the size issue continued but it was during the time when registrations, membership and exports were very high and so people tended to ignore the latter problem and would not even consider that there was indeed a problem.

One of the truly dual-purpose great herds was the Kelmscott herd

of the Hobbs family; their cattle and their wise council contributed to
Shorthorn breeding for so many years as Robert Hobbs served on
council for over 25 years.

Hastoe

Another herd founded around this time was the **Hastoe** herd of the
Timberlakes; Joseph Timberlake had helped with the management of
Lord Rothschild's Tring herd when he acquired Hastoe Farm, also in
Tring. He obtained from this herd a number of the breeding stock which
were not considered fit to be included in the dispersal sale, several of
which had their calves at foot. Among these were some very significant
animals, which many say were the most significant in the breed and
certainly were at that time: Darlington Cranford 5th with Dorothy, the
former averaged 10,174lb for ten years and the latter 10,536lb for eleven
years and the bull Royal Chief, a son of Cranford 5th. What a start! The
herd was noted for conformation, longevity, milking ability and very
correct lasting udders. Dauntless Duke 2nd, a great grandson of
Dorothy and son of Royal Chief, therefore combining the two lines,
was a major success with his progeny and at the production sale (sale
of selected stock) in 1923 twenty of his get averaged £122 10s. The sale
average was £135 11s.

More recently Double Imperial, a home-bred sire living and working
to a grand old age, made a huge mark with his progeny. Among a host
of awards far too numerous to list there were some noted successes:
Champion at the Royal Show in 1935 with Hastoe Millicent 2nd; Hastoe
Barrington 17th, a favourite of Mr Timberlake and another Royal show
Champion; Hastoe Bective 4th was placed at three successive Royals
1933-1935; Hastoe Tulip Leaf 10th a prize-winner at the London Dairy
Show and had four yields over 12,000lb with her first 4 calves, the
highest being 13,314lb. Hastoe Beauty was a winner of the Calvert Cup
at the London Dairy Show in 1933. Another stock bull, Frontier Fame
2nd from Hastoe Barrington 2nd and a son of Double Imperial, was a
very productive sire, his first 14 heifers averaged 7,641lb with their
first calves ; also Hastoe Florence 9th yielded 17,738lb. Outside breeding
also contributed as they used three sons of Iford Waterloo Rose 59.
Other notable cattle included Thornby Lord Foggathorpe 51st, a son
of Thornby Foggathorpe 30th, a famous show cow and winner of the
London Dairy Show again going back to Darlington Cranford 5th;
Hastoe Premier Fame 2nd by Double Imperial was son of Yeldersley
Lady Hermione 2nd who had 12 calves with very consistent yields;
her dam was Hastoe Lady Hermione 2nd, a milking trials and cup
winner at the 1932 Dairy Show. The Hobbs at Kelmscott were among
many who used this breeding and it was Imperial Roderick, another
son of Double Imperial, who sired a large number of stylish Kelmscott

progeny including Kelmscott Marjory 47th who won the Royal Show among many awards.

The Scotch type/MacGillivray

For many years Hastoe was a by-word among dairy breeders; a similar regard among the beef type was held for the Duthies, Uppermill and Cruggleton, and in the early part of this period the MacGillivray family herds came onto the scene. They made an incredible impact on the breed, especially when one considers the number of herds and breeders at the time. This was a time of great demand and high prices for the top cattle. What follows could be the subject of a book but perforce it must be condensed into a part chapter and so resembles a bit of a catalogue for which I apologise. These details are only the highlights but it is doubtful if any other breed can compare with this record and to spread it out would lose the impact. The MacGillivray family consisted of four brothers: John at **Calrossie**, Finlay at **Aldie**, William at **Glastullick** and Kenneth at **Kirkton,** and later Kenneth's daughter Jean at **Phopachy**. Glastulick was subsequently farmed by John's son William. John's other son, John, was sadly killed while flying a bomber over Holland in 1942.

The MacGillivray boys were born and bought up at Strathdearn, Inverness, on a hill farm where their father had a sizeable fold of Highland cattle, winning many prizes for their Angus or Shorthorn cross Highland early maturing calves. John started on his own in 1905 and bought his first bull at Perth for 40 guineas to work with 50 black cows; he sold him a year later to the Argentine for 200 guineas which he then thought was a fortune! So he bought some quality Shorthorn females, the first of which was a Floss at 40 guineas from Sanquhar and a Miss Ramsden from a Perth sale for 54 guineas and history was born as progeny from these both won Championships in Perth and Palermo! Shortly after the first purchases he bought an Augusta cow from Ireland for 810 guineas and over the years made many judicious purchases. Any non-performers were speedily culled, a discipline he considered most important. Among his other successful families were Broadhooks from Abbey Mains, Zoe from one of the Naemoor Dispersals, Paulines from Saltoun, Princess Royal from Millhills, Butterfly from Collynie, Rosewood from Cornelius, Princess Royal from A. J. Marshall.

As for so many others, the war intervened and, after serving in the Lovat Scouts, Captain MacGillivray, as he then became, really started to hit the headlines when three years after the war his first Champion of many was achieved with Calrossie Field Marshall who had beaten a hundred competitors in his initial class for this honour, selling for 2,600 guineas to the Argentine. This herd was to win the supreme award

A fine group of Scottish females.

twelve times up to 1955 when he sold Calrossie Paramount for 8,500 guineas to Australia. Eight reserve Championships were achieved in the same period as well as countless group awards.

One of the favourite sires was Royal Pride, purchased from James McWilliam for 56 guineas, cheap because he had failed the TT test, but he left wonderful progeny. Then came a succession of sires over the years which 'nicked' with the quality females so well their reputation spread around the world. Millhills Rothes King, then DSO, (yes, that was his name) followed but passed on as he did not satisfy the Captain! Then came White Prince who sired the Champion, reserve Champion and group Champion at the Perth sale in 1925. Doune Monarch was purchased for 3,500 guineas to correct certain faults, then Captain MacGillivray spotted Collynie Royal Leader at the Royal Highland Show at the time owned by Mrs Fletcher of Rosehaugh, but previously having been with Bertie Marshall. To roughly quote the Captain, 'He was the finest bull ever to walk round a show ring but some —— English Judge put him seventh, I was so impressed I went home and bought him over the phone for £2,500 despite his smutty nose.' His first success was Calrossie Control, who won Perth in 1933 and was breed Champion at the Highland and Royal Shows in 1882. He went to Kenneth MacGillivray at Kirkton were he sired Royal Pride, Champion of Perth in 1937 and also the reserve junior Champion and the groups of 3 and 5 bulls in 1936 and 1937. In this last year 33 bulls were consigned to Scottish spring sales.

Then followed the purchase of two Naemoor sires: Naemoor Ian, jointly owned with Lord Lovat and the MacGillivray brothers, purchased for 3,600 guineas, the highest priced bull for any breed that year and Naemoor Jasper, who he shared with his brothers. Naemoor Jasper, Collynie Royal Leader and Naemoor Ian were all standing as the stud bulls at Calrossie at the same time, what a group! Following a request from Windsor, Collynie Royal Leader was dispatched for a few months to the Royal farms where he sired a Royal show winner. Then followed Double Event and then Glastullich Waverley from his brother who sired Calrossie Red Baronet who was sold for 2,400 guineas after being junior Champion at Perth, to Australia were he made a huge impact.

The next bull emphasised the quest for short-legged stock: Broommount Pipe Major by Beaufort Royal Hawk, a grandson of Naemoor Jasper from Lord Lovat. He was so low-set his cows had to be dug in (stood in a hole so that the bull could make it). A so-called friend said, 'The Captain discarded all larger types as the type needed were all small and thick but were big lying down.' A bit far fetched but a pointer. Pipe Major had also been a Champion in Ireland where there were a number of Calrossie animals being used. Another favourite was Calrossie Randolph who left many quality females and again sired a Perth Champion Calrossie Prince Peter and junior Champion Calrossie Finger Print as well as his reserve junior Champion Calrossie Foot Print, all in 1940. Not content with this the herd did it again a year later!

1952 was similar but also it was almost a family take-over when Calrossie Prefect by Calrossie Welcome, who was by that time sweeping all before him, took the senior and supreme award. Aldie took the junior Champion with Aldie Jonathan Adonis. The best 3 bulls went to Calrossie with Aldie in reserve The best 5 bulls went to Calrossie, the best 3 bulls by the same sire was Calrossie Welcome reserve was Aldie Adonis. Phew!

Back to the sequence: Lawton President Roosevelt followed Randolph, again bringing Naemoor breeding. He sired Calrossie Supremacy whose first ten calves made an average of £1,084, the top average for any one bull in 1945. Moving on Kirkton Baronet produced many high priced sons: Calrossie Good News at 6,000 guineas, C. Rescue at 8,000 guineas, C. Adonis at 5,000 guineas also C. Pibroch at 8,000 guineas who went to Argentina and sired the 1955 Palermo Champion who made 250,000 pesos which was the 2nd highest price! The herd prefix was also to the fore in the USA with Calrossie Troubador at the Acadia Ranch who sired the All Breeds International steer. In 1956 in Canada Calrossie Armada for the Louada Stud had 18 sons, who averaged £1,000, and the previous year 27 of his sons averaged £ 930.

So the list goes on: Calrossie Welcome, who was mentioned above having that fantastic performance, continued the week with the top price, £10,000, being paid by the great character Sandy Cross from Calgary, Canada, for another of his sons Calrossie Highland Piper who had been 2nd in his class. The 13 bulls at that sale averaged £3,664 10s. Welcome sired well over £130,000 for his bull calves alone. Several draft sales were held, in 1945 the average was £250 for 44 head and in 1950 the average was £704 for 57 cows and heifers.

Donald MacGillivray, who had farmed with his father for many years, joined as a partner in the early 1950s; he remembers his father being a great marketer, insisting on choosing every mating himself. He also had his cattle housed for inspection in pairs by type, size and colour. He also recalls his father's dislike of the nurse cow practice, which started in the 1930s and continued as another controversy for some years.

One of Donald's memories is of the days when cattle went by train down to Perth, being walked individually to Nigg station, over the fields if it snowed, and there joining other consignments from probably thirteen other breeders to make up twelve trucks in the load.

In 1951 thirteen bulls averaged £2,008 at Perth, and this was a year Donald remembers better because it was the year when Balbithan Highland Leader by a Calrossie sire of the same name won the Championship and was bought for £3,000 by Mr E.L. Killen of the Antrim stud, New South Wales, Australia. He had also brought his daughters Mary and Diana with him. Donald persuaded Diana to be his wife, 'The best day's work he ever did'! In 1961 twelve bulls averaged £2,302, among which was Calrossie Heirloom who created a record at 13,500 guineas to the Argentine. Another high-priced bull, Calrossie Freebooter, sold to Col. Hardie of Balathie for 6,000 guineas. That same year they introduced Armagh Eightsome Reel, an Australian sire, and their first poll bull. Earlier they also purchased Banchory Orangeman from Hugh Black as they recognised that they had to improve the size of their cattle, so these two large sires were the first step to achieving it.

Captain MacGillivray, who had been invested with the OBE in recognition of his services to cattle breeding, died in 1957. A man of extraordinary character, he had been a Director of the Royal Highland Agricultural Society for two periods and Director of the Animal Diseases Research Association, also council member and the President of the Shorthorn Cattle Society, being the first to hold this office on two separate occasions, 1937 and 1950, as well as being President of the Scottish Shorthorn Breeders Association. He had judged in Argentina, in fact 5 MacGillivrays have judged at Palermo, which must be another record! He also judged in South Africa and North America as well as major events in the UK, including Smithfield. He was, as one might expect, a very successful breeder of Blackface and Cheviot sheep, winning many awards but above all he rightly inherited the title of 'King of the Shorthorns' from William Duthie. He was later referred to as one of the world's greatest cattle breeders by international authorities.

Donald carried on with the polling and size policy which was to be very successful, but in doing so he decided that in order to meet with the commercial trends the herd should be reduced. Col. and the Honourable Mrs Dewhurst purchased a substantial number, thus providing them with further bloodlines and leaving Calrossie with mainly families of Floss, Augusta, Rothes Queen, Rosewood, Broadhooks, and Princess Royals with Eliza and Ruth lines from Australia. In 1966 C.Telstar was another sold to the Argentine at 3,400 guineas but left a number of good animals before he went. A later prominent sire was Gotewich Ragusa followed by C.Coronach. For the polling Dipple Whistler was used with great success enabling the herd to win the poll Championship for four successive years, 1969-72. In 1970 Woodhead Cairngorm from the Hendersons proved a tremendous asset siring a number of winning progeny and was followed by Gregalach from the same stud and later again Newton Sovereign. AI was also used with Millhills Guestlater, the Australian sires Weebolla bolla Royal Commision and Mandalong Super Elephant, and the Canadian Banner Royal Oak all before joining in on the new experiment in the next few years.

The Argentine demand had still looked to Calrossie for sires and in 1966 C. Telstar was sold at 3,400 guineas.

In reading these continuous successes for this herd and the others mentioned, it is a sobering thought, emphasising the magnitude of the achievements that the averages over the early period nationally and at Perth were so low :

All figures averages {£ figures rounded off)

PERTH (spring sale)		NATIONAL BEEF SHORTHORNS		ALL SHORTHORNS	
1914	301 sold	£72 av.	1,426 sold	£51 av.	5,380 sold	£38 av.
1917	561 sold	£98 av.	1,515 sold	£101 av.	6,564 sold	£79 av.
1919	512 sold	£224 av.	1,710 sold	£219 av.	7,881 sold	£132 av.
1920	482 sold	£303 av.	2,235 sold	£254 av.	9,235 sold	£153 av.
1921	530 sold	£182 av.	2,024 sold	£110 av.	8,922 sold	£86 av.
1925	377 sold	£114 av.	1,762 sold	£60 av.	8,460 sold	£49 av.

The 1920 figure is up owing to the record sale of Millhills Comet for 6600 guineas.

Bapton Constructor, the highest recorded private sale bull at 15,000 guineas in 1956, with Gordon Blackstock.

Bapton

Despite the demand for the breed at this time the performance of the Calrossie herd is all the more remarkable when we remember the great herds around during some of these days such as Cruggleton, Millhills, the ever-present Uppermill and Collynie to name a few; also one which, maybe, should have been mentioned before, **Bapton**. This herd was founded in the 1860s by J. Deane Willis at Bapton Manor in Codford St Mary, Wiltshire, with a herd of deep milkers and sires mainly from R. Stratton, Garne and Arkell, all mentioned in an earlier chapter as was the detail of the Collynie not going to Argentina and William Duthie taking some (see page 18). Well, Deane Willis took 32 of the young heifers and one bull, Captain of the Guard. This transfer of stock was completed in 1889 when another bull, Archer, followed but after a few years he went back to Duthie's herd from which Bapton acquired two very excellent sires, Count Lavender also Roan Robin, who eventually went to New Zealand. So much so that in 1906 Bapton took both male and female Championships at the Royal Show, both being exported, one to Argentina at a record price in a year when 2,357 were sent to that country. The other, Golden Garland, went to Canada. From the very early days of this herd it was showing with such success that between 1885 to 1896 it won 820 prizes including 73 Championships, this continued so that in the years 1924 to 1927 they won 19

Championships, 13 reserve Champions and 56 first awards.

The herd changed hands to Sir C. Chubb of Sevenoaks, Kent, in 1924 who moved it back to Bapton Manor; he continued showing with success and sold it to J.V. Rank, from the film and milling family, in 1935, when it was moved to Edenbridge in Kent, being managed for some considerable time by Tony Morrison. The show and sale successes continued with the Royal supreme in 1933, also in 1934 when they also took reserve male and female Championships; several of these were by Calrossie Ringleader, another very prolific sire at Bapton. This herd was the main source of beef blood in the south for some time so it continued to attract much interest.

Bapton Aerial took supreme at the Royal in 1938 and he, Bapton Air Control, Bapton Air Pilot and Bapton Battleship, continued the winning show runs for this herd with their progeny. The latter went on to Lord Lovat. Bapton and Calrossie are in so many pedigrees and successes it is not possible to name them here. Mention of the latter again reminds me that after Tony Morrison, Gordon Blackstock, who had been herdsman then manager at Calrossie, came down in 1950 to Bapton as manager: a 'great little Irishman' as someone called him. When J.V. Rank died in 1954 the herd was bought by Cecil Moores of football pools fame and taken up soon after to Oldmeldrum, Aberdeen, Scotland, where it again became a centre of attraction, as Gordon Blackstock was one of the first in the UK to introduce polled Shorthorns.

Bapton Air Pilot

Francy and Benny Zeigler, two breed enthusiasts, with the famous, superb breeding bull Louada Rothes King. Compare the height of the mature sire with the humans.

Continuing to make headlines in 1952, Bapton Enterprise sired by Aldie Red Gauntlet created one in Argentina when sold in Perth for 1,220 guineas; he went to Palermo where he made 230,000 pesos (£11,000).

With the full enthusiasm of both Cecil Moores and Gordon, both of whom were determined to revive Beef Shorthorn interest which was then beginning to flag, Cecil paid the record price for an eight-week-old bull calf to Sylvester Campbell at Kinellar: 5,000 guineas for Gallant Marshall. This was an extraordinary coincidence as this same Kinellar herd had made the first 100 guinea bid for a bull calf in the 1860s. Bapton took teams of show cattle wherever possible to promote the breed with considerable success, however the whole herd was eventually sold in 1963 to Messrs Louis Cadeski and Wilbur Donaldson of the Louada Stud in Ontario, Canada, who had already created a record when they paid 15,000 guineas to purchase Bapton Constructor.

In this chapter there has, to this point, been rather a lot of beef type coverage, necessitated by the fame of the herds and there have also been references to the size of the cattle which were bred as they were largely influenced by the export demand: this was to cause so many problems later. It was true they were continuingly losing height and if one studies the photos it can plainly be seen that this was largely in the area of the pastern, i.e. below the knee. Many retained large body size but one of the associated problems was that they also lost length of body. Again this was not a worry to many at the time as the demand was still there but there were several who were concerned, very rightly, as it was a progressive problem and one which would prove very hard to change.

Gainford

One of the very old established herds which tended to steer a middle way dual-purpose course whilst initially veering towards the beefing aspect was **Gainford** at Gainford Hall near Darlington, Co. Durham. George Harrison founded the herd in 1878 with non-pedigree stock, but quickly changed over and very soon was winning awards, gaining some 2,000 prizes and Championships between 1893 and 1904 including the Royal Show, the Royal Dublin and Highland shows among a list of county successes as well, in fact almost developing his own type. He and his son John, who had similar gifts, developed a very upstanding type and maintained size which was also very well received overseas; they bred specifically for type, milk, depth and beef and managed to maintain the balance. At times very outspoken, George decried 'both the suet pudding over fat and the confetti type dairy animal that would blow away'. The first cattle at Gainford were of the Aberdeen type with the ability to milk. Like Uppermill, Gainford Hall had a series of owners in the early days. William Raine in the early 1800s had entries in the third herd book; then followed D. Nesham who had bought stock from the Colling brothers; then in 1886 George Harrison took it on, passing it on to John and his brother Robert, who took on the arable in 1927.

Gainford Ringleader from the Rosebud family was probably one of the most famous from this herd; Bertie Marshall described him as the best bull and breeder he ever owned and exported; he produced so many Royal winners and the bulls sold from him averaged 2,000 guineas. He was eventually sold to Argentina for 5,000 guineas on a photo alone but tragically died just after landing. 'The greatest tragedy the breed has ever known.' Cattle from this herd were sent to many countries overseas as well as the Argentine. Gainford also kept a herd of Galloways to breed the wonderful blue-greys and they sold a lot of bulls to Ireland and to other blue-grey breeders. One of their proudest achievements was selling two successive bulls to the Royal herds at Windsor. Later in times of slump John decided to turn more to milk and bought a son of Ringleader Stonelands Royal Ensign of the Princess Royal family. This bull's progeny proved very satisfactory: Gainford Eldorado, a champion, sold as a dairy bull to Argentina for 300 guineas, demonstrating the differential in the two types for price. The herd also used sires from the dual type Parton and Twells herds, which matched in very well. Another sire to prove his worth was Barugh Broad Sword, some his daughters giving up to 18,800lb at 3.5%. Gainford was often

Gainford Goldie. A 50,000 lb @ 3.83% cow.

high in the milk records, being second in Durham county in 1944, and sent both beef and dairy types on a regular basis to the Orkneys, having regular clients there. A sideline at Gainford was breeding Thoroughbreds and prior to that they had a prominent Cleveland Bay stud. It was the Thoroughbreds and hunters that took David, John's son's interest and the herd was sold but almost right to this time one was struck by the splendid large capacity cows.

As we progress through the century many references have been made both to the exports situation and the size factor and it is also important to recognise that the Shorthorn was certainly not the only breed involved. The superb beef breeds Hereford and Angus were also heavily involved, going for similar markets although not in the same numbers. From national figures the Shorthorn exports were probably equal to the other two breeds added together, although initially the Angus was possibly preferred in some cases to the Hereford because of the breed's natural polling ability. These two breeds which have evolved as pure beef were probably proportionately worse affected by the size factor when the problem bit home. The predicament that all three breeds found themselves in - i.e. lack of size - probably precipitated the eventual import of European breeds and the re-import of overseas strains which had not been so affected to overcome the situation, but this happened later.

World War I brought its own problems but some breeders were causing their own, for example one of the fads at the time was the black nose which cropped up from time to time in some strains. It was thought most likely to have come from a well meaning outcross in the very early days when C. Colling made a conscious outcross with a red Galloway (which was fully documented). The other possibilities involved the bulls Foljambe and Son of Bolingbroke who was known to have brindle ancestors; another theory was the crossing of the Teesdale with the Dutch cattle. Who knows, but most people put it down to the poor red Galloway! However the 'problem' became known as the 'Galloway Alloy'.

This problem reared up from time to time and indeed is still mentioned. It was thought that such an indication might produce a slower maturing beast or a reduced milk yield. The brindle was thought by some to be indicative of an outcross but did not produce lower yields and some even considered it attractive. We all know that, despite many claims, an ancestor becomes irrelevant after, say, six generations; but some of their genes can 'pop up' maybe hundreds of years later in some form. For example a few years ago a trusted breeder reported a calf being born from a supervised natural mating seeming to be Guernsey, despite the fact that he was positive no such contact had been made for at least two human generations. The problem of the black nose even became the subject of council business in 1917, some even proposing that surgical solutions should be found on valuable animals or those with potential.

One of the more constructive events at this time was the founding of the Federation of Young Farmers Clubs in 1918, which has provided such fellowship, skills and training in a number of disciplines ever since for the benefit of both town and country youngsters. The calf shows have been major events of competition as well as promotion and training. Public speaking and travel, with inter-country exchange,

Distribution of calves to members for rearing, 1934.

have given immense confidence and self-reliance as well as just a little bit of the social side! Many of us have been trying to forget some of our social activities for years!

Durham, etc

The historic area of Durham, Northumberland and Yorkshire was once one of the main strongholds of the beefing type until the clamour for more milk and the necessity of the monthly milk cheque changed their policies.

I will stay in this district with the herd of **Upsall,** founded in 1907 by Sir Edmond Turton at the historic Upsall Castle not far from Thirsk. Originally the herd had Augusta, Broadhooks and Bellona lines, and regularly sent to markets in York. It was also an excellent area for crossing bulls and pedigree sires, especially as it was not originally officially possible to send English bulls to the Scottish Association sales in Perth. The herd was carried on by R.H. Turton MP, and more recently by the Hon. Gerald Turton. As well as the bulls being sold in Britain they had quite a success selling overseas with animals going to Argentina, USA, Chile and Russia among other countries. Having used bulls from such sources as Calrossie, Collynie as well as Cruggleton, the herd was always fortunate with its milking ability but in 1960 they decided to go over to polled breeding so Hilldale Collynie came from Mr Pentecost who had already used him to great effect, having imported him from the USA. He was aged and did not live long so the bull Harold of Denend took his place as senior stock bull and in turn Constructor, out of the famous Bapton Constructor, was purchased. This combination of sires left some very appealing females and stock was again exported as before but also to New Zealand. Noted families in the herd are the Lavender, Victoria, Jilt, Broadhooks and Clipper lines, in fact a number of the original Shorthorn lines are still included. Mr Turton was one of the first to take on performance testing and has used it ever since with some success with gains around 3lb per day not being uncommon.

Again not too far away and from Booth 'country' at Otterington was the **Otterington** herd on the estate farmed by the Furness family. For generations this herd was originally associated and worked closely with the **Knowle** herd which was farmed by F.W. Furness at Kirby Knowle near Thirsk. They started pedigree work in 1930 using in fact stock purchased from Upsall and Gainford and later from Collynie, Cluny and Pittodrie to name a few, which all proved effective, with exports being achieved in some numbers to the USA, Canada and the Argentine. In about 1946 a naturally polled heifer was born at Otterington and this so aroused the interest of Miss Furness, who was sharing bulls with her brother, that she decided to develop this aspect, so the calf was called Lucky Chance. This also produced a polled calf from a horned sire. So lucky were they that her calf produced another polled heifer but this time to a polled sire. In 1955 a poll bull was born *but* the licence official said if it was a Shorthorn it must have horns! Later a more understanding official came and approved it *but* the Shorthorn Society would not register it. However it was registered by the then formed Poll Shorthorn Society and later accepted by the main Society with the Otterington prefix in 1958 so Miss Furness's perseverance paid off and a new chapter was written. She followed this up with the purchase of some more cows from Perth from Cluny, Beaufort and Bapton, of the Augusta and Rothes lines and later from the Cropwell herd of Mr Pentecost, and expanded to around 35/40 cows. Miss Furness was one of the original poll society members.

In the same district, at Tadcaster, is the **Oxton** herd formed in 1926; this herd has had a tremendous influence on the dairy side of the breed not only because of the superb and consistent quality of their cattle but because their owners, the Smiths, were so interested and involved. The herd started in Westmorland in 1931 then went to Oxton around 1941. Mr G.R.H. Smith, as well as his brewing business interest, took huge interest and pride in his herd and the breed, sparing the time become Chairman of Finance for the Society and then becoming President in 1961. Furthermore he was always looking to positive ways to improve his cattle. He was extremely interested later in the possibility using Swedish Red to help the breed regain what he was certain was its rightful place but this must wait. Geoffrey Smith was indeed a busy man with tremendous energy and directness, head of what was the largest private brewery, a racehorse owner, High Sheriff, Chairman of the Young Farmers Federation, and J.P. to name a few of his involvements.

He was also fortunate with his estate staff: J.H. Heppenstall was his farms manager and the Garnett Family were herd managers, first Frank and then his son David, who at the time of writing is still in that post. The herd had a succession of the renowned Kaberfold sires from W. J. Dent up in Westmorland to good effect as Oxton was always at the top in the show ring but more importantly with their yields. One year they had 11 cows at the top of Yorkshire milk records. They won at the Royal, the Royal Highland, the Great Yorkshire, the two Dairy shows as well as the Society shows and sales and other county shows. Kaberfold Prince 2nd was one of the first, followed by his son from a Telluria cow, Oxton Clarity, who among others sired the 1959 Royal Female and breed Champion, the first heifer to gain this award. She also produced the milk records to support her good looks! As well as having over 4.08% butterfat. Not so common in those days. Oxton Lucifer was a grandson of Prince 2nd and among his progeny were a pair of Scottish

Dairy show successes winning the coveted Grendon cup with Oxton Wildeyes 166th and Duchess 94th being reserve; then they won the pairs trophy; Duchess 94th had given 1,100 gallons as a heifer and had also been first in the trials and 2nd on inspection in 1960. Kaberfold Prince 4th and Viscount were two other well used sires and for many years they used Orma Wild lad whose daughters averaged 3.97% butterfat. Other sires used included Ravenswood White Warrior, Orma Stockman and Oxton Waterloo Duke who sired the 1,800 gallon Oxton Joan 2nd; another successful sire was Silverstream Ringer. Later on they supported the use of the A I bulls. Mr Smith died suddenly and the estate was carried on by his widow and later by their sons and the successes continued.

1922 saw the centenary of Coates's Herd Book. Many herds were founded at this time and after the war and membership was reaching new heights: 4,648 in 1925 with 20,437 female registrations plus 6,089 grade-up and 8,504 bulls. And yet the bull licensing scheme was still to come and many poor bulls were being used across dairy herds which did not enamour farmers to the breed at a time when Friesians were on the increase; in 1922 they had 2,000 members of that society. Remember in 1919 the Collynie bull sale had averaged the highest of the annual events with 24 bulls selling at £1,400 with a top of £5,535 and Perth had sold one of the highest numbers of bulls and achieved one of the highest averages of £224. Just before the slump.

There was a serious outbreak of foot and mouth in 1923/24; this came at the end of the slumps in 1920 and 1923 and all were serious blows to the industry. Apart from these dreadful problems the breed still continued its expansion. 1921 had seen the forming of the Dual Shorthorn Association by those who were convinced that was the way to go, but it did not last long and was abandoned in 1924. Do not forget this period was one of great development in agriculture, probably bought on by the war and the industrial revolution. Experimentation in techniques was springing up everywhere. The combine harvester was being developed in the USA in 1921 and people like A. J. Hosier were developing their outdoor bale system in Wiltshire as labour costs rose alongside building costs although this really came into its own a while later.

1923 saw the forming of the first poll herd, detailed elsewhere (see page 46). 1910 was the first Penrith show and sale and by 1924 they had to restrict entries but even then they got 580 forward. And the same year the national average yield was recorded as 482 gallons, no wonder there was still some way to go. This was not helped by a further slump in 1926 accompanied by the coal strike that affected all businesses. Exports also slumped from the high in 1920 of 2,589 to 393 in 1923,487 in 1924 and 390 in 1925.

There are however figures shortly after which show a much better picture: in 1928 the Ministry of Agriculture milk recording register showed 9,559 Shorthorns, 3,067 Friesians. Of the Shorthorns 5 gave over 20,000 lb; 58 between 15,000 lb and 20,000 lb; 95 between 14,000 lb and 15,000 lb; 193 between 13,000 lb and 14,000 lb; 555 between 12,000lb and 13,000 lb; 1158 between 11,000 lb and 12,000 lb; 2,544 between 10,000lb and 11,000 lb. One cow completed her third yield over 20,000lb: Pencoyd Ringlet 13th sired by Dairyman from M. and F. Perkins, had given 22,650lb, 20,069lb and 20,507lb successively in the herd of T. P. Preece of Leominster, all before her 7th calf. All the more creditable when the national average figure shows the low general standard but this breed had two thirds of all those recorded. Again the dirty nose was under discussion as it indicated 'hardness of feeding' but the consensus of thought then was that it was acceptable if the whole nose was not pot black.

At about this time the Dairy Shorthorn Association provided the Five Gold cups which were offered for yields over a period of three years, the cups were awarded to the Northern Counties, the Western Counties, the Eastern counties the Southern Counties and the Midland counties. At that time the was considerable interest with 214 entries in 1935.

Another step forward in this period was the improvement of relations with Russia, which resulted in quite a few exports through the early 1900s of the beef type and then some of both types in 1929/30 which were nearly all bulls; a number were introduced from USA because of restricted import quotas to Russia. There was excellent feedback from all of these and no doubt this aided the later exhibition in Moscow in the early '60s. The original shipments were distributed to a number of areas,

Registrations in Coates's Herd Book and Membership of Shorthorn Society From 1900 to 2003

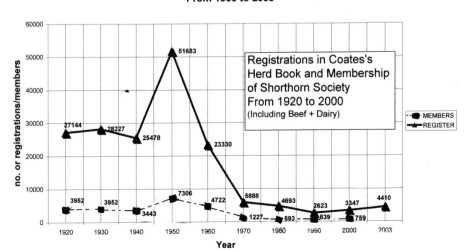

most of the bulls to the Caucasus or the lower Volga and the females went to the Sal experimental station. The original intent was to improve their beef cattle but with the industrialisation programme they decided that their milk yields needed drastic action as well but the beef type performed well with yields up to 15,240lb for 300 days.

The USA stock went to West Siberia and Voronezh province but in any case these American cattle traced back to English lines of progeny of Dairy Kings Duke and Royal Darlington. A number more went in 1932 and 1937. One from the Tory's Anderson herd in Dorset was so impressive that he was worked for eleven years. Their expansion spread along the Ukraine and Bashkira. The Russians were so pleased that by 1930 they had 181 bulls on 14 stations with over 12,000 cows mated under strict recording procedures mainly of the Kalmuck breed where their weights were increased 55 lb for bulls and 43 lb for heifers at 6 months and 123 lb on two-year-olds. So far as measurements were concerned the average height of pure bred bulls was 136.8 cm, girth was 212 cm and live weight was 1,715 lb; at the Lenin Commune the beef type crosses showed 151lb weight increase and their calf mortality dropped from 11% to 5.2% when crossed. Milk yields with the dairy type showed increases of 20 to 45% and with regard to weight two examples were provided: a half-bred bull was 1,915 lb at 4 years of age and a heifer turned the scale at 1,320 lb at six months and daily gains were reported as 2.16 lb at six months rising to 2.86 lb, one bull with two crosses of Shorthorn weighed 732 lb at 11 months, all of which was sad in a way, as the whole project was halted by the 1939 war. Perhaps we should make further approaches but having voiced this suggestion, the exports to this region and the far east have usually been with considerable price restraint.

For some time in this period concern had been expressed about the quality of store cattle in the UK and a report was produced saying that the Dairy Shorthorn Association was doing a great job being concerned with the production of milk, striving for maximum yields, promotion at shows with awards and the publishing of milk records and so on, and the Shorthorn Society was doing similar things but also primarily engaged with the production of the herd book. But, it contended, problems were arising with the very important by-product of store cattle. It was thought that this was largely due not to the pedigree breeder, but to the commercial dairyman who at that time looked upon the calf as a bit of a necessary nuisance and so bought '£20' bulls and it was decided that the use of graded-up bulls must be discouraged much the same as poor stallions had been. So a Bull Register of Merit scheme was set up in 1929 which was designed to enable breeders to find bulls which had proved their value when judged by the performance of their daughters. This was superseded in 1944 by the Improved Register of

Chapelton Crusader

Merit (IRM) and indeed prior to the latter, as this was a national problem, the Ministry of Agriculture set up the Bull Licensing Act in 1931 which came into effect in 1933.

This provided three categories:(A) was a beef bull licence, (B) was for a dairy bull who had a dam who had qualified yields which were revised in 1945 to 600 gallons with 1st calf, 700 gallons with 2nd calf, 800 gallons with 3rd calf, (C) was for a bull of good conformation but non pedigree. All categories were inspected at ten months of age. Northern Ireland originally had a rule which stated that in the C category only Shorthorn bulls were acceptable (this was in their Livestock Improvement Act of 1922). This was modified, as we know!

The effects of this scheme were a considerable improvement and resultant increase in demand for the breed; also obviously the introduction of A I had a bearing on the figures. For example in 1938 Shorthorns had 23,891 licensed; Friesians 2,671; Ayrshires 489; Lincoln Red 1,324. By 1944 the figures were Shorthorns 21,268, Friesians 11,537, Ayrshires 11,537, Lincoln Red 1,358. Overall 25% were pedigree according to Ministry figures. A very low figure.

Despite the mechanisation, impact was still to be felt and employment on the land was still high. For example as late as 1933 Colonel H. J. Cator M.C., a well known Shorthorn breeder with the beef type with the **Ranworth** prefix founded that same year was farming 1,300 acres on his Norfolk estate and reported having 58 staff although it is true to say he also had an Ayrshire herd and a British White herd for which the family have become noted in recent times. This Shorthorn herd was founded on Collynie, Chapelton, Cluny,

Uppermill and Glastullich lines with cattle being exported to South America and other countries.

Mention of Collynie again and of the Bapton herd earlier with the transfer to Scotland reminds me of a nearby herd some of which made the reverse journey. To explain, in 1937 the remainder of the **Collynie** herd was purchased by Sir Bernard Greenwell and transported to **Marden** in Kent; this became the new prefix, as under agreement the Collynie prefix was dropped. Nineteen waggon loads came by train. It was a very beneficial move for the breed as it prevented the remainder of the Collynie and Sittyton blood lines from going abroad and some 81 cows and 59 calves carrying almost irreplaceable bloodlines including the Eliza, Dainty, Lavender, Secret, Orange Blossom and Jilt lines combined with Aldie, Rosehaugh and Naemoor through the sire's lines, thus providing a very rare unit. Unfortunately Sir Bernard died so the Marden herd passed to Sir Peter Greenwell with the day-to-day management by William Cowie. Through the proximity of the war and the cancellation of most of the shows not much was heard of Marden till after the war.

Backtracking again, probably the most momentous happening during this period was the founding of the Milk Marketing Board in 1933 when marketing was becoming a problem caused by the growth of demand being supplied by a large number of small producers, with problems of supply and collection, as well as price cutting by the dairies. A consensus from the Government, the NFU and the 100,000 producers formed the board to provide some security, which indeed it did until some time toward the end of the century when the Monopolies Commission decided it was in contravention. After all the years when we all, or most of us, swore at the board for its inadequacies, we should now get down and pray for something similar as the current situation deteriorates to a very similar one to that which was in place before the Board. The industry is in disarray. Farmers then received regular payments and were able to plan their business for long term. It developed its own transport, marketing, A I services and products and, although it grew a bit like the civil service, the coming of the war with the cessation of imports meant that everyone with the MMB, as it became known, had to knuckle down and cope with the production of sufficient milk and by-products and also cope with the seasonal output swings that all added to the associated problems of food rationing.

1936 was a good year, the Society moved to Victoria House, Southampton Row, London, the Lincoln Red Association decided to return their administration and registration back to the Shorthorn Society and the Dairy Shorthorn Association and the Shorthorn Society finally merged.

1937 was a dream year for the breed and reads like a fairy tale. Firstly the Society: Dairy Shorthorns had over 500 awarded certificates for the Government register, twice as many as other breeds, this was for three years' consistent yields over 9,000lb.There were three new production records: a 10-year-old gave 33,240lb; another yielded 131 $^3/_4$lb in 24 hours with a butter fat of 4.1%; another, Broadfields Flora, yielded 10 gallons a day for 7 days and Silverstream Melody was the first to give over 100,000lb with her first 5 calves; more than 40 had life-time yields exceeding 100,000lb. The Royal Show had over 200 entries from 56 herds and Hastoe won the Championship for the 2nd time in 3 years. The dairy show attracted 78 entries and Fothering Foggathorpe 2nd was placed supreme over all breeds as well as winning the Calvert Melvin and Shorthorn Butter cups. Her average yields were 67lb at 4.09%. The breed won the Bledisloe trophy for the team of 6. At Smithfield the carcasses cross-bred classes were won by Dairy Shorthorn crosses. For the beef type the Perth average for 210 entries was one of the highest at £139 17s. Ken MacGillivray won the Championship; Captain John MacGillivray averaged £345 for 16 and Finlay MacGillivray averaged £198 for 7 bulls; W. McNair had the highest average at £466 for 6 bulls. At Smithfield the Captain won 4 cups outright and was reserve for all 7 with his second team. In Belfast H.C. Robinson won supreme male with Magheramorne Masterkey also the female Champion Glenanne Clipper 19th. At Dublin J.K. Wright won both the Champion and reserve and the group of three and the sale averages were higher at £56 for dairy and £37 for Beef Shorthorns.

Calrossie created more records when Calrossie Control won the Royal and the Royal Highland and the Captain was the first President to Judge at Palermo on the first occasion when the judges were appointed from Britain. To finish, beef bred steers won at Chicago and Toronto and the winner of the latter was full brother to the Champion the previous year. Phew! I feel I should end this on a high.

8. World War II- the '60s

This section of the history is once again one of great turmoil internationally, but also a period when agriculture made huge strides, many forced upon it by circumstances and some by reason of population increase. The years before the war were those of foreboding and uncertainty and it was obvious that a period of disruption was to come. We would need more food and milk, especially that which was home-produced, and the quicker the better. Certainly initially not much thought was given to quality of milk in the form of butterfat and this was one factor that helped the increase of the Friesian as there was no doubt in people's minds that this breed could produce more milk; but all breeds were experiencing large expansion at this time. However the black and white was prone to low fat production in this period and she needed more food so the Shorthorn continued to hold the front place; furthermore everyone wanted a bull to produce the required stores. The dual-purpose factor came more and more to the fore and that largely featured and favoured the Shorthorn, so registrations and herds continued to expand.

Robert Hobbs in his presidential address in 1938 said, 'Following the move to Victoria House when the Beef Shorthorn, the Dairy Shorthorn and the Lincoln Reds all share the same address, there is a real danger we shall lose our place as the national foundation of stock in the UK and Ireland. If no beef breeder will budge an inch from the short legged Argentine type and get more udder and the Dairy men refuse to sacrifice a few gallons to obtain better beefing and the Lincoln Red men as well, are reluctant to yield on their size in return for quality we are all going to lose the huge advantage of amalgamation and its benefits. We cannot afford to ignore the commercial trends, some people say we should not say "Dairy Shorthorn or Beef Shorthorn" as it does not help co-ordination. High milk production might be a menace to the dual purpose quality, the same problem has happened in Ireland were there is a great shortage of dual purpose Shorthorns; the Aberdeen Angus is decreasing milk yields and the Ministry are very concerned. Their view and mine is that the prosperity of the cattle trade depends generally on foundation cows of the Shorthorn type which in turn will produce a good store or beef animal as well as furnishing a large flow of milk.' Strong words but maybe needed.

1935/36 had been a great year for Dairy Shorthorns as they had won all the milking trials at Three Counties, Kent, Tunbridge Wells, Oxford, Peterborough shows, also the London Dairy Event, where the winner had 82.6lb in the day and the 38 head turn out had averaged 6 gallons per day. The breed then surpassed itself at the Royal Show when two cows beat all breeds in the trials: Huxham Duchess Royal 7th gave 91lb at 3.6% and Silverstream Melody gave 79.4lb at 3.9%. The former was a record for the breed, the latter was the second best performance for all breeds. Jerseys and Ayrshires were the runners up, a Friesian was in 8th place.

1937 was the year when the journal became *The Shorthorn Journal* but it changed again later when the beef produced their *Beef Shorthorn Record* magazine. It was also the year when J. C. Robinson of Iford Fame gave £800, a considerable sum, in memory of his brother A. E. Robinson towards the provision of progeny group prizes at principal shows. Their herd had a very satisfactory reduction sale of 99 head, which averaged £53 12 shillings which was very good considering the looming war; in fact it was the highest average for 5 years. Eaton also held a draft sale of 75 and the average was higher at £69, probably because the drought experienced earlier had broken. Also there were 32 calves at foot against 5 at Iford. This was also the year when Cherry broke the record as reported elsewhere giving 143 $^3/_4$lb in a day and 961lb in a week for Messrs Wort and Way of Amesbury. A further record was by Metchley Daisy 4th for Messrs Follows and son of Edgebaston when she completed 165,225 $^3/_4$lb in 13 lactations.

1939 was obviously a very difficult time and many were apprehensive about the outcome of the sale of the **Aldenham** herd of Pierpoint Morgan which was called just after the outbreak of war. This herd had been noted for its excellence for some years but many seemed oblivious of the impending problems, or they were taking advantage of the situation: an average of £67 10s. was obtained, with one of the top prices of 200 guineas being paid by Major Leslie Marler for Aldenham Florentia 8th, twice a winner at the Royal Show and female Champion at the Centenary Royal show a few weeks earlier. He also paid the top price of 240 guineas for the 2,000 gallon cow Aldenham Kirklevington 20th who had achieved this yield with her first calf. These two went into the **Wavendon** herd started in the 1930s where a number of quality animals were kept near Bletchley, Buckinghamshire, but it was dispersed owing to business commitments in 1957. Again I am delighted to record this prefix was another to be reborn, in the later years, although in a beef context.

In 1939 the Royal Agricultural Society held its centenary show at Windsor, a great event for Shorthorns despite the impending problems, with 250 entries from 49 herds. The female Champion was, as recorded, won by J. Pierpoint Morgan's Aldenham Florentia 8th and the male Championship was won by Eaton Rose King 23rd for Major W. E. Mann. The Beef Shorthorn classes or 'Shorthorns' as they were classified then were won by Capt. MacGillivray with Muirside Ramsden King. The female award in this sector went to Wing Princess Royal for Miss A. S. Brocklebank who had a great show winning the group award as well.

Interestingly, because of the size controversy which was growing apace, official society measurements were taken, all quoted in inches:

	height	**girth**	**length**	**age**
Florentia 8th	53	86	74	4 years and 4 months
Wilds Rosedale Abbess 6th (reserve Champion)	49	79	67	5 years
Eaton Waterloo 7th	52	79	57	3 years 4 months

Eaton Rose King 23rd was 61 at withers and 89 from base of horn to tail root. Follow now the measurements of Cherry the world record breaker who yielded 41,644lb in 365 days for the Wort family recorded elsewhere: 91 girth, 93 barrel, 59 wither to pin, 55 height. Garrard the famous artist in the 1800s recorded all his subjects' measurements in inches as: shoulder 60. Poll to tail 93. Chest 91. Breadth of hip 26, bone of fore leg 9, height of knee 14, all for a bull and for the female: shoulder 59. Poll to tail 98, chest 87, bone of fore leg 8, height of knee 16. Now if you have a second take a measure to some of your herd, and see how yours compare for size. Back to the history, as I deviate again!

In 1939 the pressure of the demands of war was felt, with 4 million more acres under cultivation. From 1940 until 1945 agricultural shows were ceased, with a few exceptions. The council decided to maintain the same President throughout hostilities. They were very fortunate in the elected choice, Norman Lee, who had just sold his Stonelands herd, and shouldered this responsibility with all the extra problems that arose. Even in normal times the holder of this office can be called upon to carry out many duties and take often difficult decisions, frequently at short notice. One of the remarkable achievements was the Red Cross Agricultural Fund which was so well supported by all breeders including the Royal Family, donating stock for sale. The society raised well over £35,000 with auctioneers and their staff also donating their time and commission; donations were also received from Canadian and Australian breeders.

This fund is worthy of explanation as it was part of the main Red Cross and St John Fund that up to 1942 had raised £15 million from donations, a staggering sum. More was always needed at this time as they were spending £12,500 *per day* for parcels for our prisoners-of-war; they had spent £3 million on medical parcels and £1 million on 'aid to Russia' for that country suffered horrendous casualties in terrible circumstances. The agricultural section of this fund had raised almost £2 million to 1942 and so was a considerable effort of support.

Later on in **1940** the London Office was evacuated to Medmenham, just outside Marlow, Buckinghamshire, following the increase in bombing activity, the staff having spent most of their working time in the basement. Staff numbers were very reduced owing to some not wishing to move and others having joined the services.

One of the herds prominent at this time was the **Scotsgrove** herd at Thame, Oxford, owned by Lt. Colonel Ashton, OBE, JP, MP, who had served as President twice, first in 1936/37 then later in 1951/52 and had been Chairman of the Herd Book Committee. He was on the British Mission to South America, also the RASE council and that of the BDFA as well, so he was a busy man!. He was first of all in partnership with C.J. Maurice and later with G.M. Hibberd; originally he founded the herd in 1907 with the former and in fact the whole basic herd came from five animals: Timbrell Queen, Barrington Princess, Lacey Musical, Ranksborough Cynthia and Timbrell 21, most of whom went back to Cranford breeding, demonstrating the immense influence that herd had, being used by all the successful herds of this time. They developed a number of families: principally Cynthia, Cinderella, Camilla, Clara, Carol and Barrington. Probably their best remembered cow was Scotsgrove Musical 8th, a beautiful animal who was breed supreme and reserve overall supreme at the 1947 London Dairy Show, giving 81.7lb at 5.31%in 24 hours. They used a succession of excellent well chosen sires which produced a number of other noted daughters, among the former were such bulls as Knowsley Precentor, Foxbury Wild Prince 6th, whose 1st 14 daughters averaged 7,336lb with their 1st calves, and Fothering Foggathorpe Duke 2nd. All going back to Darlington Cran 5th. There was also Wicklesham Fairy King of Hastoe breeding, Andersea Marshal Cran with 5 crosses of Damory Kirklevington 5th, who gave 17,000lb with her 15th lactation and lived a productive life to over 20 years of age, and Andersea Empire Barrington. To name a few. The herd was consistently in the top flight at many shows and incorporated in many pedigrees.

The **Fylde** herd of R. Silcock and Son at Thornton in Lancashire was founded in 1898 and proved a substantial influence in that region for a number of years, recorded from very early days producing both excellent yields and also a multitude of show ring successes in both interbreed and Shorthorn competitions. T. B.Silcock had been one of the very early Dairy Shorthorn Association members and was very keen on obtaining top yields from his herd. How much they were helped by the use of that company's products is not too clear! But they certainly got the results. Fylde Cherry 11th was one of the earliest 2,000 gallon cows giving this in three successive lactations around 1925. The herd followed fashionable Bates lines with Oxford, Duchess, Foggathorpe, Barrington, Wild Eyes families as well as Morwenna, Rosebuds and Moss Rose lines. The Silcocks only used progeny tested sires once they became established and among their bulls used were: Babraham Bridegroom, Sir Rafe 16, Kelmscott Tarquin 16, Fylde Peer 4th and 10th, Fylde Jester 12th and Dairyman 2nd, also Imperial 29th, Ilford Lawrence and Favourite Blend, Histon Royal Oxford and Royalist Darlington, also Royalist Duke 3rd and Lord Waterloo 26th, Hastoe Wild Bruce, with others which demonstrated the use of lines from all the principal herds of the day. All with great results some of which are listed, all with the Fylde prefix: Merrythought 5th averaged 12,438lb with 8 lactations the top of which was 22,017lb, Empress 2nd averaged 10,650lb with 7 lactations. Morwenna 47th 11,000lb with 9 calves, Rose 13 10,960lb with 9 calves and with a herd average consistently of around 10,300lb for cows and 7,600 for heifers. It demonstrated the breed's productive longevity and the consistency of the herd particularly if one remembers the national averages again.

One of the fascinating histories of the Dairy Shorthorn farms is that of the **Wreay** herds outside Penrith. I use the plural, as, like Uppermill, there have been several owners. Thomas Richardson farmed this smallish farm for many years with the real dual type so appreciated by the Irish, originally being a substantial size but with distinct dairy abilities. He retired around 1919 after 46 years and Walton Jackson took the tenancy bringing with him a herd which he had at Wigton as a foundation; this was also of the same type and very popular overseas as well. Walton Jackson was keen to be involved in the trend for milk and recording and this unit was dispersed in 1928; he purchased Bates type animals nearly all of the Wild Eyes family. Walton had two sons both interested, Edward and William, and the latter was particularly interested in this Wild Eyes family, although it was realised that this one family was not too practical on its own despite the fact that they came from several branches of the Thomlinson farming families so other families were added, Gwynnes, Barringtons, Foggathorpes, to name a few. Edward Jackson had got married and took his part of the herd with him nearby to found his own herd, **Lifton**, again just outside Penrith at Clifton. Then on to **Bellmount** using that prefix later to be dispersed in the '60s. William died very young, in 1942, and as his father had retired the herd was dispersed in that year with a storming sale attracting members from all over the country. Sixty-two lots sold at an average of £264 with a top of 550 guineas for W. Wild Eyes 117th paid by Miss Vaughan. F. Morris of Groby paid 520 guineas for W. Wild Eyes 100th and then 500 guineas for W. Wildeyes 115th; many other premier herds were anxious to buy this beautifully bred stock.

The bull Orma Special Blend sold at 450 guineas. The average set another record as the highest since 1920 when H.A. Brown of the **Grendon** prefix averaged £291 16s. for 56 head from his excellent herd and the same year he exported his herd sire Grendon Royal Sovereign to Chile for 2,500 guineas.

William had a son known by all as 'Bill', who was left fatherless at a very young age but was guided by his uncle Edward before eventually taking over in 1961 and building a very high reputation, again on Bates lines, with skilful selections of Wild Eyes, Barringtons, Waterloos, Thorndale Roses and Foggathorpes and this reputation for quality was maintained until the herd was dispersed in 1998 but this takes it into another period so I will leave it there for the present.

1942: although this was a crucial stage in the war, it was again a good year for the breed with over 28,000 total registrations and over 3,500 members. Sales were surprisingly high in view of all the international uncertainties. Mr C.A. Brown of Woodstock held a reduction sale with the eventual outcome for his Glympton herd averaging overall £225 14s.for 42 head: the highest average since 1921. It was an interesting note of English fashion at this time when the report mentioned that in the June heat 'many were forced to remove their jackets and in some cases even their waist coats'!

The Society show and sale at Reading in November produced the highest ever average to date at a society event of this type, £177 for 125 lots; included in this were 5 bulls from W.H. Vigus's Revel herd which averaged £362 17s. The Champion was from Oxton, Foggathorpe 9th, which realised 800 guineas and the reserve was Brackenhurst Telluria Maid which made 420 guineas. Consider again the comparison with the Perth sales top price, which was 3,100 guineas with an average of 196 guineas for 186 head.

The **Brackenhust** herd, from Southwell in Nottinghamshire, owned by Sir William Hicking BT, was one of influence at this time, and again comprised of Bates families. It had gained a very substantial number of awards including no less than five Royal supreme awards as well as winning outright the Thornton Cup for groups in 1928,29 and 30, and also the Grendon Cup – the only herd to complete this feat to that date. Probably their best remembered cows were B. Bonnie Jean and B. Cerise Royal both sired by B. Red Prince who won the Bradfield Cup over all breeds in 1934. In 1942 the spring show and sale Champion was Brackenhurst Butterfly who sold for 850 guineas, the highest price gained at auction for 19 years. Unfortunately the herd was sold the following year with 44 head averaging £359. Again it is pleasing to report here that the herd was reformed under this prefix in the late '80s when the Agricultural College established a new Shorthorn herd.

The other herd which featured in the 1942 sale report was the **Revels** prefix; coupled with it needs to be the **Revelex** herd as they were so interrelated, also **Revelsmill** and **Revelsware.** To explain! Walter H. Vigus founded the Revels herd around 1920 and it became so large, with over 400 head, that in 1946 he decided to allocate some to his four sons: Joseph and Robert took over Clements Farm, Brickenden, Hertfordshire, using the Revelex prefix. Frank took over Mill Farm, Hertingfordbury, and used the Revelsmill prefix and Geoffrey used the Revelsware prefix at West Mill Farm on the Buxton Easneye estate at Ware. So, as with the MacGillivray family, a complex history arose, although with hindsight the last two did not rise to so much Shorthorn prominence.

Revels cow families of Daisy, Cressida, Lady Lee, Barrington, Altrusia, Lottie, were the most prominent and prolific. The first was from Col. Abel Smith's Michaelmas Daisy from which a phenomenally successful family of descendants evolved. The most well known was the superb R. Daisy Chain who won a huge number of awards including 5 challenge cups, 7 Championships including supreme at the 1947 Royal as well as yielding over 94,000lb of milk. One of her sons R . Imperial Duke was male Champion at the Royal in 1948, furthermore 3 of his daughters won the progeny group. R. Red Vale 3rd produced 46,201lb in 3 successive lactations and with 9 calves she yielded 128013lb; by 11 calves this had risen to 139,808lb and her stall mate R. Altrusia yielded 122,801lb lifetime yield. Sires used included Hawkstead Mainspring who traced back to the Taylor's Mainspring, Pennbury Lord Barrington who sired many winners as did Wicklesham Barrington Beau who was the sire of Revelex Daisy's Premier that sold for the record 3,000 guineas to the USA in 1950. Then there was Brickenden Crispin 14th, R. Wildeyes Warrior, who was sire of R. Daisy Warrior sold to USA for 1,050 guineas, Glympton Lord Darlington 3rd, Tilsworth Barrington Bandit, Histon Waterloo Lad, Earlsoham Rose King 2nd himself a Royal Show Champion who sired among others the reserve Champion at Reading Show and sale in 1942 and 1943 and the Champion in 1944 as well a string of other winners. Revelex Imperial Duke was male Champion in 1948 and supreme in 1951.

Another famous cow was Revels Cressida, who won a huge number of Championships among which was the 50,000lb class at the Royal which she won in 1951 and then later when she was 11 years of age she secured a 3rd prize in the same competition having given over 93,000lb by then. The herd was top of the Eastern Region and indeed top of the National Records many times; it also exported to South Africa, the USA, Canada, Australia, New Zealand and Kenya.

Some idea of the national situation at this time can be gained by the following tables:

Female population in 1942 was:

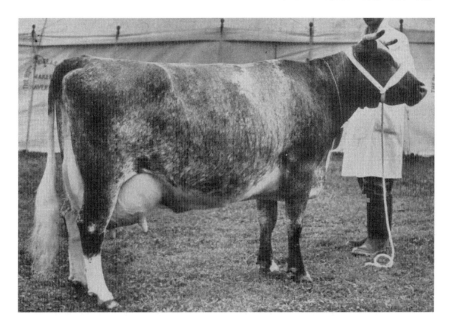

Revels Cressida

Shorthorn 41,000. Friesian 38,100. Ayrshire 11,040. Jersey 18720. Guernsey 16,980. Red Poll 11,080. Lincoln Red 5,880.

The bull licence situation was:
1938. Shorthorn 23,730. Friesian 2.671. Ayrshire 489. Out of a total of 31,252.
1943 Shorthorn 21,268. Friesian 9,096. Ayrshire 1,101. Out of a total of 34,971.

The Ministry of Agriculture was concerned that there was a great shortage of Shorthorn bulls even at this time when work was progressing fast in respect of Artificial Insemination procedures, with the first centre to be set up by the MMB in **1944**. Way back in 1938 the Shorthorn Society insisted that anyone contemplating A I should notify the Society. Another statistic which surprised me was that out of those licensed 80% had no recorded breeding or milk records. No wonder the ministry had cause to worry over the future quality of stock.

Another major development for the industry in this period was the completion of trials in the USA for the X19 strain, for immunisation against contagious abortion, which was to save millions of pounds in the national herd. The ministry introduced a scheme at a charge of 2 shillings per animal to encourage the use of S.19, as it became known. One of the surprising facts with regard to animal health was the

Revels Daisy Chain

reluctance or difficulty of attaining attested status especially in view of the human ability to contract the tuberculosis disease from cattle. Although Shorthorn show and sales had been required to be TT *and* agglutination tested for some time; even by 1948 125,000 out of the possible 162,000 national dairy farmers were neither TB tested or attested. Thankfully the human level of infection is now almost a thing of the past but there is currently an upsurge of the tubercular problem in cattle which is very disturbing. Opinion is divided in that many consider the problem has arisen due to infection from badgers but there is a strong lobby against this view. Hopefully before this is published the source will be defined, but it seems doubtful.

Controversy continued with Capt. Milne Harrop setting out his ideal Shorthorn in 1945; among his statements, which indicated that the breed must maintain its quality, he advocated that 'cows must be deep bodied with short legs but be able to accommodate a milking machine' which bought forth a storm of protest from all quarters. Another controversy which had been smouldering for a while was one that mainly affected the beef type: the principle of nurse cows, mainly to help bull calves, which were going for sale, reach their maximum potential. I remember personally seeing some herds of Herefords and probably others some of which had 15 or 20 nurse cows to boost their calves and produce them in fine coat and maximum flesh/fat cover. Gordon Blackstock, when talking on the two problems as late as 1963, rightly said, 'Put two bulls in the ring, one short legged and fat and one with growth potential but up on the leg and longer and narrower and the buyer will pay more for the short fat one which will weigh 12 to 14 Hundred weight than for the one which will weigh a ton at three years of age.' He was right at the time as that was the fashion. It was also the case that females would be far too fat to enable them to breed properly but again buyers favoured the over-fat beast; this again caused a problem as when the animal got back into to the commercial situation the flesh 'fell off'. For a long time this was also the case at shows with both beef and dairy animals far too fat; at this time if your animal was in working condition she was marked down. The practice of over fitting was the ruination of some heifers.

The situation got to such a pitch that the Shorthorn Society and probably the others were approached by the Government in the '40s to bring this practice of nurse cows to an end, not an easy thing to police; the system declined to everyone's advantage, especially as the implication grew that the breed did not have sufficient milk in its sucklers. Most good breeders supported the need to stop this system. Another ridiculous ruling and fashion was that, 'No animal without horns could be admitted to the grading register nor could they be shown to compete for Society prizes.' This was an edict in 1943 which was not withdrawn until 1951 for females when it said de-horned females could be shown and believe it or not it was not until 1962 that de-horned bulls were permitted to be shown. Even then the vote was narrow, and we wonder why some decry breed societies! One can see why prejudices are slow to change and indeed why it took the Society so long to recognise that the breed was getting seriously too small.

There were fortunately some who were concerned and outspoken The first to be taken notice of was Lord Lovat DSO, MC, who was appointed President of the Scottish Shorthorn Breeders Association in **1947.** His **Beaufort** herd had been established in 1869 and, although beautifully bred with a reputation for quality females, it had not achieved much fame despite a large number of successes at shows and sales and good exports to the USA, Eire, Chile and Australia.

To explain the Scottish situation briefly: the Scottish Associations had till 1936 consisted of four small associations: the Scottish central, the Aberdeen, the Banff and Kincardine and the Northern counties. These held little sway separately but they amalgamated in 1936 and also became a limited liability company, all of which gave the reformed organisation considerable clout. They, like other associations, appointed their President and committees; the Presidents are listed in Appendix IV from this date. A number of serious steps were taken as their members were at last aware that things had to be changed if they were to stay 'in business'. Lord Lovat ,who had a very distinguished war record and in any case was very respected, determined that the confidence in the breed should be maintained as the writing was on the wall despite the fact that the catastrophic decline did not start until 1949 when the peak was reached with 25,781 female registrations, 15,517 in the grade register and the bulls just starting to decline at 6,707. The peak for the grade register was actually in 1950 when an amazing 20,859 were recorded. Lord Lovat was conscious, as were a number of others, that the breed was losing size and that inevitably it would be difficult to increase size as small usually begets small.

This coincided with the early maturity with its added problem of laying on fat. Demands were changing, or had done. In an article on size Lord Lovat emphasised his point by comparing recent calf sale prices at Newton St Boswells where the averages for over 3,500 calves were: Hereford cross £38 13s., Angus cross £38 11s., Shorthorn cross £30. 'This is a very serious situation. Other breeds have their problems, Angus seem to rely on paper pedigrees, Ayrshire breeders once laughed at Friesians going to the London Dairy Show,—— there is nothing wrong with the Beef Shorthorn that cannot be put right but like many of the younger generation I refuse to be associated with the mistakes made within the last 20 years.'

Another breeder who spoke out, although some time later, was Denis J. Cadzow of **Duncrahill** of East Lothian, when he reflected on the lack of profitability in beef production that had applied for some time. He reflected that possibly the fall in demand was because we were trying to sell 'an out-of-date model' and he decried the use of bulls in this country that were the 'left overs' from the Argentinian market. Strong words indeed, but with some truth. Perhaps some considered him presumptuous as a comparatively new breeder of Pedigree Shorthorns whose herd was started in 1940. But he knew cattle, therefore felt able to speak out so his herd was quickly in the front at shows following Butterfly, Princess Royal, Broadhooks, Lancaster lines with Calrossie, Pittodrie and Cluny and Beaufort Sires. He brought out the supreme Champion at Perth in 1950 with his junior Champion Duncrahill Ambition by Pittodrie Impression. Duncrahill also won a number of fat stock shows, winning senior steer at Smithfield 1953, breed Champion Edinburgh 1952 and 1953. He also had faith in the breed as he and his family were to found the Luing breed in the 1940s using the Shorthorn crossed with the Highland to produce the very hardy cattle, in fact using Cruggleton Alastair initially. The breed was officially recognised in **1965**.

In striving to find the right 'prescription' for both and dairy, as the latter were also becoming conscious of a problem, breeders were trying several steps to correct the trend and some of those not happy with what was happening were the Dales breeders who wished passionately to retain their hardy but fine type which had been bred in their hills

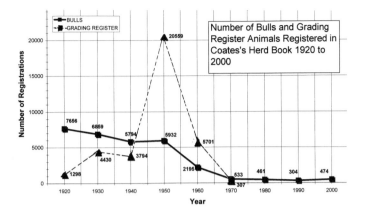

for many years. A group broke away in 1944 to found the Northern Dairy Shorthorn Association. **1945** saw the move back to London of the Society staff but in **1943** the Lincoln Red Society had decided to go it alone with their administration being carried out in their own county.

1944 also saw the improved advance register set up for females and the improved register of merit for bulls and it was also the year when the MMB took over all responsibility for milk recording from all other organisations. 1946 was the year when the Society decided to regularise the Regional Associations, as, although there were a number of such bodies doing sterling work, there was a need for a reasonably common form of constitution and guidelines so that maximum benefit could be achieved. Eleven regions were established, making a total of 14 regions. As always fantastic work was done for the breed. Most Secretaries are honorary or receive a very modest fee and do a wonderful job coercing their members to participate both in social functions and other events that publicise the breed through open days, local herd and calf competitions, regional sales and contacting new members, etc. These activities not only serve to help the breed, they also provide those concerned with a common ground for discussion, advice and comparison, as well as contact, so are invaluable for the members. **1946** was the year when the world record cow Winton Gentle 2nd sired by Iford Lawrence 4th died, having produced 15 calves and yielded 223,917lb on only twice a day milking and being kept out night and day all her life.

It was surprising also how long the effects of the war lasted; even animal protein foods were rationed during the war, so every step was taken to produce it or its equivalent, at home; it was also the time when silage started to become favoured, mechanisation was evolving, another factor combined with our famous climate, or weather as it is better described! Human rationing also continued in some forms until **1953**.

Production of milk had expanded greatly over the war years and in

1944-5 a total output of 1,070 million gallons were produced in England and Wales alone. There were two distinct ideas on production: on the one hand there was the low input system and low cost epitomised by the Hosier Bale system used by people such as Rex Paterson who also developed the buck rake, now so universally used in some form or another. This system was mainly used by the commercial man. The other end of the spectrum was an emphasis on maximum production per animal and it took some time to arrive at a happy medium; this was governed to a certain extent by the cost of concentrates and also milking parlour development. The added factor has been the cost of labour and it remains to be seen how many cows a man can be expected to milk and care for efficiently, many will say that economic pressures today have forced us to unreasonable limits at the time of writing, but back to the period in hand.

One of the south country herds mentioned previously from time to time is the **Anderson** herd of the Tory family in Dorset started by H. J. S. Tory at the start of the century at Damory Court. He purchased stock from the legendary Taylor herd and later from Kelmscott. R.N. Tory then transferred the herd to Anderson and from this sound foundation he developed Moss Rose, Darlington, Wild Eyes, Waterloo and Furbelow families, added to this the excellent choice of stock bulls one of which, Anderson Champion Bates, who was well named as he won at the Royal Shows of 1926 and 1928. One of the Damory prefix Kirklevington 5th had a long productive life breeding a series of well known sons as well as giving over 17,000lb with her 13th calving. She bred such bulls as Anderson Matchless Bates sold to the USA for 3,000 dollars, A. Royal Bates Champion at the 1929 Royal, and A. Priceless Bates whose progeny from the Hunts Green herd averaged 114 guineas. The Anderson herd sold many stock bulls to well known herds throughout the country as they were very genuine heavy milkers on strictly commercial lines including two 2,000 gallon cows, Spetisbury Rosie and her daughter. The herd also won a trophy, presented by His Majesty the King, for the highest herd average in Wiltshire of any breed, five times. They exported to the USA, Australia and South Africa. In recent years the family have been famed worldwide for their flock of Hampshire Down sheep, what a pity they don't still have Shorthorns! But while they did they certainly made their mark.

It is an extraordinary fact that so many successful herds go back at some point to either Taylors of Cranford or Rothschild of Tring for their base. G.T. Burrows, the Editor of *Live Stock Journal,* and many writers in the Society Journals of the '40s reported that before and after the Cranford sale over 100 herds had purchased stock and in the case of the Tring sales the figure was nearer 200 which had benefited and 'it would take a book of over 30,000 words to do justice to their influence.' I am doing my best!

Another that made an impact was the **Churchill** herd of the Rose family at Kingham in Oxfordshire. And this is another fascinating history. The Garne family, one of the original names mentioned in the early history, previously tenanted this farm. George Garne was son of Thomas Garne and grandson of William Garne (who was farming 150 years before), all Shorthorn breeders of repute. The farm may well challenge Uppermill's record for the length of continuous Shorthorn habitation. They rented from another Shorthorn breeder, J. H. Langston of Sarsden, who benevolently built on extra rooms because they had so many visitors from the USA to see the two cattle herds who needed to be accommodated!

In 1880 Urban Rose became tenant of Churchill when the ownership had passed to Lord Moreton, himself a Shorthorn breeder and President of the Shorthorn Society in 1885/6; he had an excellent Bates type herd at Sarsden, so the 'plot thickens'! Urban went to Hobbs for his foundation in 1892 and purchased two, Bessie 22 and Fanny 40, both tracing to the first herd book. He started registering in 1920 and began a regular export trade: first to South Africa with Bessie 74 who won every principal show in the union for the next four years; the calf she carried out turned out to be the most famous bull ever in South Africa, Haslop Bradman. Which was reported as never beaten. Exports continued to South Africa on a regular basis and also to Argentina, USA, Australia, New Zealand, France and Newfoundland. Over the years his herd has had so many winners and used so many stock bulls they cannot all be listed but a few prefixes or individuals follow: Gaiety Rover, Orma Barrington Lord 4th, Eaton Rose King 36th, a fantastic bull so prominent in several herds; Stirzakers Lord Ringlet 11th, Brackenhurst Gay Lad, Brilliant Boy and Paragon; sires from Kelmscott, Anderson, Checkendon, Thornby, Calstone, Stockwood and Great Tew, all noted quality herds also they used home bred sires such as C .Lord Cactus 2 and 3. The herd grew a reputation for selling productive sires but in 1962 Dick Rose reckoned that A I had reduced his income from that source by 80%. The surplus males were steered and records showed that they finished at around eight and a half cwt at 13 months. The Rose family was always willing to try new sires and ideas to keep their herd in the front line with great success. In 1968 Dick Rose became President of the Shorthorn Society and later still was awarded Honorary Life Membership in rare recognition of services to the breed as it was he who really pushed the scheme that revitalised the Society and the breed (see later). He also was the initiator of the concept of World Shorthorn Conferences on a regular basis. Churchill sires and female cattle went into many herds. It is also Interesting to note that when later Sir Winston Churchill started his herd he could not use the expected prefix as it was already booked, so he took **Chartwell**!

A little earlier I referred to Capt. Milne Harrop with reference to the extreme views expressed by both camps (those who wanted change and those who did not) but his appreciation of good stock was fully recognised, which can be demonstrated by the fact that he successfully bred dogs, pigeons and Welsh pigs, all of which were prize-winners, as were his geese which won a number of gold cups at York, Crystal Palace and London dairy shows for the best bird of any kind exhibited. A claim not many can boast! His prefix **Gweryllt** was based first near Wrexham where the herd was founded in 1925 then Ruthin in Clwyd, Wales, with stock from the Grendon herd of H.A. Brown and from Samuel Sanday from whom he bought Moel Oxford 3 and Oxford 5 from which he built up a quality herd with much expertise, mainly on Bates lines. One of his 'stars' was Lucy, who yielded 66 tons of milk in 9 years during which time she won the area gold cup no less than five successive times. His first sire was Plaspower Conjuror by Kelmscott Conjurer 56, Champion at the 1916 Royal and sire of several other Royal winners; this bull's progeny were winners of many trophies including milking trials at the London Dairy Show. The herd also had two leading Iford sires, Royal Waterloo 26th and Laurel 13th; these were followed by two Deenwood sires and a senior sire, Great Tew Trickster, purchased at 10 years of age. Capt. Milne Harrop was President of the Society 1948-49.

One of the main problems in writing such a history is selecting which herds or events to include and I am very conscious of this as I go through the years but I can only console myself by looking at Sinclair's History, which took 1,000 pages to cover just the beginning of the Society. It is so difficult to describe a herd's many years of development in a few lines, particularly the large ones, but the next one contributed to the breed by its policies and skill. The policy was to run the business in a strictly commercial way and breed cows that without being pushed had the capacity for very long productive lives in the herd or in the herd to which they were sold. Their breeding spread all over the dairy world and their productive longevity ensured their buyer's satisfaction. I refer to the **Theale** herd owned by the Cumber family that has farmed their land in Berkshire and Wiltshire since the 12th century.

It was founded in 1919 by grading-up from existing stock as well as very astute purchases. Lockinge Darling, purchased for £14, had well over 80 descendants; Buttercup and Maude were also very prolific families and made early contributions: T. Buttercup 2nd gave over 136,000lb with 15 calves; T Buttercup 9th gave over 100,000lb with 11 calves being sold to B.W. Brazil of Nettlebed after 9 calves, and both the Brazils and Cumbers are still in business. The herd had an enormous number of 100,000lb cows in the register and some of these were Vespers, another graded-up family; the Valentines originated from a pedigree purchase, Chalfield Valentine, who gave 62,885lb with 6 calves. Cliveden Snow Queen was another profitable purchase, still milking after reaching 17 years of age, she gave 134,772lb with 13 calves; Revels Butterfly 3rd bought in the same year gave 106,000lb with 10 calves; Beadlow Wild Queen gave 117,065lb with 10 calves, Mathers Tiny 2nd gave 100,740lb with 10 calves and was a member of the Bledisloe team at the London Dairy Show and went on to have 13 calves; Stourhead Barrington Duchess 54th gave 10,000lb as a heifer and gave 5 subsequent lactations of around 14,000lb. Theale Maud 12th gave 203,875lb with 7464lb fat with 12 lactations.

So the list goes on, but when we think of many Holstein herds averaging only 3 or 4 lactations it certainly makes one wonder why. Surely productive longevity must be better, leaving so many progeny for sale or choice, even if solid-not-fat levels have to be considered which they were not then. The herd ran up to some 530 head with about 150 milkers. The steers were an important asset and W. Cumber and Son (Theale) Ltd, as the firm was titled, were loyal supporters of Smithfield with regular exhibits; their steer in 1950 for example had a daily live weight gain of 2.72lb, higher than any other breed exhibit over one year old: he weighed 12cwt 20lb at 16 months. A group of 122 steers aged 35 months averaged 10 cwt 3 qtrs all on mainly home grown feeds. With up to 10 bulls at a time in stud duty it is hard to pick out particular ones, but perhaps Earlsoham Rose King 14th, Checkendon Brilliant Boy, sired by Churchill Brilliant Boy, Streetly Lord Barrington 4th who worked for 15 years leaving 145 daughters will give a flavour of the quality. Exports were numerous selling to USA, Malta, Uruguay, Equador, Azores, Peru and Egypt.

I wrote about my dilemmas a few lines back but the Society also had problems in the late '40s and early '50s; these were problems of scale as the membership was in excess of 6,000 and the number of herds was reported as over 5,000. There was a problem with the number of representatives on Council; with the area entitlements plus the President and 8 Past Presidents bringing attendance to a possible total of over 50, it was all in danger of being becoming unmanageable. In those days the South-West region was the largest with 800 members; which makes one so sad when one realises that within 30 years the membership had sunk to considerably less than this in total.

From one of the more up-to-date herds we move to what is probably the oldest and also one of the youngest. The **Ireby** herd of the Ritson family has played a very important role for longer than our records recall as it was established at Ireby Hall, Ireby, near Carlisle in 1855 by the current family's ancestors, the Hopes. This herd was mentioned in Sinclair's *History of Shorthorns* and in those days had around 70 head, with Duchess Emmas, Duchess, Tulip, Buttercup, Greenlea, and Forester lines. One of the first to do so, they started recording yields in 1909 and later joined the Shorthorn Association scheme in 1918; it is in all probability the oldest herd in one family's care in one place. It has always been noted for the excellence of its stock and has been one of the first places other herds have gone to seek sires as well as being regularly in the top flight at Penrith shows and sales in more recent years. Their most numerous and favourite family being the Greenleaf, supported by Duchess Emmas still going on as were Foresters, Foggathorpes, Rubies and Darlingtons. Among sires used were Greencroft Marquis, winner of the Royal Show in 1935, Morning Sun, Deansbiggin Warrior, Mollies Heir, Burndale Space Rocket and A I bulls like Histon Dairy Premier, and Orma Wild Pretender followed by some of their own Ireby Moonstone, Playboy and Premier. Unbearably this wonderful herd was one of those lost in the **2001** foot and mouth outbreak. Such an experience must be horrendous in any circumstance but to lose one so old must be unbelievably hard. Like some others the Ritson family are tenacious and have started again, even finding some Greenleaf animals to ensure some continuity and one has every confidence they will once again be at the front of the show and sale line-ups.

In all the chaos, loss, and inadequate handling of the 2001 outbreak this breed was reasonably fortunate in that not many herds were lost but another such was the outstanding **Chapelton** herd of the Biggar family. This family, like the previous one, has been in the agricultural public eye for many, many years. Walter Biggar, who died in 1941, was one of the early exporters and a cattle breeder of great repute, farming at the Grange, near Castle Douglas, Kirkudbrightshire, Scotland. Walter had the oldest herd of Galloway cattle in the world, with cattle registered in that breed's first herd book and although their Shorthorn herd was only registered in 1942 the number of this breed's cattle they had handled must run into many thousands as Walter was among the early men to export to Argentina and he quickly gained a worldwide reputation for his integrity and skill. He judged around the world and must be the only man who had judged Chicago show in USA thirteen times. In between all this he found time to have four sons (or rather Mrs Biggar did)! It was James who had the hard task of following his well known father. Leaving school, he worked with Bertie Marshall and quickly gained a unique reputation. Like his father, he travelled around the world and judged in a number of countries so gathering a unique knowledge of the requirements of all the regions; in fact his first overseas assignment was at 16 as assistant cattleman to a load of cattle being shipped to Canada.

Perhaps it is at this point that I should mention that it was largely his urging that persuaded me to write this book to occupy some of my retirement so you can understand what a skilled persuader he was! I am only so sad that he did not live long enough to see its completion, despite ringing me fortnightly to ascertain progress. I would add that it was he who assisted me with his advice when I was founding my Hereford herd as he helped so many to achieve their ambitions over the years.

This book's subject is cattle, not people (although they play a huge part in any history) so I will continue. In a way this herd was founded by accident in that a group of cattle from the Cruggleton herd were due to go to a special client, but they had to cancel the order, so they went to Chapelton. Six Cruggleton heifers in calf to Cruggleton Perfect and the herd was born. Brights, Rosewoods, Brawith Buds, Augustas, Rothes Queens, Floss, Nonpareils, Orange Blossoms, Charity Clippers, Rosewoods and Pye and other families followed as did quick success; his second bull in Perth from this unit, Chapelton Brigadier, won his class selling for 3,000 guineas. In 1941 C. Bonus was the highest price at Palermo fetching 40,000 pesos; in 1950 C. Crusader was Supreme Champion at the Royal Highland. The first stock bull was Calrossie Supreme, who was considered too leggy at the time but after only one season he left a host of influential sires: Chapelton Ambassador was probably the most noted, as he dominated the scene in Australia for some years; C. Crusader in the Cluny herd, C. Baronet at Aldie and C. Royalist at Saltoun. Calrossie Contribution followed, who sired another Australian success, C.Coronation, who then went on to Argentina. C. Comet at Dungarthill and then South Africa. Cruggleton Balmoral followed from which C. Bright Star and C. Banner both went to South Africa at substantial prices. Other sires followed, among which were Kinellar Broker, Calrossie Contribution, Erimus Galant, Cruggleton Reminder, Chapelton Commando, reserve senior Champion at Perth, who was sold to the Bapton herd at 5,100 guineas, then Deenend Glendrossan followed. James Biggar reduced his herd in 1962 with the fall-off in demand. He also ran a very successful Hereford herd founded in 1976 which was herd of the year in 1995 and also produced the Interbreed Champion at the Royal show in 1988.

He had been President of the Smithfield Club, President of the Galloway Society, President of the Shorthorn Cattle Society in 1959/60 and President of the Beef Shorthorn Society 1972/73. There will be more of Chapelton later as, like only a few of us, James Biggar had the God-given gift of always being able to have whatever the trade demanded ahead of most others.

Another such character was Richard S. De Quincey, otherwise known as Dick, who founded the **Erimus** herd at Bodenham, Hereford. He had bred world-renowned Champion Sealyham dogs, humming birds, Welsh Cobs, orchids, Clun Forest sheep and Hereford cattle, the last it is said, by chance, as he was on his way to look at Shorthorns but called on a friend who bred Herefords on the way! Be that as it may his Herefords were renowned throughout the world in a very short time.

The Vern (his prefix) cattle were sought in every country and his Vern Robert and Vern Diamond, Julia Vern 40 and Vern Logic were all record breakers and trendsetters and were household names that everyone wished to emulate. Even his eventual Hereford dispersal was a record in 1966 when the average was £1,696.

He had always claimed he had no training in agriculture or genetics but in every species he was gifted with the eye or knack to know what was required; he also modestly claimed he never instructed his stockman how to feed or manage. He controlled the breeding and also had a strong disregard for 'breeding boffins'! Added to this he was very vociferous about those who thought that four or five bulls with the aid of A I could do the job within a breed: 'one would have thought the technicians would realise that the overspreading of one sire before he had been proven was an absolute disaster.' He was adamant that the future of a breed should be in the hands of small pedigree herds with good breeders that were the safety element for lasting improvement in cattle breeding. One of his other hobby horses was calf shows which he considered were 'the graveyard of good breeding as animals were over fitted.' At last in 1943 he had got round to Shorthorns: his first purchases were Augusta Heather Anne, Larbert Princess Royal 28th, reserve Champion at Perth and Clipper Mona; these were mated to Larbert Leader before this bull went to South America, then Balathie Command followed by Clipper Captain and Calrossie Evening News, Moonshine and Superb, both the last to were subsequently exported to Argentina. Female lines were Goldie, Floss, Graceful, Clipper, Rosewood, Miss Ramsden and Queen Rothes with a number related to Calrossie Randolph, Glastulich and Kirkton lines. In 1951 the top price at Perth was 6000 guineas paid by Westdrums Boots herd for E. Emeritus 5th.

In 1949 the Erimus herd had the top Perth average at 1,344 guineas. There is no doubt in my mind that if he had been alive today his cattle would have been those at the top; they would have been adapted to meet demand. A.L. Smith-Maxwell from Upton-on-Severn, another Hereford breeder, who was making the change to Shorthorns, eventually purchased the Erimus herd. In 1965 he had also purchased one of the oldest herds of the time, **Aldsworth**, which had been founded in 1825 and farmed by the Garne family thereafter, near Cirencester. They were assisted by Albert Forsythe, their stockman for over 60 years. They developed families such as Pye, Royal Prince, Jubilee and Brawith Bud, breeding a number of well known stock with many prize-winners including some exported that made their mark: Aldsworth Royal Prince went over to Australia and was Champion at their Royal in Sidney where a few years later his son and daughter created a double at the same event by winning both sex Championships. At home the prefix was prominent in several major herds including Millhills with

Aldsworth President that sired a number of champions. Aldsworth Village Lassie was Champion at Smithfield and Birmingham in 1911. After Archie Smith Maxwell purchased the herd he went on to retain the prefix trading as **Aldsworth and Beeston**.

Demand through the high days of the '40s was incredible and herds and membership were increasing so one can understand why not many took note of the critics in the various controversies. In any period there are always some who disagree and often this is healthy as it creates an awareness of alternative possibilities but in this case and in hindsight it serves to remind us of the words of Richard Stratton quoted earlier when he questioned what would happen when the Argentine trade was ended or declined. This trade was still a major factor and was evident by the fact that in 1946 no less than 70 animals out of 110 total sold for export at the Perth spring sale went to the Argentine and this from an overall total forward of 309. The extraordinary thing about this sale was: (1) It was when all records were smashed when the all-time top price, through auction, was achieved: **14,500** guineas was paid for Pittodrie Upright to go to Ralph Smith of USA and to be shortly after followed by Upright's brother Pittodrie Uprise at **14,000** guineas paid by the previous underbidder Col. Hardie of Balathie. (2) In that same sale 158 bulls were sold at under 100 guineas.

The South American trade had already declined from the high days, which for them were the days following the Great War. The trade to that country was now in the 50-100 per annum rather than the many hundreds which had gone before but exports continued at a reasonable level partly helped by the need of Europe to replenish losses incurred during the war; also other regions requiring to make up for the slowing down of trade during that time. Some of whom had followed the trade for the short-legged variety like Canada and USA at that time. However, quoting Lord Lovat again, 'Meat and milk are no longer the perquisites of the wealthy, they are the necessities of the better paid workers, they will soon be the requisite of the whole world. The Shorthorn has milking ability, early maturing abilities, weight for age performance and the ability to up grade native cattle and so is the best breed to assist in the global shortage but on the minus side it will never succeed if we do not bear in mind that substance has to be bred in not fed in. ' He went on, 'We are in danger of evolving a breed that cannot walk or even suckle a calf and the present chunky animal has already affected the reproductive powers of both the male and female in the two senior Scottish breeds.' Again, strong words.

1948 marked a major step in the breed when a group of breeders commissioned a selection of polled cattle to be imported from the USA despite the reluctance of the Society to register such cattle; the Poll Shorthorn Society was formed in 1950 as described more fully elsewhere (see p. 46). This provided the cynics with the question of

Denis Cadzow with his 1950 Champion Duncrahill Ambition.

how could you have such a contradiction in terms as Polled Shorthorns! The same year saw the Revised National Attestation Scheme being launched by the Ministry of Agriculture. 1947 had seen the Argentine Government abandon the slaughter policy for foot and mouth and this had meant a massive task of vaccinating three and a half million cattle a month but still today many regions are affected by this scourge.

1949 was marked in the Society by the retirement of Leonard Bull as Secretary after 50 years service; maybe he had decided to go while the Society was on a high! I jest, as after that many years and so many changes he had certainly earned his retirement and was succeeded by Arthur Furneaux who had already been with the organisation for a number of years.

1950 Perth sales were considerably brightened by the presence of the film star Greer Garson, star of the epic 'Minerva Story', who was here to buy white Shorthorns for her ranch 'El Rancho Blanco' in New Mexico, with her friend Frank Harding of Chicago to advise her. They eventually purchased six, which proved very successful winning the

Champion male, Champion female and reserve Champion female at the New Mexico show a few months later and in fact won 9 awards with 5 animals at that event. Later still she experimented with crossing the white Shorthorns with white Santa Gertrudis to create heat- and insect-resistant cattle for tropical conditions. She reported after 4 years that using the bull Philorth White Knight, that Mexican Champion from Perth, **all** calves over the period had come white. It is interesting also that in Argentina at that time there was a herd of 500 white cows breeding white calves continuously. I think the only UK herd to be all white Shorthorns was one in Norfolk which was dairy oriented bred by Francis Key!

The Perth Champion in 1950 was D.J. Cadzow's Duncrahill Ambition; after this he spoke out on the size issue mentioned above and his Champion is photographed here to illustrate how small he is compared to Denis Cadzow and note also how the Canadian photo demonstrates the similar problem with a more mature bull.

Mention was made of the **Pittodrie** herd above, from Pitcaple, Nr Aberdeen, owned by Mr R. Laidlaw Smith and managed by Mr Fowler; its quality ensured it a place in this study. It was founded first in 1901 and then re-started in 1931 with excellent choice females such as Calrossie Rosewood Kate who went on to be a fabulous breeder leaving among others P. Jubilee, a Champion who sold for 3,200 guineas, P. Gold Standard, reserve Champion Perth, selling for 2,000 guineas; P. Banker, a Perth Champion, selling for 4,750 guineas and P. Onward 3,300 guineas and another, Aldie Keystone a very successful sire breeding both the Perth supreme and junior Champion in 1943; P. Banker was sire of the best three bulls by one sire, also the best three by any sire: Regalia and Mascot selling for 1,500 and 1,000 guineas respectively. Other stock bulls came from Millhills. The senior sire at this time was Bapton Upright who sired the two record breakers above and who also sired a number of other Champions including P. Royalist , who sold for 2,335 guineas to Argentina and P. Impression, who was first in his class at Perth and sold for 1,000 guineas as well as a host of others. A later successful sire was Cruggleton Raeside. Female lines were Rosewoods, Broadhooks, Goldie, Orange Blossom, Queen of Rothes, Augusta and Brawith Bud. Other prominent herds such as Bapton, Duncrahill and Baldowrie all had great success with sires from here. This herd was sold in 1959 on the death of Mr Laidlaw Smith, with an average of £331.13 shillings with a top of 1,300 guineas for Pittodrie Minerva.

Drynie was another herd in the front line in the '40s and '50s, having been started in 1901 in the Black Isle north of Inverness by the Maclean family but transferred about as far south as it could go – to High Hurstwood in Sussex. They ran similar families to the previous herd with foundation stock coming from Calrossie, Fingask and the Aberdeen sales. Their bulls came from De Quincey's Erimus herd with Miguel, Quest and Intrepid but the favoured bull was Naemoor Immaculate, a white bull who left a string of prize-winning progeny, many of which went to Argentina and the USA, notably Drynie Warden to the former and Drynie Royal Oak and Drynie Wonder to the latter. Westdrums Polaris followed and proved an excellent show bull in interbreed beef classes in the '60s.

Another MacGillivray herd, **Glastullick,** often in the pedigrees, was owned by William MacGillivray, son of Capt. MacGillivray, founded with a draft from Calrossie and farming also at Nigg, very close to Calrossie, there was obviously close co-operation and bloodlines from the master. Glastullick was soon in the money, G.Captivator was sold to the Argentinian Ambassador for 1,050 guineas; having used him at home he resold Captivator for $50,000! G. Fortress by Lawton President Roosevelt was reserve Champion at Perth but was considered of such quality he was retained and went on to produce some grand stock; G. Supremacy sold at Perth for 3,500 guineas in 1934. In 1947 G. Smasher was supreme Champion at Perth selling for 5,000 guineas. In 1956 G. Gay Lad was also supreme selling for 6,000 guineas. Their 6 bulls averaged 1,424 guineas. Later G. Highland Bob sold to Carlos Duggan, Argentina, for 5,600 guineas. Such was the quality of the herd that at a reduction sale they averaged £222, and out of 13 shows at Inverness they won 11 Championships. Later the herd was sold *en bloc* to the world's largest mink farmer (he had around 100,000 of them), Otto Grosse, from Carey Illinois, USA.

A herd previously referred to was **Saltoun,** farmed in Pencaitland, East Lothian, by Capt. Talbot Fletcher and started in 1917; but he had run down the numbers until after the war when he was able to devote more time to it. He was then able to use the Goldie Blossom and Butterfly families that he had retained so he quickly built up the numbers again adding Broadhooks, Orange Blossom Miss Ramsden, Clippers and Paulines. Bulls included Newton Renown, and Burgermaster, Sanquar Grand Courtier, Naemoor Druid also such well known sires as Saltoun Gold Dust, Saltoun Crusader, who was in fact the sire of Naemoor Jasper, also Saltoun Cruiser a most successful show bull. In 1945 Saltoun was reserve for the best 3 bulls at Perth, which sold for 2,000, 1,000 and 690 guineas respectively. Capt. Talbot Fletcher always bought quality and reaped the rewards.

Although the decline of the Shorthorn had started as has been mentioned and recognised by several, the period of the early '50s was very active. So many reasons for decline in demand were given at the time, lack of size, no colour marking, too early to fatten, not enough milk and several others. Many had an element of truth; but the counter arguments were equally valid. In the event the British farmer decided that he would follow a swing in fashion and also there was a change in the market requirements. Demand on the beef side was for a larger animal which did not tend to put on fat with early maturity. The fashion after the war favoured the Angus breed and on the dairy side there was a swing to the Ayrshire as it had made more progress towards attestation. Nationally there was also a change of emphasis to mark the solids not fat aspect of milk content which had not happened before. This helped the Shorthorn.

The Shorthorn was deemed to be too small and fat in the beef sector and in the dairy sector some said it did not give enough milk and was too shelly and small. As it can be seen on the graphs (p. 116), the decline was relentless year by year and people seemed not to remember the huge assets of the breed: the **wonderful docile temperament**, the **ease of calving, excellent feet and legs, heat resistance**, the **dominance of the genes which gave improvement to other breeds, mothering ability, quality of marbling, the highest ratio of percentage protein to butterfat** also **the ability for dual purpose production** if required. In fact some said it was possibly this last aspect that resulted in the swing away from the breed as it was not in a position to challenge the Friesian for milk yield and the fashion was changing.

Nevertheless at this time many hundreds remained loyal **or** did not recognise the problem or indeed the problem was not affecting them as they had not followed the trend.

1952 was the year when the Society finally agreed to allow females without horns to be shown and **1952** was also the year of the incredible **Cruggleton** dispersal, as mentioned in a previous chapter. It not only marked the end of an era with the passing of that great genius Bertie Marshall, it came at the time when the Australian Authorities and those in South Africa had lifted their ban on imports because our problems with foot and mouth disease were over; furthermore it came at a time when people were beginning to appreciate the problem of lack of size and the fact that this unique herd had scale. A train was organised (see p. 145) to take the herd from Wigtown to Perth, pictured above, and cattle were sorted into the appropriate carriages for their lots and then they were unloaded and walked through the town to the old market; well over 200 head were before a capacity crowd of spectators and buyers, some from Australia, South Africa, New Zealand, USA, Canada. All these countries took cattle home, and prospective buyers were also from Europe as well as the UK and Ireland. The exporters were also there in force.

Selling took place over two days; after the first when 137 lots had sold at an average of £495 with a large proportion going overseas, home breeders were concerned that all this unique breeding would go

Demonstrating the organisation for the Cruggleton sale: cattle being driven to the train in loading order so that they were in lot order for penning when they got to Perth.

overseas. Some £40,000 worth had gone to those clients for 66 head with money changing hands at the rate of £450 a minute. **Top price of the day was 4,000 guineas** for Cruggleton Guthrie who went to Illinois and was much sought after as he had a double dash of Bertie's favourite bull Cruggleton Perfect in his pedigree. Many were seeking this breeding. The second stock bull Cruggleton Bilsland stayed at home going to Finlay MacGillivray of Aldie fame. People were wondering what the second day would bring and they were not disappointed as 103 cows, some with calves, averaged £614 with a gross for the day of £363,316 of which £14,100 was spent by overseas buyers. A total of 94 sold for export. More than 25 lots sold at over 1,000 guineas. Of the home buyers Calrossie, Cadzows, Lord Lovat and James Durno were major purchasers and several new herds were started. An 11-year-old cow with her heifer calf went to the USA when Major Allan of Maryland paid £1,500 for Princess Cembra. Twice was 1,800 guineas reached for yearlings when Boots Pure Drug Co. bought Princess Dossie and Robert Bryce purchased Princess Meada for 1,800 guineas. At the end of the day a train was laid on to transport the export lots back to Cruggleton. The auctioneer Lovat Fraser and the stockmen led by Billy Maxwell must have been exhausted. The total aggregate of **£134,000** for **240** head

was the **highest such figure ever reached for a dispersal** which was all the more remarkable as it followed on a recent reduction from this herd prior to Bertie's death and there had also been the Millhills reduction sale just before. This had produced averages of £177 for 29 bulls and £175 for 19 heifers with a top of 2,000 guineas paid by F.E. Gourley of Canada for Millhills Jubilee. It was a tragedy that this whole herd came on the market shortly afterwards, owing to Mr D.M. Stewart's sudden death.

Mention above of **Aldie** brings me to the remaining MacGillivray family herd to review. Owned by Finlay MacGillivray, this herd like the others was noted for its success and quality but it also suffered a major setback (foot and mouth) after being founded in 1920 and built up to 84 head with a number of Championships including junior Champion at the Highland with Goldie in 1923 and supreme at the same event in 1924. She was mated to Calrossie White Prince and produced Aldie Goldie who in turn produced Aldie Benefactor exported to Argentina at 2,800 guineas and it was a Goldie who produced the famous Aldie Air Raid by Naemoor Jasper. Air Raid was eventually bought by W. Snadden of Coldoch in whose herd he produced a series of champions in both shows, sales and fat stock shows. Other lines like the Broadhooks that produced so many champions including Aldie Conqueror that bred so well for Millhills and his progeny also bred well for the Lawton herd of Mr W. Henderson. This herd had so many good cows both at home and overseas it was a tragedy when it was cut short by foot and mouth in 1942. Finlay was not to be defeated and moved to Pencaitland, in fact leasing from Capt. Fletcher of Saltoun where he again built up a reputation for his cattle with Clipper, Brawith Bud, Lovely, Princess Royal and Goldie lines but he was beaten by poor health and decided to sell in 1956. Buyers again attended this event from many countries and the top price of 2,000 guineas was paid for Aldie Judy by Boots farms. An average of £273 was paid for 55 head which included the sire Cruggleton Bilsland above at 120 guineas which was sad; stock went to New Zealand, Canada and the USA. Since the second start bulls used came from Calrossie and Pittodrie with Adonis and Regalia respectively. Prices were not too good because there were temporary political problems.

Back to better times: **1952** was the year when Calrossie broke records again at Perth with their 13 bulls averaging £3,664 having won the Supreme Champion with Calrossie Perfect, the best 3 bulls, the best 5 bulls, and the best 3 by the same sire, Calrossie Welcome, and Aldie won the Junior Champion and was reserve in the team events so it was nearly a MacGillivray clean sweep! To follow this Calrossie gained another record when Sandy Cross from Calgary paid 10,000 guineas for C. Highland Piper who had been 2nd in his class which had 3 Calrossie bulls in the first three places. The Champion fetched 6,100 guineas. There was also progress in the presentation in that the judge, Mr R. Guardhouse from Canada, commented on the amount of 'breeders' bulls forward and also that the overall condition of bulls was much improved with very few being over fitted. But there was a down side as Mr R. Watherston, President of the Scottish Association, commented that, 'If one assumes that £250 is the cost of bringing forward a bull, more than half those forward were sold at a loss.'

On the dairy side there was comment on the poor quality of female stock put forward for the Reading Sale which was over two days but it did produce the highest ever average for bulls: 66 made an average of £251 12s. with the top of 2,200 guineas being given by the Irish Department of Agriculture for Felden Spartan 2nd. The reserve Champion Fordson Lottery, went to the Northern Ireland's Ministry of Agriculture for 1,200 guineas. However the female average reflected the quality at £107. Beef averages were much higher than those for dairy, as was the top price of £2,000 (beef) compared with £1,000 for dairy.

There was great success at the Scottish Dairy Show when Aiktonhouse Blossom 67th from the Royal Mental Hospital Farm gained the breed Championship for the second time as well as giving 95.1lb in the trials; her previous Championship was in 1950 when she missed the Interbreed Supreme as well by one point.

1953 was a bad year as it was marked by 30 herd dispersals but vendors had taken note of the adverse comment as the November sale at Reading was reported to have had the best display for years with the Champion Whatcote Lord Barrington 26th selling to the Isle of Man Ministry of Agriculture for 700 guineas but 2 bulls went again to the Eire Ministry of Agriculture for 1,000 guineas each, Rycote Lord Kirklevington 2nd and Kirklees Lord Walnut 3rd and 4th in the same class as the Champion.

This year the council upgraded their schemes for the improved register of merit for bulls which must have 6 daughters or more in the herd book or grade register with not less than 60% of daughters registered and approved by inspection with records of:

1,000lb milk @ 375lb of butter fat calving @4 years and over

8,500 lb milk @ 330 lb of butterfat calving@ 3 years and under 4

7,500 lb milk @ 300lb of butterfat calving@ 3 years and under

All at 305 day lactations except for Ireland where 315 days apply. There were 282 qualified in 1953.

On the plus side there were 65 new prefixes registered but it is some time before a new herd can contribute much. Perhaps Mr Robert Tory of the Anderson prefix had some explanation when he spoke and wrote that many disappointed farmers were suffering their problems because they were using bulls of unknown performance or breeding, which in those days was quite probable; their heifers were coming in with poor udders and low yields, also heifers bought in also had bad performance, so who could blame the farmer for being disappointed and going elsewhere in future. Many breeders had climbed on the bandwagon and reared and sold everything instead of having a rigid culling policy and the breed was now reaping the result. Even prominent breeders of the day for example like the Mills of Bishops Sutton and the Jackobi family of Southweston, to name but two, were examples of disenchanted breeders, went to Jerseys and were equally successful.

The decline had started but the beef sector was worse affected initially. One of the dairy loyal successes of the time were the Robarts brothers of the **Kimble** herd prefix in Northwood, Middlesex, who this year had their remarkable cow Dorothy who beat all cows in all breeds with a record for three years averaging 22,261lb. She had won the interbreed Harold Jackson trophy and her daughter was runner up. This herd was founded in 1924 and graded-up to be registered with the Kimble prefix in 1938; so successful was it that it won the society Gold cup for the area on no less than 22 occasions over 35 years. It was owned nominally by the brothers J.W., E.K., and M.J. Robarts and run actually by E. K. Robarts, the Chairman of Express Dairies; he would eventually become Chairman of finance after being President of the Society in 1974/5, which were difficult times. Arthur Mason, a superb stockman and manager, who was there for over 30 years, managed the herd on a day-to-day basis. One of the many winners was Mercers Spot 19th who produced 150,000lb in her lifetime as well as countless prizes, including the dehorned Champion all breeds in 1965; another was Kimble Rose 68th who won supreme at the Royal in 1977. This herd later entered the blended programme (see p. 175). The herd had also had more winners at the London Dairy Event over a number of years: Kimble Daisy 7th won the Melvin cup in 1949, Swanford Duchess won the inspection all breeds in 1974.

From 1939 the average at Dairy Shorthorn collective sales rose from an average of £36 up to £116 in 1943 and dropped to £96 by 1952 with 2,500 animals involved. Dispersal sales rose from an average of £33 up to £127 in 1948 and back to £70 in 1952 with nearly 2,000 animals involved.

1953 was also the year when the long-running radio series 'The Archers' began; it was originally based on two Shorthorn breeder families!

1954 was quite a year for the breed and the society as it was the Bates centenary year when the anniversary of Thomas Bates death and his achievements was celebrated. It was the year when Shorthorns set up a record which is unlikely ever to be beaten as they won **both the Dairy and Beef Burke Trophy awards** at the Royal Show.

Berkswell Sharon Lad 3rd from the Wheatley-Hubbard's herd and Histon Waterloo 24th from the Chivers herds were the two dairy stars and the beef pair were the Durno's Princess Maude and Erimus Ghost from Lord Rotherwick's herd but bred by R. De Quincey: these made up the pairs which were presented with this trophy by Her Majesty The Queen at this memorable Windsor Royal. Compared with some of the

Burke Trophy teams in 1954, with beef on the left and dairy on the right. Compare the heights of the beef and the dairy with later winners.

Calrossie Welcome

actual trophies competed for, this cup is rather insignificant among the splendid array but the competition that this event arouses is immense. This year's teams were all consistent winners at major shows but the picture here with illustrates how the short-legged beef pair epitomised the style of the day. Note the comparison with the dairy pair. Later in the year there was a Centenary Dinner held at the Savoy Hotel in London attended by over 300 guests; they were entertained by the Band of the Guards, the bill for which was £26. How times have changed!

Back to more serious matters, it was a year for records that would tend to block out the problems. A February bull calf at the 3rd Millhills reduction, Millhills Majestic, sold to Hugh Black for 3,000 guineas and 29 bulls set up an average of £428 and the continuing world reputation of this herd brought buyers from Argentina, Ireland, England, Scotland, Canada, USA, Uruguay and New Zealand. Perth also surpassed the previous year with 302 bulls sold at an average of £670 13s. but this was helped by the purchase of Calrossie Claymore (by Calrossie Welcome) who was 3rd in his class for 10,100 guineas. Supreme Champion this year was Alex Anderson's Burnton Bank Book by Calrossie Crocus Count; he sold for 7,300 guineas. The same herd produced the reserve Champion Burnton Rowan who sold for 5,000 guineas.

There was also a record set in Inverness when Glastulich Drambuie from William MacGillivray sold for 1,200 guineas, the highest price achieved by any breed for over 80 years at this centre. Drambuie was Champion at the event and sold to Capt. Maclean of Drynie.

Exports had also risen, which again boosted morale, they had been high in 1953 at 823 but this was because there had been quarantine and transportation restraints the year before so this had virtually meant a doubling up. They were 509 in 1955. A I was really taking a very important part in the scene at this time as there were 137 Shorthorn bulls in the service and 4,283 Shorthorn bull registrations, but still the ministry reckoned there was a shortfall. The breed was receding still slowly but was still very much holding its own with 420 in the 100,000lb register and 6,208 members registering 19,494 females and 15,474 in the Grading Up section. The registrations and membership recovered quite well for the next two years, as will be seen.

1955 was a year when Scotland was much in the Dairy Shorthorn news as 287 of this type were licensed in that country which the department reported was a 55% increase. Dairy Shorthorns also excelled at the Scottish Dairy Show winning the Supreme Individual Interbreed Championship; the team of 6 won the McAlpine Trophy with a maximum score. R.W. Moffat of Penrith with his five-year-old Maggie won the individual and also the breed milking trials with a yield of 78.4lb and gained top points of 161.8. To top it all the team of 3 won the Bennochy cup which was again an interbreed competition for three animals.

The London Dairy Show was remarkable in that the Champion was a repeat performance when Mr C.Gush of Haslemere, Surrey, gained the award for the second year in succession when Wendest Florrie 20th was drawn in as supreme Champion. She was 1st on inspection and 2nd in the trials, gaining a total of 161.22 points.

Mr R.W. Moffat from that family of cattlemen again had a super event as he had Dawn 2nd in her class and 4th in the trials; Rita who was 5th on inspection and highly commended in the trials; Rosebud 1st in her class on inspection and reserve breed Champion and Highly Commended in the trials; all three were in the grading register and won the Thornton Cup for a team of three on inspection. What a year for Mr Moffat and what a show for Mr Gush and his herdsman Roland Moss.

This year coincidentally was also the first stock judging competition at the Royal Show that was so popular for many years and so competitively fought, as were the preliminaries that were held around the regions.

One of the greatest enthusiasts in support of the younger element of this competition was **Richard Roper** of **Lenborough** who was a legend in his lifetime. His father had started this herd in Buckinghamshire in 1914 from non-pedigree stock by the grading-up process but the enterprise had started many years before, in about 1878 at nearby Manor Farm where his grandfather farmed. His father, Mr Corbett Roper, married a Miss Roadknight of another famous farming family in 1905 and built up a well known farming unit after moving to the Laurels Farm. He decided to grade up his cattle and it was his and his son's proud claim that not a single female had ever entered the herd since its foundation. Richard never married, and he and his sister Evelyn continued to live at the Laurels but built up arguably the best farming estate in Britain winning countless awards for its excellence both in agriculture and later conservation in more modern times when he won the Civic Trust Award in 1979 out of 1,100 entries from all over Britain and the Channel Islands.

The herd was built up to 900 head of cattle of which probably one third were his surplus heifers and steers as well as a flock of around 600 sheep and at one time a large flock of poultry as this was one of Richard's early successes in the showing of livestock when he won medals at both the London Dairy Show and Birmingham fat stock shows in 1933. He had won stock judging competitions at the age of 13 and, although not having children of his own, took an immense interest in assisting and teaching the younger generation. He also took a huge interest in his staff many of which had been with him from when they left school and several of whom worked with the family for 40 to 50 years. One, Mr Alfred Mead, was born on the estate and worked there for 67 years with his father who had given 30 years service before him.

Each year he held judging seminars that turned into large social occasions with friends and young people coming from miles to attend and learn. His stock won every possible event on both the dairy and beef side but the latter were with Dairy Shorthorns as he was one of the main and regular exhibitors at shows from Scotland to the south with his cattle at events as diverse as Smithfield and the dairy event and local area shows with his steers and female stock winning everywhere and consistently. The herd achieved 7 supreme and 2 reserve supreme awards, 25 breed Championships and 124 first prizes; the winning Bledisloe cup team in 1969 included 4 of Lenborough breeding and 3 times Royal Show Champions, at least 9 Smithfield Champions, the Hylton Brook Trophy for young stock, all of which were just a few of the successes. The Lenborough herd built up 24 families, the best known of which were Dubbie, Fillpail, Rose Cowslip, Whitetail, Pansy, Dairymaid, Strawberry, Tulip; bulls used over the period were of course numerous but a few are featured here starting with Kelmscott Grand Master 8th, Kelmscott Imperialist, Heather Prince, Kingsthorpe Fairy Duke and Raspberry Duke 3rd, Anderson Lord Conjuror 3rd and more recently Stockwood Lord Barrington 2nd, Swepstone Foggathorpe Premier 9th, Amber Prince Regent, Maxton Silver Fox, Stockwood Dignity 22nd as well as a number of home-bred sires such as Lenborough Conjurer 285th and Field Marshall 115th. Several of the families go right back to his originals like Cowslip 818th, Tulip 349th. The livestock side was more recently managed by Eric

Osborne B.E.M., who had been evacuated to Lenborough aged 14, and the arable side by Peter Stilgoe, both in company with Richard Roper who died in 1986.

Another similar graded-up herd also farmed by bachelors was the **Stockwood** herd founded in 1931 near Worcester by Messrs Harry and Jack Hillman. The family was very interested in the Thoroughbred business as well and kept one or more stallions at stud. On the cattle enterprise the family policy was to retain the purity of the Shorthorn breed as they knew it and not venture into the later blended scheme and in this Richard Roper thought on similar lines. There were five single partners in this business: F. C./H.M./J.P./J./and Miss A.M Hillman. The brother principally concerned with cattle was Harry and was his in-born skill of breeding and stockmanship that led the herd to such prominence that at one time there were few herds that did not carry some of this breeding. It was also this family referred to above as one of those on which the 'Archers' series were based! Their Foggathorpe, Digitalis Tulip, Lily and Dumpling lines were most prominent. Over the years these cattle retained their correctness but tended to lose size; Harry's attention to bloodlines and breeding skills ensured the demand for their cattle. Like Richard Roper the Hillmans retained their herdsman, Bill Kitchen, who worked with them for over 35 years.

The century was rolling on: 1956 was significant in the beef sector as the **Millhills Dispersal** sale attracted many established and new breeders although not so many from overseas. It was a sad day as it followed the death of Mr D.M. Stewart and brought the end to one of the great herds. There was a heartening increase in interest although prices were much reduced: 137 head averaged £262. The cows were headed by a 1,400 guineas bid to secure, for the Bapton herd of Cecil Moores, Scottish Buttercup 58th by Calrossie Highland Leader but the stock bulls Bapton Balmoral gained the top bid of the day from the MacGillivray family when W. MacGillivray and the partnership of J. and D. MacGillivray joined forces to acquire this bull for 5,400 guineas, which had been purchased in the February sale of 1955 for 2,500 guineas. Banchory Metaphor, one of his progeny, looked so promising that he fetched 3,600 guineas, again more than his purchase price in 1955 of 2,900 guineas. Both these sires had very fine breeding in their pedigrees, the former being sired by Cruggleton Balmoral who had served so well at Chapelton with his progeny averaging 2,257 guineas and Balmoral being considered one of the best sires bred by Bertie Marshall. Banchory Metaphor was by Bapton Eldorado, one of the best of Hugh Black's breeding. At the sale 14 went overseas to Australia, Canada and the USA, all at very reasonable prices. The poll lots were mainly purchased by Mr E.L. Penticost then of Cropwell, Nottingham, who was doing much experimental work with this type. It was also of interest that Ian Henderson started to change his Hereford herd for Shorthorns at this sale and it was the Hendersons that really started the turn around later in the story.

Mention of the **Banchory** prefix is made in the exporter section as well as above and although a small herd founded in 1929 at Banchory, Couper Angus, it was originally farmed by James Sidey who was an exporter. He was later joined by Hugh Black, his nephew, in the business and this unit was also famed for the flock of border Leicester sheep as they held the top prices and top average at Perth for 20 years out of 27. The export business was equally successful as for example in 1919 they sent 300 cattle and 1,000 sheep to Argentina and organised the return from there to Antwerp of loads of cattle. At home they fattened bullocks and sheep as well as their Shorthorn herd of about 20 cows. Bapton Eldorado mentioned above was his most successful sire but others were Banchory Brawith Boy, Champion of the Highland show 1933, who was later exported to Canada; another was Banchory Orangeman who went to Calrossie as stud sire for some time, later going to Argentina; Broadhooks Nanette 7th was a successful female taking second twice at the Highland. It was his Maude and Brawith lines which were most prevalent in his herd.

It may be of interest to see how the national wages and yields were progressing through this period. In 1941 the average wage was 48 shillings a week and the average yield was 484 gallons. By 1951 the wages were £ 5 8s. and the yield had moved up to 537 gallons. By 1958 the figures were £7 8s. and the average yield had moved up to 893 gallons and the individual breeds were Northern Dairy Shorthorns 730 gallons, Dairy Shorthorns 806 gallons with Friesians on 992 gallons. Poor progress had been made by Shorthorns with regard to butterfat as in the past 15 years the average for the breed had gone from 3.62% to 3.56 %,whereas the Friesian had gone from a poor base of 3.29% to an acceptable 3.55%, so there was a need for definite steps to be taken to improve this in the case of Shorthorns: it was another thorn in the flesh.

1957 was the year when there were fierce protests to the government by the Shorthorn Cattle Society council and those of other breeds against the proposed importation of a large quantity of Charolais cattle; as may have been noticed, the government did not take much notice!

1958 saw the end of the requirement of birth notification forms to be submitted and I was amazed that it had taken so long for the Society to arrive at this decision with the huge entry numbers involved! It was also the year when Wing Commander T. B. Marson died, another great character recognisable from his size and his unique top hat who after his retirement devoted his time and energies to the breed, its publicity and writing a number of books on hunting and farming; he wrote *Scotch Shorthorn* and *Scotland's Shorthorns* the former being of assistance to

Bapton Northward Bound, Bull of the Year 1959.

me on some of the research for this book as in 1945 he visited each beef herd in being at that time, recording their breeding policies.

This year was also the time when the beef breeders pressed at last for their own section within the herd book despite misgivings on some breeders' parts; it was agreed to and once achieved it was conceded it was an excellent move as breeders would be sure of the genetic trend and influence in both sections which would greatly help all those without a complete knowledge of the variety of bloodlines. Further to this the Beef Shorthorn Association also changed to the Beef Shorthorn Cattle Society in **1959**. Also in this year there were **long service awards** made to a number of staff of the Shorthorn Society, 5 having served over 25 years. A. Castle had completed 42 years. S. W. Grossmith completed 40 years. H. Macpherson 33 years. Miss W Rush 32 years. Mrs G. Simmons also 32 years. Quite a record of loyalty and also a tribute to the Secretaries, L. Bull and A. Furneaux, for the way they ran the Society offices.

1960 saw the export, after much negotiation, of 67 bulls to Russia and this was followed in 1964 by the Society's attendance at the Russian Exhibition in Moscow. Both of these events had been greatly helped by the performance of the previous cattle to go which was reported earlier.

The two other major details in that year were firstly that owing to there being a risk of blue tongue disease in Australia they imposed a ban on all imports from the UK for further notice and the second was the Ministry of Agriculture declaring the whole country Attested.

9. The '60s and Early '70s

The start of any year in the cattle and Shorthorn world calendar is always the Perth Bull sales in February so it is no wonder it attracts so much attention. Added to this the Angus and Shorthorn breeds have customarily been the breeds that start the show and the sale week as it is now, so it is a reasonable indication as to the trade and interest and although more recently the continental breeds have enjoyed higher prices later in the week.

1960 was no exception and there were the usual excitements with Uppermill Leopold selling to Boots farms for 7,100 guineas. Such prices are often a recognition of quality as well as competition but also of faith in the future, so when Lt. Colonel S.J.L. Hardie of **Balathie** paid 14,000 guineas for Pitodrie Uprise this gave breeders a new challenge and purpose. Col. Hardie had been the under-bidder to the previous record bull in 1946. Later, when he and Captain Rutherford, who had acted as Col. Hardie's factor for a while following his service career, paid 13,000 guineas for Calrossie Fortitude in 1958, this gave the breeders a new challenge. The Balathie Shorthorn herd was one of three breeds on this estate, the others being Highlands and Ayrshires. The founding Shorthorns were from Uppermill, Cluny Lawton and Cruggleton, all of high quality on which he used a number of Cruggleton and Calrossie sires to great effect.

Breeders were at last beginning to accept that whilst there had been a very lucrative market in the Americas, the situation was changing due to a number of factors. The main one was the changing demands on the beef market, also agriculture was changing. There was now an acceptance that so far as corn was concerned it was possible to grow continuous crops, whereas before it had been taboo; this was due to new strains of crop. Also the economic situation was changing in that it was essential that any beef enterprise must pay its way whereas in the past quite often the only benefit to the farmer was that of building up his land fertility and productivity and the profit factor in the accepted sense was not in the equation. On beef demand, fat had become a dirty word despite the fact that it was the fat that ensured the excellence of the taste of the product, but the term 'marbling' was not used at this time and the fat was considered as something that would have to be trimmed off.

There was also a move to more intensive beef production in this part of the world and barley beef was coming into vogue, provided of course that the grain remained at a reasonable price. Added to all these changes the A I facility was increasing in popularity thus reducing the demand for bulls and also there had been a complete change in attitude with regard to importation: the Charolais importation had been a success, particularly as the requirement by then was for a different type of carcass. From this it became 'part of the game' to introduce other Continental breeds, first the Limousin, then others – Simmentals, Murray Grey, Belgian Blue, Pinzgauer, Gelbvech and others. The British Friesian was changing the type to move more towards producing a very acceptable carcass but it was the first three in the list that captured the beef trade and the fashion albeit over quite a period. Nevertheless each took a large slice of the available market particularly as the 'doubting Thomases' had been proved right in that the Shorthorn *was* too small. It is comparatively easy to breed cattle smaller but one heck of a task to get them with more size so there was indeed a problem.

Another development at this time was the increase in the speed of introduction of Performance Testing and Beef Recording in a meaningful form although it was extremely slowly accepted by the British Shorthorn breeders despite the growth overseas of the huge feed lots and the effects these had on their management.

Many pedigree Shorthorn breeders considered that to enlarge their animal would take too long; added to this they considered that there was more money to be gained by getting involved with the 'new breeds'; so the slide had begun but in the '60s there were still a number of breeders who remained loyal to the breed as they were convinced that there could and would be a change. In the dairy sector there were many who went towards the Friesian but again there were a number who resisted the change for a variety of reasons, loyalty being one, and those points outlined in the previous chapter were also very relevant.

A number of prominent breeders expressed their views, some stronger than others so maybe I should not include their names! 'The decline and exclusion of the Shorthorn in some quarters has had a marked affect on the quality of the UK stock and its inherent qualities are the same.' 'The shorthorn produces the superb Blue grey and the excellent Highland cross and it also crosses very well with the Ayrshire.' 'Our bulls are fitted to a far too high degree but this is currently the same in all breeds and the benefits are open to question.' 'I am absolutely against using the polled strains.' Another wrote, 'If we are to survive we must forget the thick blocky short legged type.' Another, 'What is the objective of the Shorthorn breeder? He has not got a clue. He sold his birth right and allowed the foreigner to dominate him. If our beef industry was better managed we could get all our beef from that source.' Another, 'The Shorthorn gained its reputation on Fleshing, size, and ruggedness and suffered a recession in the market and the opinion that the breed has lost its size has spread among the farming public. We must think more positively about size than we have for 20 years. We are selecting on fitness at twelve months rather than later. Emphasis is on fat rather than muscle and we must change before it is too late and we must use the polled shorthorn.' Three more, 'We wish for the Shorthorn of 20/30 years ago the biggest don't necessarily breed the biggest but the smallest always breeds the smallest.' And, 'We are now getting to a situation were numbers will be so small there will be insufficient selection.' This last was a little premature but the sentiment was proved right later. Finally, 'The breed set the fashion in the past let us not be found wanting, where the breed fitted in a few years ago it does not now. Commercial men tell us we have lost the growth and ruggedness. The selling of 10 months old bulls has just served to encourage too early maturity.'

Differences of opinion but most with the same theme and all from major trusted breeders of the day. It is also true that any breed must have a variety of types within it if it is to survive differing needs but it was simply that at that time there were too few of those with quality and scale.

This decade started in the Society with two of the best known Shorthorn families to the fore again: James Biggar of Chapelton was President in 1959/60 and Jack D. Webb of Streetly took over in the habitual way in mid year for 1960/61. The **Streetly** prefix was one of the oldest in the Society as mentioned in the first chapter; F.N. Webb, Jack's ancestor, was one of the original founders of the Dairy Shorthorn Association. This herd was taken over by J.D. Webb, the founder's nephew, in 1939 and in the course of its development had held two very successful reductions in 1951 and again in 1964, having built a reputation for large-framed stock with excellent records. The continued success was due partly to Hastoe Dukedom 2nd, followed by another excellent sire for the herd Parsenn Cragsman who later became one of the first sires to be sponsored by the Society and who did a wonderful job on the herd which had been started as early as 1838 and then built up on Bates and Cranford lines. They were one of the first to use A I and again were successful with **Streetly Lord York** out of a twice 2,000 gallon cow **S. Lady York 23,** then came S. Wild Magician followed by an outcross to Kimble Bright Spot and Collingham Grand Duke Darlington 2nd, a bull that had done very well in the Harrogate Trials. The main lines of the herd were Barrington, Wild Queen, Waterloo Rose and Red Rose, originally mainly bred from Cranford cattle. Their records at the time of their sale supported their excellent qualities; as for the last ten years the average was 11,445lb @3.6% for cows and 9718lb for heifers, a very significant performance in 1966. The family had also been renowned for their Suffolk horses and Southdown sheep, both of which had a world reputation.

1961 saw the threat made earlier by Lord Lovat carried out in the sad dispersal of the Beaufort herd for an average of 220 guineas with a top of 1,000 guineas for Beaufort Princess Royal selling to USA.

Up to 1961 the export certificates issued for both dairy and beef by the Shorthorn Society exceeded over 61,000 but as can be seen on the export graph (see p.80), numbers had been falling very fast for some time.

The Beef Shorthorn Society, as it now was, had elected Capt. Gideon D. Rutherford of **Baldowrie,** Coupar Angus, as its President in 1960. His herd had originated in 1836 but was re-started again in 1945. Bulls used were Glasstulich Smasher, Calrossie Silver Mascot, Kirkton Heir and Cruggleton Justinian to name a few. Capt. Rutherford was to be elected President of the Shorthorn Society in 1970 at a particularly difficult time (which will be clarified later); there was a series of events which had contributed, among which were controversies which had arisen in the formation of the two separate bodies within the Society, also the decrease in the popularity of the breed and the resulting financial problems for the Society which did not do anything to improve the situation. However there were good signs among the bad and as was said at the time: Unity is strength. The **Poll Shorthorn Society,** which had started virtually out of necessity, was at that time finding out the difficulty of running a small Society but one with growing interest so it was agreed in **1962** that they and the **Beef Shorthorn Cattle Society** would merge, which gave the advantage to both with administrative strength. A phrase was published at the time: 'Let us go forward as one force, The Shorthorn first and always with a single purpose of advancing the interests of the world's most useful breed ' which was to become more important later. It went on, 'disunity and petty jealousies can only put a brake on progress and expansion'. Another advantage of the merger was that polled and horned could participate in the same classes at shows; also the following year the poll bulls got both a licence and the beef bull premium so this was progress indeed as was the decision that polled bulls could at last compete. Sense was beginning to prevail, but in the dairy sector, the rule that bulls without horns could not compete still applied!

This year also the record-breaking sire Bapton Constructor returned to Britain as part of the contractual arrangement but he died in 1963 after a long and productive life.

The Beef Shorthorn administration had for some time been carried out at 17 York Place in Perth very close to the market and the costs had been very effectively shared with the Highland Cattle Society and Perth Hunt, but as everywhere costs were beginning to cause problems.

Glamis Benefactor, bred by Robert Adams & Son.

1962: the Royal Show was also another great success for the Beef Shorthorns as their team included the great bull Glamis Benefactor who had won no less than 8 Supreme Championships and was undefeated for the Adams family. He had been purchased by the Bapton herd and was joined by Tolquhon Crystal Ramsden, bred by John Sleigh and owned by The Hon. Mrs Dewhurst to **win** the **Burke Trophy** for the beef sector of the breed again. A fantastic performance as the Beef Shorthorn team of four had come reserve at the Royal Highland with these two unbeaten animals included. Benefactor had started his year by winning Perth under the discerning eye of Frank Young, one of the most experienced and respected UK judges, who had noted the bull's dark nose and thankfully disregarded the controversy as evidently did the seven other judges! Frank Young was incidentally the first UK judge to officiate for many years at Perth for the second successive time as he carried out the task again in 1963. Another definite sign of progress. It was also a second successful year for Robert Adams and Son as they had won in 1961 with Glamis Trademark who had the same sire and was out of a sister of Benefactor's dam. The latter was followed by Naemoor Escort from Mrs Dewhurst who had saved the superb Naemoor herd from export when Major Mowbray had been forced to sell owing to ill health. This herd had played such an important part in the breed with so many wonderful cattle over the years it would have been a tragedy if it had gone overseas.

Demonstrating the changing beef scene, Stephen Williams of Boots Pure Drug Co. summed it up in the following when describing the customer requirements, 'Beef must be cheap and therefore lean. Beef must have no waste and therefore lean. There must be taste and therefore lean. Beef must be easy on the dentures and therefore lean and tender. It must be good for making sandwiches and eating in the dark and therefore lean! All of which because the housewife was now demanding convenience for her meals'.

The Beef Shorthorn President in 1962 was Lt. Col. H.L. Dewhurst of Dungarthill, Dunkeld, who was also to become President of the Shorthorn Society in 1972. The **Dungarthill** herd and the **Ardbennie** herd were naturally closely associated, the latter being founded in 1959 by the Hon. Mrs Irene Dewhurst with the purchase of Pittodrie Rhode Blossom at that prefix herd sale, a good buy as she had already produced three Perth bulls. She was followed by ten heifers and then in 1961 they sold their first Perth bull and bought three more heifers, one of which was the aforementioned Tolquhon Crystal Ramsden who had such success, only being beaten once in her life. One of her sons bred the Supreme Champion at the Palermo show. Another of her animals from the Naemoor purchase was reserve Champion at the 1962 Perth sale selling for 2,000 guineas to Canada. In 5 years they bought out three reserve Champions and seven four-figure bulls at Perth and the female Champions at both the Royal and the Royal Highland. Lack of space caused a reduction in 1965 with a very healthy average at that time of 117 guineas for 54 head. The herd was always progressive using several overseas bulls mainly from S.G. Bennett of Scotsdale, Canada. UK sires included Bapton Crocus Robin purchased for 3,500 guineas in 1963 just before the Bapton herd was sold to Canada to the Louada property. He sired A. Keystone who became the third Ardbennie reserve Champion at Perth Uppermill Pagan, Rushden; Brandy followed the latter being Perth Supreme Champion in 1983, then the Royal and Royal Highland. Probably their highest price bull was A. Horoscope, another son of Crocus Robin, selling for 8,000 guineas to Carlos Duggan in the Argentine.

They also used imported semen from New Zealand from interesting sires Kai Iwi Burgundy and Commandant, later Maine Anjou breeding in the shape of Uxmore Goal, also used by Capt. Rutherford, and Echard. Sadly the herd was dispersed in 1985 with a lot of interest. The top of 1, 600 guineas was paid for A. Pauline Daisy and her bull calf, A. Butler, purchased by Major Gibb of Glenisla. An in-calf heifer, A. Flossy Rosa, reached the second top price of 1,200 guineas; Uppermill Brandy sold at 1,000 guineas to a new herd in Kent that was to make its mark later for Mr Sandys. The overall average of 589 guineas was attained.

Dungarthill: founded with very sound choices of females in 1950 first from the Naemoor herd; these were followed by stock from Bapton, Chapelton, Cruggleton and later Erimus, Millhills and Baldowrie and the Calrossie females mentioned elsewhere. All cared for over a number of years by Duncan McNab and later with Jimmy Findley. Over the years the herd had used a number of successful sires, Kirkton Great Expectation, Baldowrie Braemar, Glastullich Repulse, Chapleton Comet and Celtic, Dron Xerxes to name a few; the latter bull sired the 1963 Reserve Supreme Champion D. President to Capt. Rutherford's Supreme Champion Baldowrie Neptune. But the top price on that day in 1963 was for the Adams Glamis Supreme Commander who went to the Argentine at 6,800 guineas for the Duggans. The average was £421 for 147 bulls.

Every breed needs several differing types within it if it is to meet changes in demand and in times of stress some sectors feel that they need to intensify demand for their type or, alternatively, feel that their type is endangered by current events, as the Northern Dairy breeders did in 1946; in **1962** the **Whitebred** breeders considered something had to be done on behalf of their Cumberland bred type. This and the Northern Dairy situation is covered in more detail in chapter 3.

The Dairy Shorthorns were not by any means without success and the **Stonethorpe** herd of the Woodford family established in 1873 was enjoying the limelight, having had Stonethorpe Darlington Pretender 1st in his class at the show and sale at Reading and selling for 2,000 guineas to the Northern Irish Ministry in 1961; they also sold S. Darlington Dairyman for 1,000 guineas to Ceylon the year after and S. Dairy Premier the year before for 1,100 guineas. This herd had attained a herd average of 1,200 gallons at 3.7 % for over 30 cows for a good 4 years so it was no surprise that buyers would be interested in their bulls. Unfortunately this herd sold up in 1963 but the event drew huge crowds who learned that their neighbouring herd the Kyford herd established in 1953 would continue the Stonethorpe herd. The average of £106 was low but the times were difficult.

The Royal Show Supreme in 1961 was won by a successful show winner, Kelmscott Bold Lord 8th, and his breeder Robert Hobbs was there to see it at 85 years young! Although he was owned by a comparatively new breeder, H. Eaves. The female Championship was won by Mrs N. Fielding Johnson's Effjay Beggar Maid 57th who went on to take the all-breed award at Yeovil and Frome soon after.

Despite these happy events there were voices expressing concern from several sources that improvements and changes must be made. Radical ideas were being formulated concerning the future direction of the breed and the Society. The Secretary Arthur Furneaux had retired and been succeeded by Arthur Greenhough; there were thoughts of moving out of London as the lease was expiring; several breeders were wondering about introducing the Swedish Red breed or using it to improve dairy performance. This breed's average was an impressive

9,453 lb at 4.1 % at that time and had been developed using the Swedish Red Pied with a percentage of Shorthorn and also Ayrshire. These thoughts were regarded by many who were purists as completely unacceptable but nevertheless several breeders made a trip to view the prospect. Their rationale was that the original Shorthorn had been created from an amalgam to suit a need as had several other breeds before they were stabilised. The dedicated reckoned that there must be genes somewhere in the world that could help the breed regain its size, yields and status. This last sentiment was also held by the beef type breeders. Despite this reticence a cross-bred dairy register was set up in 1962 to accommodate the more adventurous to experiment and for these to be officially recorded so that their efforts could be traced; fittingly it was called the experimental register! It was originally thought to be to accommodate the Swedish Red enthusiasts but in the event the government did not approve the import for quite a while, owing to the fact that Sweden had a leucosis problem. During the intervening period there was much discussion and of course rumour, the result of which was that very eminent people were to be drawn into the discussions, which will be detailed later.

1963 was the year when the Stoneleigh Park site at Kenilworth became the permanent site of the Royal Show which at the time seemed an adventurous step but the costs of a peripatetic event were becoming prohibitive. Since then there have been many developments in the use of the area and at the time of writing there are expansive plans to create it as the main centre for agricultural interests which it should have been for some time but economics and politics have prevented it.

At the autumn Dairy Shorthorn Show and Sale at Reading, the male Championship was won by Streetly Barrington Prospect; Mr Webb declared it had been 'his aim for 20 years'! The female Champion was Orgreave Brenda 14th to the delight of the Hill Family but the averages were low with females at £96 10s. and bulls £170, helped by the Champion selling to the Northern Ireland Ministry of Agriculture for 420 guineas.

The win by the Hills was another milestone for them as it was their first time showing at this event; although comparatively young, their herd, **Orgreave,** near Burton on Trent, was to become a major contributor over the next years. Mrs Hill had been widowed early leaving her with the farm and a large young family in 1942 which was formed into a company, Messrs J. Hill and Co., which started grading-up but after a while it was decided to reduce these and add some pedigree stock. John Hill bought Barton Park Masterpiece from Tom Bullock; then the decision was made to base the expansion on Hastoe lines, Lady Hermione and Barrington, a policy which certainly put this herd on the map. Hastoe Grand Dukedom followed and then

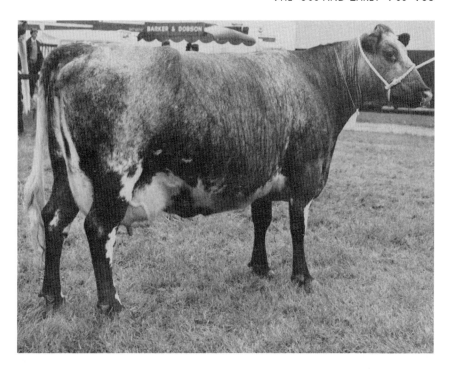

Orgreave Lady Laura 12th

Barrington Defender both followed by Hinxhill Barrington Beau who was full of Hastoe breeding. The herd's first major success came soon when after Orgreave Marion 7th had made several attempts at dairy events she won the Championship at the Scottish event in 1958. One of their other entries, Overton Whisper, paired up with Marion to win the pairs award at the same event. In 1959 Wychbridge Ruth 3rd won 1st on inspection and in 1962 she won the trials. These achievements were to be the start of a long line of show wins. And a long association with Terry Foley as herdsman. One of the famed cow families was the Laura line, started with the purchase of Libbear Laura which John later said proved to be the best £50 he ever spent, winning many championships and breeding Orgreave Lady Laura, the mother of 10 calves, 3 proven sires and 4 VG daughters while giving over 150,000lb of milk. At the London Dairy Event she gave 93lb of milk and her progeny went on to win so many awards for Orgreave and other prominent herds she and her family of well over 100 must be considered one of the greats of the modern breed.

   Writing of families of cows also reminds me of Gilbert Withers who not only bred wonderful cow families, but had an interesting family history of his own. It is quite complex but the history goes back to around 1915 when Alfred Batstone, farming commercial Shorthorns in Somerset with two brothers decided to go to pedigree stock, so specialised in Barrington Foggathorpes, and Musicals. Gilbert was a cousin of Alfred and one day went to visit just after he had taken over the management of his own family's **Gateshayes herd;** he was only the tender age of 14 and almost immediately won the Bradfield cup for the best herd average in the county of any breed. He was so impressed with what he saw he purchased a bull calf. Later the Batstones joined forces with Gilbert and his wife Minnie, bringing their stock with them and in fact Alfred subsequently married Minnie's mother!

The combined skills of these two families created a unique herd. In 1943 Gilbert joined the Shorthorn Society and decided to grade up some of his best families such as the Fillpails and shortly after the two men went to Yeovil Show and Sale, long a favoured venue for the West Country breeders, and bought two sires, Roundhill Darlington Duke 2nd and Leycroft Wild Lord, who both went back to the Tory's Anderson Imperial Cran. The Leycroft Sire bred six Champions and a reserve Champion. Gilbert later took a fancy to a heifer that came before him at a show he was judging and he subsequently purchased Libbear Barrington Duchess 2nd. So successful was she that she won over 20 Championships and 17 spoon trophies. Gilbert had an incredible memory for cattle, remembering features and pedigrees years after. (Believe me, I tested it!) It also became obvious that he could not resist his cattle as several times in his career he sold up: the first time in 1960, but a few months later he would start again! At his final dispersal, as previously mentioned, he stopped the sale momentarily saying buyers were paying too much! Such was his integrity that a nearby commercial dairyman with 250 Shorthorns bought 5 successive sires for his 3 farms. Gateshayes cattle were always impeccably bred and correct and Gilbert was a great show man with many show triumphs.

He and Minnie had a daughter Margaret who inherited the cattle skills of her parents going on to win stock YFC judging both nationally and internationally, then marrying Raymond Burrows and starting another Shorthorn herd with the prefix Whimple.

1964 was an interesting year for several reasons. One being that as usual for some time the dairy breeders held an annual conference (as did the beef at another venue) to discuss matters of general interest or concern as transmitted by the regions; however on this occasion the concept was widened as there were representatives in the country from South Africa, Australia, USA and Australian milking societies, as well as the English, Welsh and Irish members all with a fee which will make modern conference goers a little envious – £2 + £2.2 shillings if the dinner was also required. As well as the normal discussions the conference decided that a world conference would be a wonderful idea for all sectors of the breed combined on a periodic basis. The idea caught on and it was agreed subsequently that the first official world conference would be staged in South Africa with representatives from as many countries or continents as possible. The first took place in 1968 as a means of exchanging experiences, ideas, problems and for visitors to see the systems and cattle in the host country as well as experiencing the country and its hospitality. So again more later!

It was also the year when the dairy sector of the breed gained the coveted Burke Trophy for the second time since its inception in 1951, with Sir John Armytage's bull Kirklees Truman 3rd and G.T. Wooster's Pennbury Elizabeth 14th. The trophy was presented by the Duke of Gloucester. What a way for Mr Wooster to start his Presidency as of course the President is elected at the AGM held then at the Royal Show. Both these exhibits were Champions in the dairy sector but of course this is not necessarily the case in this competition as the cup is for the best pair of the breed also it is split into dairy and beef breeds.

The **Kirklees** herd was managed by Billy Goodman who was there from the foundation in 1949 and was attending his 41st Royal. Truman had won the Royal in 1961 and Championships at many other shows. The **Pennbury** herd also had a long serving herdsman in Albert Pickard although Mr Wooster had been forced by poor health to reduce his herd from around 100 head to about 35 for a time; it was now reaching its former numbers but in 1966 it became necessary to sell the milking portion of this herd which included Elizabeth 14th who made £220 when the average was £114, with the top being Elizabeth 16th at £235.

1965 was an encouraging year for the Society as it was the year when the **Northern Dairy Shorthorn Association** decided to re-join the parent Society after a prolonged negotiation described in chapter 3 but their ability to identify their type in the herd book was assured. Dairy breeders were also encouraged as in the autumn show and sale they achieved their highest average for bulls for 10 years. Twenty-eight bulls averaged £263 10s. A sale total of 78 head averaged £163 7s. and in fact it was Gilbert Withers who bought the top price female, Stirzakers Wild Eyes 39th, for 200 guineas; top price bull was the Champion Stockwood Principle purchased by Richard Roper for 800 guineas to follow his other Stockwood bull Statesman. Improved figures, perhaps, but once again compare them with the Beef Shorthorns at Perth this year when the average was £566 for 139 bulls helped by the Champion at 10,000 guineas to Denis Cadzow of Duncrahill for Denend Ragusa bred by Gordon Blackstock, the first time he won this honour for his own herd. The bid was especially salient as it was the opening bid and designed very effectively to discourage the Argentine bidders! The year was also marked by the major reduction of a sector of the Calrossie herd part of which was bought by Lt. -Col. and the

Hon. Mrs Dewhurst who bought some 35 head. Later in the year they also had a reduction which included some of this consignment as well as some Dungarthill and a few of the Naemoor females; their average was low at £117.

The Championship at the 1965 show and sale was to prove in retrospect a fitting tribute to Gordon Blackstock as he was tragically killed in a motor accident in August 1966. A great Irish character who had achieved so much in his short life, he was only 46 when he died. He ran first the family Rosemount herd in Ireland, then went to Calrossie; following this he went to the Bapton herd in 1950 where he achieved great things and when it was sold to Canada he started on his own again in 1963 with the **Denend** herd. Obviously with a great breeding skill he was also helped by his former owners who encouraged him to buy what he considered the best and invariably he proved his point. Awarded the MBE for his services to cattle breeding, he was outspoken at times but his skills at promoting both his herds and the breed were never in doubt.

In the autumn Perth sale his herd was dispersed so it was again fitting that his Denend Glen Lake, a show winner through the previous two years, should reach the top price of the sale at 560 guineas. Averages were again low but this was the order of the day at that time: 56 polled animals £124, and £140 for his horned stock. The top female was the dam of Glen Lake for 460 guineas to the Henderson brothers at Gifford who will be seen to play a major role in the turn around of the Shorthorn fortunes. Female Champion at this event went for the seventh time to the highly skilled Adams family at Glamis with Glamis Princess Nona who eventually went to New Zealand. I need make no apology for quoting Gordon Blackstock again as he was proved right when he said, 'Who can blame the breeder when he takes 8 small thickset bulls to Perth, one makes 8,000 guineas to the Argentine and the others are far too small for crossing so make 60 to 100 guineas a total of around 15,000 guineas another breeder takes 8 big strong, honest bulls and sells them for an average of £300 a total of 2,500. What would you do?' At the same conference he said, 'Why is it that a commercial farmer will pay the equivalent of 8 lambs for a ram but when it comes to buying a bull he expects to get one for the price of one or at most two steers? An extra £100 or £200 would repay him many times,' a very reasonable assessment. Speaking about the fall-off in Irish demand he said, 'The Irish government made a disastrous mistake when they tried to correct the small Shorthorns by the use of dairy bulls, the store buyers would not buy the weedy products but they would flock back if we could provide the big rugged old fashioned Shorthorns of yester year when they would give around 750 gallons but had huge Scale and ruggedness, this was when 70% of Irish cattle were red and white.'

Another Irishman was to be the President in **1966:** Mr R.D. Best. He farmed in Co. Antrim and was the first President from Ulster and the first Irish president for about 50 years. He ran a Beef Shorthorn herd but also had many other connections being on the boards of several agricultural organisations including being Vice President of the Royal Ulster Agricultural Society. There was much internal discussion this year on the new dairy issue, firstly members wondering if the proposed idea of experimentation was the right way forward and secondly, if it was, how it should be progressed. There were strong feelings on both sides; in March the President called for further discussion on this aspect with the famous geneticist Dr Alan Robertson from Edinburgh at the meeting to answer what must have been an immense number of queries. Some considered the Meuse Rhine Issel (MRI) and others the Danish Red would be better, the former as it had a closer relationship with the Shorthorn or the latter as it had more size than the Swedish Red.

A principal speaker at this event was **Henry W.S. Teverson,** who was to become so important in the eventual scheme. Educated at Cambridge University and owner of the **Stowfield** herd with a superb brain and communication skills, he also had the gift of a photographic mind. One of his pastimes was commenting at agricultural events in this country and Ireland with particular reference to the cattle competitions. These he carried out with supreme skill and continuity with few if any notes, just a study of the cattle lines beforehand. He also acted at dairy events, the Royal Dublin Show, the Royal Show, Smithfield Show and many other major events. He was to become chairman of the eventual experimental scheme and the Breed Development Committee as well as President. He was passionately interested in the future progress of the breed as well as having his own herd at Stow Bardolph, Norfolk, where he practised his theories and always was able to demonstrate his point of view and experiences. Tragically for his family and the breed he suffered a brain tumour and passed away at a critical time in the progress of the changes so was unable to see many of his visionary ideas come to fruition. He achieved almost impossible successes in gaining the trust of so many understandably sceptical breeders by his ability to see both sides and to demonstrate his answers through his own herd. His contribution to the breed's survival was incredible and arguably unmatched, as even those who were not converted to that solution respected his view and his successes. Without such a man the transition would have been almost impossible as not surprisingly feelings on the subject ran very high and many organisations would have been ruined by the strength of the debate.

Many changes were to come; one that affected the whole dairy sector was the **revision of the classification scheme**. For the benefit of students or others who are not sure what is involved, it is an objective opinion of any beast to establish on a sliding scale the aspects of conformation which make up that animal. This is carried out by one or more people regardless of type or pedigree and it enables the society to assess the good or bad points of say a female's progeny. Basically a beast is assessed for a number of traits resulting in a total assessment of either excellent, very good, good, average, fair or poor, dependant on a series of points awarded to such traits as legs, feet, udder attachment, body, etc., and includes an assessment of as many as 56 structural aspects, so that one may find out what good or bad points are transmitted within a family group. For a long time this breed had been slow to accept this as an important breeding aid but as the years went on and as computers made analysis so comparatively simple, awareness increased. In this year there were a number of demonstrations in differing areas of the country attended by over 100 members at nearly every one and the events were supported by the Past President Mr W. Woof, the current President Elect Mr G.R. Maundrell and a further past President Mr G.J. Wooster.

It was Mr Maundrell who, among many others, was very forthright in his views of the experimental scheme saying, 'There is nothing wrong with the Shorthorn, if you cannot get on with the breed there is probably something wrong with you! There used to be a lot of bad Shorthorns about but they have been culled out. Don't, by Mischievous meddling ruin this wonderful breed, go elsewhere.' However notwithstanding his strong views he kept an open mind. He intimated his opinion that the current problems were largely due to the indiscriminate use of bulls, 'Too many bad bulls and not enough good bulls have been used for far too long.' His herd was the **Calstone,** founded as a non-pedigree herd in 1912; it had made a huge contribution to the breed with its ruthless culling policy with well chosen bulls and had graded-up to pedigree status. A sire, Calstone Lord Cactus, proved through A I to be one of the most improving sires of his time, another being C. Premium Bond. Another bull used by the Maundrell brothers was Earlsoham Premium Bond. Others used included Stokely Cross General Premium, Lenborough Pansman 50th, Gateshayes Dairy Premier and Calstone Blarney Stone. Their herd influence in the West of England was immense; they were successful at shows as well as in production, winning 7 supreme interbreed Championships, 2 reserve Champions as well as 124 firsts, 90 seconds, etc, during the previous 10 years. Their final Champion was in the 1968 Royal Show with Calstone Nancy 62nd. The herd was sold in two parts, first the milking herd in 1970. Unfortunately the herd had an unexpected temporary accreditation breakdown shortly before the sale which may have affected the outcome. The young stock was sold in 1971. The first sale averaged £118 for 90 head and the second averaged £187 for 38 head.

1966 also saw the long association with Thornton and Co. the auctioneers, who had recently amalgamated with another organisation, cease. Thornborrow and Co. would conduct the autumn sale at Reading with the future emphasis of the Society show and sale being moved to Crewe partly because it was thought that to move it to the real dairy area would attract more buyers. The other change was the start of a **Young Bull Proving Scheme** which initially asked for bulls over 15 months to be offered to enable semen to be taken in a scheme involving the Milk Marketing Board(MMB). Later the Society examined every bull's pedigree in detail in conjunction with the MMB in order that the potential could be assessed. Shorthorns were one of the first breeds to be also involved with the MMB through Contemporary Comparisons (ICC) which enabled one to assess the relative performance of bulls as when used in one herd it is comparatively easy to gauge but when used in AI across a number of animals in differing herds it is another matter. Again the significance of this was a little slow to be recognised.

Back to **1967** as it was again an eventful year for both sectors. Firstly there was a bad outbreak of foot and mouth disease which curtailed several events and sadly several herds were lost. For the Beef Society it was marked by a change of Secretary as **Miss Pat Ramsey** had decided to get married and become Mrs Macdonald! After 18 years service, she was succeeded by **Mr Tom Lang** who was assisted by his wife **Barbara,** both came at a difficult time as exports were fast declining and the Society was, like the dairy, accepting that their cattle must alter or fail, all combined with a shrinking membership and falling funds.

There was some interesting news from Canada in that although it and North America were virtually closed to exports there was a surge of interest in the breed and the value of the poll Shorthorn was at last being appreciated. This had resulted in a world record $30,000 for a $^1/_2$ share interest being paid for Gloriadale Bonaparte sired by Constellation of Bapton by T.C. Stuart of the Tutira herd near Quebec from Roy Philip of the Gloriadale herd Ontario.

The 103rd Perth show and sale was the start of a very successful year for Mr Durno's Uppermill herd as they started with Uppermill Bydand achieving the supreme Championship following the male Championship and the herd also won the cups for the best 3 bulls, and best 5 bulls. Top of the day was Denend Golden Miller at 2,100 guineas, Bydand fetched 2,000 guineas The reserve supreme was Calrossie Treasure Trove. The averages were £284 for 142 bulls and females were £125 but other breeds were suffering reduced averages. Uppermill also gained the top sale average herd at £645 for 10 bulls. One of the encouraging things about this sale was the purchase of no less than 31

The winning Bledisloe team

bulls for the Ministry of Agriculture's scheme to assist the crofters and 11 bulls went to the Argentine.

Uppermill went on to win supreme at the Royal Show and the Royal Highland in 1966 and 1977 with Uppermill Ballot. It was also the start of serious beef bull performance testing as the Scottish Milk Board were able to allocate space at their Scone Centre; unfortunately this fell through at the last minute, however fortune went their way as Oatridge Farm West Lothian was being set up as an Agricultural Training Centre and found room for 11 bulls.

For the dairy sector there was the triumph of **winning the Bledisloe Trophy** at the Dairy Event. The team of Maundrell Bros Calstone Spark 53rd, R. Vigus's Stoke College Foggathorpe 2nd, J. D. Spalton's Ancliffe Gladys 5th , J. W. Cook's Mercers Isabella 9th , J.Hill and Co. Orgreave Lady Hermione 7th , S.J. Callwood's Woodcall Burrows 6th all made up the team, the latter having won the Supreme Individual Inspection Award.

The team first of all won the inspection shield under an Ayrshire judge and then clinched the trophy when their production points were added: the first time since 1935 that the breed had succeeded in this competition. It was a great boost to morale as during the year council had finally bitten the bullet and decided they should move out of London. At the same time they would reduce staff and alter the committee structure to provide committees as follows: Dairy Shorthorn, Publicity, Finance and Administration, Artificial Insemination, Herd Book, Rules and Discipline, Regional Associations and Judges. These were to be revised again later as numbers fell and duties were further combined.

1967 also marked the launching of the Government's brucellosis scheme which was welcome but belated as countries like Norway had been free since 1953, Sweden since 1958, Finland since 1960, and the Swiss and Germans since 1962; our excuse was that we had more cattle which when compared with Germany did not sound too good.

Mention was previously made of Sir John Armytage and the **Kirklees** herd. This estate had been owned by the family since 1565 and had registered their herd of Shorthorns as long ago as 1870 but they had lapsed until after Sir John had been invalided out of the army. In 1949 they were re-established on Bates Lines from a number of sources, principally Revels and the Astonia herds, and families were developed, the most favoured being Eves, Foggathorpe, Telluria, Wild Eyes, Grand Duchess all building up to around 250 head run on commercial lines. The first bull in the new herd was Cliveden Lord Foggathorpe out of a 3 times 2,000 gallon cow; he was followed by Kirklees Lord Nelson 2nd whose dam averaged 18,666lb at 3.8% so they had a wonderful start. Kingsland Lord Wild Eyes and Thrimby Lord Barrington 2nd followed before the star, Truman 3rd who had immense success in the show ring. The herd had a very happy association with its manager Billy Goodman who at one time had owned his own small herd before coming to Kirklees. It was thanks to Sir John renting him a small farm that his dream of again being an owner came true as he purchased the major portion of the **Earlsoham** herd, owned previously by Major Mann and managed for many years by Albert Mullinger, which had had its own degree of fame with yields of 2,000 gallons and a large number of show wins including first at the Royal Show as well as several prominent sires, some already mentioned in other herds. Success in this herd came mainly from Eaton Rose King 23rd. Principal families in this herd were Wild Eyes, Barringtons, Foggathorpes and Sharron Rose; they developed with several sires from the Orma herd and Earlsoham Sharron Warrior. Billy Goodman was another very skilled showman who attended some 37 dairy events and over 40 Royal Shows.

It was about this time that the death of Hugh Haldin deprived the society of another personality who had contributed much through his **Hinxhill** herd near Ashford, Kent, as well as his work on the council and being elected President in 1963. The Hinxhill herd was always a successful one in the ring as well as the pail, founded and maintained almost completely with Hastoe breeding, the careful management, assisted by Bob Gibbs for many years, ensured much success and wide acclaim as evidenced for example by one of the open days which attracted over 1,000 people from all breeds including those with top herds. All came to view the expertise in the herd which had maintained average yields of 1,186 gallons over 11 years, with around 200 head, and a beef unit of some 300. The estate held other enterprises including a well known Romney Marsh sheep flock of some 2,000 head and a large turkey unit of 6,000 birds. Some of the herd sires used were Amershill Superior, Hastoe Master Dukedom 5th, Duke Beau, Royal Dukedom 3rd, Grandeur 6th, Double Grandeur and Orfold Double Magnum. Probably one of this herd's best known was Theale Maude 12th from the Cumbers, who created a record with yield of 203,857 lb over 12 calves. In 1970 this herd was dispersed by Mr R. Houcghin, who had taken over ownership following the death of Hugh Haldin. Prices were modest, with a top of 250 guineas for H. Countess 5th by David Yates from Scotland and a low average but the buyers were nearly all long established breeders who appreciated the breeding.

1968 became significant as the **Shorthorn Society of Great Britain and Ireland** had moved out of London to Green Lodge, Great Bowden, Market Harborough, Leicestershire, with all that entailed. From the beef perspective the end of the year bought great celebration as the **Supreme animal at Smithfield was a pure Shorthorn, Phoenix Freeze from David Sinclair of Inchture, Perth:** the first Beef Shorthorn to win this accolade since 1915. He was sold for £3,100.

1969 saw the reorganisation of Thornborrow and Co. in that John D. Thornborrow decided to move to Leamington Spa, the importance of which will become clear later.

Writing of this period it is hard to fairly convey the attitudes of the membership when these major developments were initiated, as the concepts of many were severely challenged and the proposals were very different to those mammoth steps taken all those years before by the likes of Bates and others, when the breed was being established. These had been done almost in isolation and communications then were so slow. Nevertheless they were breaking new ground and while this current new ground was revolutionary to some and even unspeakable to a few, it was to others a way of ensuring that the breed could bring itself up to the modern requirement and survive. To this group it was as stark as that.

How it was to be done was the problem. The 'purists' wished to preserve the wonderful breed they knew with the good points outlined earlier to be retained. The experimenter wanted to retain those same good points but build in new ones with which to meet the new challenge and restore the Shorthorn to its deserved prominence. In so many ways their wishes were the same but the former group tended to overlook that all those years ago their predecessors were attempting almost the same but from a differing perspective. Technical advances today were such that although it was very, very late the breed could be bought back. To do so would, to quote Churchill and others, 'take blood, sweat, toil and tears'.

Eventually this love of the breed was to succeed not necessarily in getting all back together but to arrive at a point of mutual tolerance. Part of the success of the project was that unlike in other breeds where money played a huge part, as the Shorthorn had gone out of fashion this conflict did not arise. Those that were left were almost all absolutely dedicated to the breed.

Exactly the same conflicts of thought were going on with both the dairy and the Beef Shorthorns and they were to take enormous decisions, as will be described; although the clouds were slowly clearing such moves in both sectors were, by their very nature, going to take some time before positive results were seen and more importantly recognised, so inevitably there would be further declines before the recovery was noticeable.

The positive thoughts returned, even if they were to be challenged many times and the change in the membership's relationships was eventually to be greatly admired; if it had not occurred the breakdown of plans would have seen the breed go to extinction.

The other point to recognise concerning the future was that in the case of the dairy, the numbers were relatively small in relation to some other breeds but the labour involvement with a dairy unit is considerably greater than a beef unit of similar size. So it was more noticeable that with the labour cutbacks that took place in this period changes of the dairy sector would inevitably be slower. Furthermore the starting numbers of the Beef Shorthorns and their members at this time was very low compared with that of the dairy sector.

In **1969** Dick Rose of the Churchill herd fame was President and he had invited **Sir Richard Trehane** as **Chairman of the MMB** to address the breed council to explain his ideas on the proposed scheme. Sir Richard related experiences of both Russia and Hungary, both of whom had carried through similar improvement schemes with significant success, he stressed every situation was different and suggested that the Society should certainly carry out the pure breed improvement as the breed had commercially fallen behind others and there might well be genes overseas or somewhere which could help the return but he fully recognised the potential and the qualities. He also recommended that some form of experimental trials should be organised but he also warned that it would be some time before reliable results could be assessed. Above all he assured council that they would have the support of the MMB Production Division and suggested that around 2,000 cows should be initially selected and a geneticist should become involved. Shortly after this the experimental committee met with MMB officials and the meeting was so successful and positive that the President volunteered his Churchill herd as the first step to the work. Sir Richard had also given assurance that if a well planned programme could be provided he was sure he could achieve the support from the Ministry of Agriculture who were currently not very in favour of cross-bred bulls. Before this a few had carried out their own brief experiments among whom were the Atlantic herd of Mrs Tanner and also the Stowfield herd so there was already a provisional start to an official scheme.

Soon after this Professor John Bowman from Reading University became involved in drawing up a scheme. Subsequently he became fully involved, giving incredible support and advice on the Total Breed Improvement Schemes for a number of years.

As if in response to this the challenge Col. S. Watson's Ballingarrane herd bought out 3 Champions at the Royal Dublin Show with Ballingarrane Wild Cherub as reserve breed and male Champion and then the breed and female Champion with Ballingarrane Belle 57th. Sir John Galvin bought out the reserve male and reserve female Champion with Loughlinstown Seraph and Seraphina respectively, the latter by an English A I sire Stukeley Imperial Ringmaster. An A I sire Gillshill Lord Wild Eyes 2nd was also responsible for Cherub.

In addition to this the Dairy Shorthorn team won the inspection shield for the Bledisloe award at the 1969 dairy event with C. M. Robarts and Sons' Kaberfold Barrington 9th, Lenborough Pansy 112th and Pansy 123rd and Cowslip 464th as well as Lenborough Daisy Chain 18th, all from Richard Roper; Orgreave Whisper for John Hill. Unfortunately Greaves Joy 9th, the breed inspection Champion, was not included as she was slightly (.06%) short for qualification but she had been shown by the Society's present Secretary Frank Milnes who had taken time off from Harper Adams College for the event. This was the second time for the breed to win this shield in three years.

The **Greaves** herd, founded by Frank's grandfather John and carried on by his Father J.S. Milnes on the high ground outside Sheffield, was incidentally one to be reckoned with as it had been top of the Yorkshire National Milk Records for 4 years with averages of 12,244 lb at 3.60%; they were also 5th in the breed's national milk records for the country. Greaves Topsy 13th, winner of the regional gold cup, had averaged 68,409lb at 3.8% with 5 calves. Greaves Joy 9th had achieved a yield of 93,786lb with 6 calves and went on to challenge the daily milk yield record by giving 112.5lb with twice a day milking. (The actual breed record was set in 1939 at 129.5 lb by Eva from Mrs Hollas.) She was definitely not just a 'pretty cow'! In **1974** this herd again hit the highlights at the dairy event when Greaves Barbara 43rd broke the record for this event for *all breeds* when she gave 112lb in one day on twice a day milking; this had previously held by a Guernsey with 107lb or for three times milking when a Friesian gave 111.3lb. Yet another outstanding cow in this herd was Greaves Vera 36th who gave 109,092 in her first five lactations, an average of 21,819lb with a top of 29,393lb with over 600lb weight of fat and protein. She was also an excellent breeder as her first daughter yielded 27,464lb with her first two lactations and was first in the heifer class for production and inspection at the dairy event in 1978. Greaves Joy 9th went on to be the first cow to be awarded a 75,000kg certificate as in her 16th year; having had 13 calves, she reached 172,994lb (78470kg), demonstrating the economic longevity of the breed, a feature evident in so many Shorthorn herds. Longevity is not too hard to achieve, but the test is for it to be economic as well, as one is not much use without the other in dairy farming.

Another response early in **1970** was the setting up of a Pure Bred Improvement Committee following a further suggestion from Professor Bowman after an idea from Gilbert Withers. It was under the chairmanship of John Hill of Orgreave. The plan was to see increased yields, monitor growth rate and feed efficiency, all as well as carcass composition. A further step was the determination to form a company to market and promote Dairy Shorthorn semen so **Dairy Shorthorn Breeders (DSB)** was formed. **Cattle Breed Improvement Services Ltd (CBIS)** shortly preceded DSB to obtain and market semen for the experimental sector. These two committees could have proved very divisive within the Society but on the contrary, although there was naturally some competition, the progress made by both sectors put new heart in the members. This could largely be attributed to the combined efforts of the respective Chairmen Henry Teverson and John Hill.

It was an incredibly exciting and busy year, generating as it went a very refreshing new attitude of hope and even competition, with each sector keen to prove its point. The previous year saw the appointment of John Bowen as classifier and this year Paul Hocking as Technical Officer who would work with Dr Bowman and the Secretary to process and evaluate the large amount of data that was to be generated in respect of the schemes. He had an Honours degree in Animal Production and a diploma in genetics and in fact later made the scheme his thesis for his eventual doctorate.

Obviously there was much happening at this time apart from these developments but I feel it is better to outline the experimental process now so that it is not fragmented; therefore for those not interested and the beef breeders perhaps you should skip a few paragraphs, but your time will come!

The experimental dairy blending concept and pure-bred improvement

The objective was to produce a red, red and white or roan hybrid, based on the Dairy Shorthorn, which would be suited to the economic production of quality milk and meat and would be able to compete with the best milk-beef breeds in the world. This would be done with professional direction and monitoring with advice, but would leave considerable personal choice because of personal or local situations. It would involve, as outlined, collection of data and the required processing of results. This would then involve the inter-breeding of the most promising cross-breds one to another with the object of eventually producing a closed strain. With co-operation and good fortune this would take about 15 years with the intermediate stage of achieving say 50% Shorthorn, 25% of one outside breed and 25% of another, this being achieved in about six years.

The practical interpretation of the scheme would ideally involve herds and the distinct wishes were (1) that the attributes of the pure Shorthorn should be retained and (2) at least one third of that herd should be retained as pure both to ensure retention of the genes but also to enable comparisons to be made within the same conditions and management.

Council set standards to be achieved:

After calving at 30 months or under 1080lb solids= 8500lb milk at 12.7% or if calving at over 46 months 1524lb solids = 12,000lb milk at 12.7%. There should be a minimum of 12.5% solids. The breed to retain early maturing and weigh 1,000lb at 2 years of age.

The following breeds to be involved and the averages shown were those of the time:

breed	av/yield	av/ lb	av/weight b.fat %	weight fat.lb. female
Dairy Shorthorn	8,712	3.61	315	1,232
Red and White Friesian	11,093	3.64	404	1,400
Red Dane	9,823	4.26	418	1,430
Finnish Ayrshire	9,251	4.26	418	1,200
Swedish Red and White	9,447	4.50	416	1,250
Meuse Rhine Issel Simmentals	9,240	3.61	342	1,430
Simmental	8,730	4.03	352	1,650

These next were the figures that applied for comparison:

breed	av/yield	av/ lb	av/weight b.fat %	weight fat.lb. female
British Canadian Holstein	10,309	3.79	391	1,452
British Friesian	10,108	3.68	372	1,400
British Ayrshire	9,081	3.86	349	1,000

All the progeny to be registered in the hybrid register and the progeny of the females to be mated with one of the parent breeds, every effort to be made to weight record the steers and where possible their carcasses should be analysed.

Any of the breeds that failed to make a useful contribution would be dropped from the scheme.

Milk records would be analysed and the animal's type classified.

To that date any experimental work had been self-financed and this would continue but it was hoped that grants might be obtained for professional direction and recording.

It will be noticed that the British Ayrshire was not included, which created some surprise at the time but this was because it was currently lacking in size. A problem they too were addressing.

Despite these radical moves the life of the Society went on! Again the Society were first as they put **dairy bulls on test** at the Harrogate showground with the permission of the Great Yorkshire Show and under the supervision of the Meat and Livestock Commission (MLC). Bulls were from the Mercer herd of Jack Cook, the Twells herd of Joe Wyatt, the Collingham herd of H.J.Crocker and the Drisgol herd of L.V.B. Thomas. All to provide a wide choice of bloodlines and all were inspected. This consignment was soon extended.

It was also the start of the Irish Improvement Scheme, largely sponsored by the Irish Department, which was to bring a huge change in the Irish cattle as recorded in the Irish chapter.

The RDS bull sales also showed renewed confidence and determination as 3 made over 1,000 guineas and the sale averaged £315 for 29 bulls. It also seemed the government departments were keen as the Eire Department bought 7 that day, the Northern Agricultural Ministry one, with Sligo A I centre taking 3. The Champion Caufield March On from Sam Kelly was, after a battle with the Eire Department for the top bid, sold to the Loughlinston herd of Sir John Galvin for 1,200 guineas. The Northern Irish Ministry took the reserve Champion, B. William's Dairy Chancellor at 1,100 guineas and the 1,000 guinea bid was for E. Larmer's Newbliss Orderly which went to Sligo A I centre.

Bledisloe winning team, 1969.

Back on the mainland: the Royal Show was a triumph for Leslie
Thomas of the Drisgol prefix; his fine bull Drisgol Dairyman 2nd had
won the male Championship in 1969, and this year he took the supreme
award to add to his string of winnings. The reserve Champion was the
female Champion from the Hole family's Amber herd, Amber
Barrington Duchess. It was also a repeat in the Beef Ring as the female
Champion and supreme went to Morphie Lady Bridget and the
previous year the supreme had come from the same herd, Morphie
Clipper Warbler. Lady Bridget had also taken the 1969 Royal Highland
award. Dr Durno of Uppermill was reserve to her with his Flossy Floral
and again at the Royal in 1970 he was reserve but this time with his
bull Uppermill Watchman. Definitely a year for repeats as Lt. Col.
Dewhurst gained the Championship at Harrogate both years: with
Ardbennie Minstrel in 1969, and the female Champion was Dungarthill
Emerald Queen, and in 1970 with Dungarthill Bright Dazzle. These
two Dewhurst herds had made a bit of a habit at this show as they had
won a string of championships here over the last few years.

The Perth Show and sale event was won by Morphie Ballymoss
making it quite a year for this herd; reserve to him was Uppermill
Cowley (this herd won all the three group male trophies). This sale
was marked by the return attendance of many overseas visitors from
Brazil, Argentina, South Africa and New Zealand and it was from the
latter that the Champion was bought at 1,100 guineas by R.G. Whyte.
The Department of Agriculture again bought 8 to add to their Inverness
stud of about 80 bulls, which were available to the crofters on the
Scottish islands, and the 113 bulls showed a much improved average
at £303. Unusually, Roly Fraser of MacDonald Fraser and Co. stood
aside and invited Senor Roberto Lldarraz of Argentina to sell two lots
which was a fine gesture but Senor Roberto was definitely on holiday
as he usually sold some 70,000 head a year in his home country! Another

overseas success during the year was a further consignment of beef bulls to Russia.

The **Morphie** herd of W.L. Anderson had been started in 1939 with several Balthayock and Aldie cows, and later additions from several sources and using a run of influential and successful sires such as Bapton Commando, and Calrossie Crocus Count, two of the most influential of their time; Beaufort Chevalier and Graduate and Chrichton Buzzard all contributed to enable phenomenal success in the late '60s and early '70s, winning the Royal Highland Female Championship 5 times in 7 years with differing animals; it was also successful at the Scottish fat stock shows, with 2 Perth supreme and 2 senior and 1 junior Championships and featured twice in the Burke teams to name a few. As well as those mentioned they went on to win the 1972 Royal with Morphie Galaxy also the reserve female with Morphie Broadhooks Elizabeth. The Champion was once again from Uppermill with Flossy Floral.

1972 Perth Show and sale saw the first supreme Championship for a very loyal supporter of the breed, William McGowan of **Fingask**, Cupar, Fife, with Fingask Prince Charming. 'Willie', as he is known, founded his herd in 1946 and built up families of Lancasters, Brawith Bud, Crocus, Beauty, Orange Prudence, Princess Royal, and others. Successful sires included Saltoun Red Ensign, purchased from Uppermill, followed by Bapton King of Diamonds and Controller; the latter had been stock bull at the Naemoor herd and more recently Woodhead President by Mandalong Super Elephant introducing some Australian breeding; also the Canadian bred Scotsdale Havelock who had a considerable influence. Later Scotsdale Tradition had similar success when he was on loan from the large herd of Campbell Graham. This medium-size herd has had considerable success both at shows and fat stock events like Smithfield and the Scottish Winter Fayre, especially the latter: they have won the Mclaren Cup over 22 times, one could almost say outright!. From the 1970s this herd was to feature in a number of awards for Willie and his

A Morphie group

daughter Elizabeth Lang who coincidentally got married in 1972, making it quite a year for this family. Both Willie, who was awarded the MBE for his services to agriculture, and Elizabeth contributed so much and both served as the Beef Society Presidents.

Average prices at the 108th Perth Show and Sale in **1972** were up again to £439 for 110 bulls. At this time the poll bulls had their own Championship which this time was won by Calrossie Milky Way who also achieved the second highest price of 1,100 guineas. Top was Woodhead Ensign at 1,500 guineas to Uppermill. This event was judged by W.A. Spiers from the Northern Irish Ministry of Agriculture so the result and the valued top price demonstrated the changing attitudes of both officials and buyers when one remembers that originally polled stock were even refused licences for a while.

Some readers may be confused by the Presidency years as, although the year is quoted, since the Beef Shorthorn Society gained its status, their AGM has taken place at the Perth Bull sales in February and the change of office occurs then, whereas the Shorthorn Cattle Society AGM takes place in July and for many years it took place at the Royal Show which was the time when most members were gathered together. More recently the latter has been held a little later for ease of administration. The original presidential term was for a year but this was later amended to two years as it was considered more could be achieved. Be that as it may, the year 1971 for the beef sector had been a sad time as it marked the passing of one of the Shorthorn 'greats', Dr James Durno C.B.E., Patron of the Beef Shorthorn Society and Honorary President of the Royal Highland Agricultural Society. These two titles were the highest that could be bestowed in recognition of his untiring work for both organisations not to mention what else he had done.

Two other major contributors were also to be much missed: A. Watt Taylor OBE, Director of Watt Taylor Ltd, and President of many agricultural companies including the Beef Shorthorns and owner of the Philorth herd. The third loss was R.H. Watherston, CBE, another who had done so much for the Beef and Dairy Shorthorn Societies and the Royal Highland Society, who had died almost exactly a year previously. On the dairy side Capt. R.H. Stallard M.C., K.T. Timberlake, G.R. Maundrell and R.W. Kidner had died, their input and skills were to be sorely missed as were T.J. Thornborrow and H.M. Dare, both senior partners in their respective auctioneering companies. Shortly after these John Harrison of Gainford also died. Seldom have so many contributors and achievers to the breed, as well as those not recorded here, been lost in such a short period. A severe blow.

It was a difficult time despite the renewed optimism; the breed was still in decline as can be seen by the graphs (on p. 184) because, as stated, any turn around would take time, firstly to achieve and then to convince the customers. The problem was increased because the newer breeds were attracting such attention and fashion, the benefit of which was new members for them and this naturally meant a falling off for the Shorthorns. Nevertheless the tide was slowly turning as the smaller cattle were disposed of and loyal and determined breeders selected more from strains that had size, the dairymen also seeking increased yields with a new intensity. Some were looking overseas to Australia, which was a sound concept but, as some said, most of those genes originated in the UK. The pessimists, or were they realists, considered that once the benefit of hybrid vigour was past there would not be any lasting or large enough increase. Those who were seeking to improve by the alternative route (the 'blending' breeders) asked the question, 'What is so different to the black and white breeders seeking improvement from the Dutch Friesian and the Canadian Holstein as their genetic relationship was no closer than some of the breeds involved in the new plan? 'Again a very reasonable question.

1972 was the 150th anniversary of Coates's Herd Book and one step to celebrate this was the enclosing of a supplement in the Society Journal outlining a very brief history of what had gone before. News from the Harrogate Trials was that Twells Moss Trooper 4th had excelled, in that his figures showed the best of all breeds weight gain of 3.1lb per day. An outstanding performance for this bull whose dam, Twells Moss Rose 5th, was supreme breed Champion at the Royal in 1971 and was to become a major influence at home and overseas in the next few years. He was followed in the first group tests by Henshallbrook Premier Supreme. There had also been a further intake bringing the total to twenty-one at this stage. The call also went out for more progeny recorded and inspected (PRI) bulls to aid in the drive for improvement. It was soon after this that the search for Australian bloodlines intensified, following the visit of Joe Atkinson of the Willow Park Stud in Australia to judge the dairy sector at the Royal Show.

He picked Swanford Duchess from C.M. Robarts and Son's herd and E.J. Sumner's Swepstone Wild Premier as his female and supreme and male Champions respectively. The Willow Park herd was about 350 strong and held a number of price and yield records and it was from here that eventually after red tape delays semen from Willow Park Stockman 85 and 211 arrived to provide the pure strain input towards the return to commercial appeal. Both have British ancestry.

Whateley Musical 13th from G. Snape and Sons of Alcester broke the record this year with a staggering yield of 4,149 gallons in 365 days (3,529 in 305 days) with a peak daily yield of 137lb all at 3.66% and all on twice daily milking.

The **Swepstone** herd mentioned above and owned by S.J.(Sid) Sumner was founded in 1935 in Leicestershire, eventually going pedigree in 1939 and run on strictly commercial lines and assisted by his cowman Peter Chevin who worked with Sid for some 20 years, quite how no one was ever sure as Sid was one of Shorthorn's characters! The herd had numerous successes in the show ring and in the dairy events mainly with Wild Eyes, Barringtons and Foggathorpes. He had a policy of using a number of sires and laying them off for a while for future use before A I became more popular. Theale Lord Barrington 4th, Earlsoham Matador, Collingham Premier Darlington, Gateshayes Barrington Supreme and Orgreave Barrington King were some. Average yields were sought and achieved at around 10,348lb at 3.78% but Sid was a great believer in durability and female family influences, particularly the Bates lines. Shows and events would have been sometimes dull without him and his nearby friend and adversary Terry Hawksworth. The main part of this herd was sold in 1973 when he gained the highest average for 24 years, 89 sold to a top of 550 guineas and averaged £311, reflecting the quality and breeding.

The 1972 autumn Perth Show and sale was something of a landmark as one or two beef breeders were endeavouring to raise the stature of their stock by using dairy bloodlines, one being Mrs A. Laing of Forres Morayshire who offered several sired by Moy Roosevelt whose sire was the great Bapton Constructor but those on offer were out of dairy blood females. The favoured bull was Gunter, out of an Ireby cow, who, although placed 5th in his class, had an MLC recorded weight of 1170lb at 400 days. He drew a final bid of 1,300 guineas, the top price of the sale, going to the Northern Ireland Department of Agriculture. He and his 6 companions were 100lb in excess of the current Beef Shorthorn average. At this time and for quite a while it was common for the dairy breeders to send both bulls and females to this event not only for crofters' and shepherds' cows but for use of beef breeders as well. Beef bulls at this event showed an increase amounting to the average of £451 for 56 bulls. The Champion at the event was Woodhead Eglinton from the Henderson brothers, one of those herds which were to go initially down the dairy bloodline route, although their Champion this time was by Denend Golden Miller.

James Biggar, Beef Society President in 1973, speaking in his address after he had been to a number of countries, made reference to the continuing demand for Shorthorns but only for the best and was emphatic that heavier culling must be done as nothing did the breed more harm than poor quality cattle being offered. He considered there were signs of hope for the future as beef was still in demand and grain prices were rising which would mean that producers would need to produce off grass, a thing the Shorthorn was perfectly suited to. He also made reference to the huge drain on the breed's genetic resources by generations of exports which would have finished a lesser breed decades before.

The Perth Champion gave W.L. Anderson his third Champion at this event, this time with Morphie Galaxy under the judge from Argentina, Pendril Gunningham, who went to that country from the UK a number of years before. Galaxy was bought later by the Scottish Milk Board for 2,500 guineas, top price of the day and several other relatively high prices ensured the 6th rise in 6 years at £615; the reserve Champion went to the **Henderson's** Woodhead General and their other entries were in demand giving them the top average of 1,375 guineas and indeed they also gained the 1974 Championship as well with Newton Gold Coin so may be it is appropriate that I review their herds at this point especially as Ronald Henderson had started his own herd with the prefix **Newton** only four years before. (Incidentally Newton Gold Coin sold for 8,000 guineas to Watt Taylor Ltd which was the highest price for over 10 years.)

Shorthorns had started at **Woodhead** in 1940 when R.J.Henderson DSO,MBE,TD, rented the farm; but as he was away in North Africa on military service the business was managed by I.C. Henderson, his brother, the latter well known as a Scottish Rugby International (as was the third brother J.M. Henderson). Ronald and Ian subsequently formed a partnership in 1955 and Woodhead was purchased soon after and later still when Ronald retired from his many business commitments he purchased Newton Hall. Both were adamant for a long time that the breed had lost its popularity owing to the loss of size and had been some of the first both to speak out and do something about it. Ronald bought a number of the dual type from the **Mickle** herd of T.T. Hewson of Wigton and others of similar type as he was convinced that this was the first step to achieving size. Later they purchased an Australian sire from the celebrated Weebollabolla herds described in another chapter. Royal Commission was his name and again later in 1977 they imported semen from another similar Australian stud, Mandalong Super Elephant. Both were to have quite an influence not only because of their progeny but also as the gestures backed up what the brothers had been forcibly saying for some while. They, like James Biggar, believed the decline had been due almost entirely to the lack of demand for the smaller bulls and such stock must be culled. Shortly after the Mickle purchases they bought the Keith herd, one based on similar thoughts so the families blended very satisfactorily together to produce a string of successful bulls. Several sold at high prices both at home and overseas with a number sold to commercial herds in the UK, which was their aim. The dairy lines had included Waterloo, Tulip, Wineberry, Golden Queen, Foggathorpe and some of the beef lines were Crocus, Princess Royal, Floss, Fair Clipper, Nonpareil all based on Cruggleton breeding and bulls included Saltoun Orderlie, Denend Golden Miller, Denend Glendrossan, Chapelton Brigand as well as some of their own breeding. Over the years the initiatives and

Beef Shorthorn Registrations From 1960 to 2004

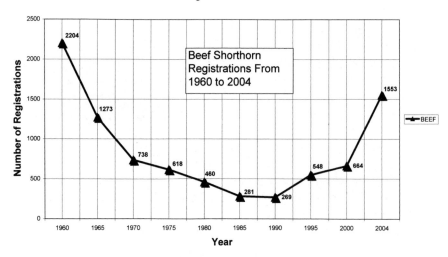

Dairy Registrations From 1960 to 2004

examples as well as the enthusiasm from Ronald and Ian, who both also insisted their success was largely helped by their stockman Lackie Balsillie over a number of year, proved a real turning point in the breeds fortunes. Ronald Henderson was to also serve as President of the Beef Society from1974-1976.

!973 and **1974** were difficult years in the dairy industry, reflecting the economic situation in the country; this resulted in a loss of confidence and meant sadly reduced prices at sales and especially dispersals of which there were several. One of these was the **Booker** herd of Dick Kimber, near Marlow, first started 1933, graded up using HastoeLord Dukedom and Amershill Darlington Senator and late in 1960 Stonethorpe Dairy Senator to gain size. Dick Kimber served on council

Mandalong Super Elephant

for a number of years before assuming a distinguished presidency in 1972 so it was a sad day when owing to labour shortage he decided to sell on a very low market. Some sold from retirement and others from disillusion or taking advantage of grants, at the time to encourage a switch to beef, by the EEC. One such was the excellent Bates bred herd of Tom Bonser, **Oxhay,** who had built up a reputation for very sound stock using bulls like Kirklees Lord Foggathorpe, Earlsoham Matador and Mickle Criterion followed by Swepstone Lord Foggathorpe 15th. Having quite good results at shows all were disappointed when he only averaged £157 for cows with a top of 300 guineas for Bates Duchess 18 who went to the Maxton Herd of David Spalton.

1974 was again significant in the history as it was the first of the **International World Conferences** as visualised during the Presidency of Dick Rose and the visit of Glen Leary, Secretary of the Shorthorn Society of South Africa as well as several other overseas personalities. So in March of that year 50 delegates from 8 countries arrived in the wonderful Kruger National Park to start the learning curve! The principles were decided and the committee formed. On this occasion the countries present were: Argentina (2) Australia (6) Canada (2) New Zealand (1) Rhodesia (1)South Africa (4) United Kingdom (4) United States (1) the brackets show the number of official delegates. Accompanying these were a number of wives, friends and other representatives of their respective countries. The first President to be elected was A. R. D. Halse (South Africa) who acted also as Chairman, Vice Chairman was G. R. Starritt (Australia). The UK delegates were John Hill as President, Dick Rose as past President, Ronald Henderson as President of the Beef Shorthorn Society and A. Greenhaugh as Secretary of the UK Society. It was subsequently agreed that South Africa should draw up a suggested constitution to be debated and confirmed at the next conference. And these to be held if possible every 3 years in differing countries. It was also agreed to accept Australia as the next venue. C.D Swaffer of USA was elected as the first Secretary. All who attended found the experience memorable as well as internationally very useful as a forum to discuss world or national problems within the breed and to learn how to overcome them as well as seeing at first hand local cattle and methods.

Subsequent conferences were held in Australia (!977), Canada (1981), USA (1983), Argentina (1986), UK (1989), New Zealand (1992), South Africa (1995), Australia (!998), Canada (2001), USA(2004).

Presidents have been R. Halse of South Africa (!974-86), P. Gunningham of Argentina (1986-95), R. Procter of Canada (1995-98), Major J. Gibb of Scotland (1998-2004), J. Roche of Australia 2004-.

Secretaries following C. D. Swaffer were J. Wood-Roberts1981-1999, F.Milnes 2000-.

From the first it was established that Ireland and Scotland would be entitled to their own representatives. As one would expect the attendance grew considerably, as did each tour, as experience was gained obviously personalities changed but the drive and enthusiasm of the presidents as well as the variety of experience has created continuing interest despite international problems. Sadly the attendees from outside the host country have in the main been largely of the senior age groups as the younger breeders can not spare the time away from their businesses particularly as many are very economic on their labour, furthermore probably for the same reasons there has been a greater emphasis on beef except in the UK and New Zealand events. It was eventually decided not to have a constitution but the expressed aims and objectives were to be 'To promote the exchange of ideas and achievements between Shorthorn enthusiasts in the pursuit of excellence'.

The 1975 Perth Championship was awarded to Major P. Henderson, DFC, of the **Lawton** herd. It was founded in 1907 at the Balthayock dispersal; later stock was bought from Uppermill and others, giving a wide selection of Booth and Colling families to combine with well selected bulls starting with Boquhon Champion who bred an excellent following of females, then Dunglass Chieftain, later Lawton Jamie, Collynie State Express and Coldoch Cairngorm, who was the sire of his Champion Lawton Albany, who only made 750 guineas but the averages were down at only £412 for 66 bulls. The reserve Supreme went to Woodhead Juggernaut and the brothers also won the bull group awards. Later in the year their Newton Discard won the beef recorded classes at the Royal Show over 23 others of all breeds. The event was another double for W.L. Anderson with Carstrad Stroller who had won the Royal Highland two weeks before. The dairy Royal leaders were male Champion Maxton Housemaster and the supreme was Lenborough Fillpail 272 giving Richard Roper yet another win and whose herd had now won Smithfield champion for 6 successive events (1969-74), demonstrating the dual capability of the breed and Lenborough cattle in particular.

A West Country Dairy Shorthorn herd cow **Kingsley Musical 3rd** owned by Mr and Mrs Blake at Clevedon, Avon, who was later to change their cattle to Beef Shorthorns, **broke the world record for lifetime production giving 210,875lb with 8,086lb of butterfat with 12 calves. An outstanding performance.** His cattle had won many awards at shows including the Dairy Show.

One of several sales forced by the increasing uneconomic size of the herd and facilities was that of the Collingham herd of H.J. Crocker whose family had farmed Lincoln Red Shorthorns as they then were. However Mr Crocker decided to turn to Dairy Shorthorns as he considered he needed more milk to go with his beef steer production so he made several judicious purchases among which were Redrice Duchess 18th and Darlington 4th and 15th, Claydon Wild Queen and Knells Elliott Fernleaf 2nd, all of which bred exceptionally well, producing families of Blush Rose, Barrington, Cressida, Choice, Crans, Fernleaf and Darlington for the herd. Bulls included Thelveton Wild Lancer and Wild Darlington; both bred exceptionally well followed by C.Darlington 5th and 8th and C. Granduke Darlington 2nd with outcrosses to Parsenn Favourite Duke 4th and then back to Collingham Lord Yorkranford. This herd maintained averages around 1056kg at 3.96% and won many championships at county shows and the Royal tended by Leslie Lane as herdsman for a number of years.

Shorthorn breeders had, despite these successes, no room for confidence or complacency, if they worried about the figures, as in fifteen years registrations for the breed (dairy and beef) had sunk from 15,434 females and 2,195 males to 3,667 females and 423 males, a catastrophic fall and the grade register had gone from 5,701 to 207; however the later was slightly compensated by the experimental register which recorded some 670 and of course the figures looked much worse if one went back to the 1950s as you can see on the graphs but as always it is no use looking back and indeed the breeders of the day were extremely hopeful that they had taken at least some of the steps to correct the situation with the experimental registers and the seeking of potential improvement from overseas bloodlines.

10. Late '70s and Early '80s

During the book it has only been possible to record some of the herds that have had an influence on the breed at any one time but in fact all the herds and breeders have made huge contributions by their input and participation. The same has applied to sales, venues and shows; owing to space only a few of the more prominent have been featured. The shows, of which over one hundred had classes for Shorthorns at one time, are the places where one can show one's wares and the sales are where people can either obtain new bloodlines, sires or of course commercial requirements or replacements or alternatively where breeders can market their achievements or surplus stock. Somewhat obvious, might be the reaction of the reader, but for a time many breeders had tended to ignore the other option of culling to the slaughterhouse and a number of cattle had been on the sale market which should not have been or alternatively had been crossed with black and whites in an effort to achieve some improvement. In many cases bull breeders were selling at a figure way below the cost of production and occasionally even below butcher price, as mentioned by Mr Watherston when he was President, before they decided to give up or change their system drastically or even leave this breed.

This had had several effects, one being that countless bloodline potentials had been lost in addition to those exported and the other being that cattle buyers or fatteners did not like what they saw and went elsewhere. This had happened in Ireland as well as the UK and the breed found itself in a spiral of decline added to which the spread of bloodlines was drastically reduced. So much so that the number of breeder members registering pedigree Dairy Shorthorn had sunk to 335 in 1976 and Beef Shorthorn breeders were almost at the all-time low of 45 registering herds.

The purist breeders had several misgivings as mentioned; another very real worry held by both sectors was that by the introduction of another breed a disease or some heritable defect might be introduced as well. The Shorthorn had been extremely clear of any such problems throughout the world. For example around this time there were problems of dwarfism in calves of both Hereford and Angus in certain strains. For this reason, among others, several of the beef breeders tried the use of Lincoln Red and others used the dairy strains, as has been outlined; others had bought in Australian and Canadian strains with some success. Dairymen used the Illawarras and also the pure lines from Australia and in fact the same type of experiments were progressing in Canada and USA. The search for other suitable breeds was also going on but in the case of the Beef Shorthorn breeders several went towards the Maine Anjou breed from North-West France founded in 1860. It was 62% Shorthorn in its make-up, the other part being Mancelle, a breed which had subsequently become extinct but was a white-faced animal similar to the Normande. The result was one of Shorthorn type colouring standing about 154 cm (just over 60 .5 inches for the old fashioned) at the wither, weighing around 1,250 kg for bulls and 900kg for females as well as having a reasonable milk yield. Interestingly this breed had been used in the founding the Rouge De La Ouest by being crossed with the Amorican in the 1960s, another one which had used the Shorthorn in its make-up.

The dairy experimental programme was going better than anticipated as over 3,000 cattle had been offered to the scheme compared with the 2,000 which had been hoped for and 100 herds were involved to a greater or lesser degree. It was still a little early to obtain meaningful answers to the challenge that had been set; great care had been taken in the selection of the breeds involved as each was viable in its own right: the red and white Friesian was the world's most popular milk breed; the red and white Holstein had the highest milking strains; the Red Dane was the best butterfat-yielding breed in the world; the MRI (Meuse Rhine Issel) was acknowledged as the best veal producer, and the Simmental from the Swiss strains was the largest dairy cow and the most popular. Dual purpose breeders were asked to use more than one sire of the outside breed to aid comparisons and the Meat and Livestock Commission (MLC) were also involved to assist with carcass evaluation; hybrid steers were performing better than pure Shorthorn or Friesian ones. No increase in calving difficulties was experienced and heifers were being bought in to calve much earlier at around two years of age with an increase of around 140 gallons in heifer yields being achieved, but longer tests were needed to allow variations to be analysed.

The Irish scheme was also progressing as some 13,000 animals had been rigorously inspected and only 350 were selected in the first year that these were entitled to a grant of £15 with a further £15 if their female progeny were retained and calved to an approved Shorthorn bull. The numbers soon increased to 703 in 1974 in 431 herds. The selected cattle and their progeny were placed in a special Register of the Herd Book.

The Perth sale result was mentioned earlier but **1975** was the time when it was decided that in future all animals would be officially weighed and measured as well as inspected at this event. 1976 was the first time a poll bull was selected for the Championship at the Royal Highland Show with Miss Furnace's Calrossie Roan Rover; she also won first in the junior class with Otterington Artic Kestrel. Roan Rover's win was also the first time the Championship had gone south of the border since 1965. The Royal Show was quite an occasion for W. McGowan, who won his first beef Championship at this event with his Canadian Bull Scotsdale Havelock. Blythsome Joan won the beef female award for Uppermill as well as the cup for the best exhibitor bred to add to their incredible list of successes, as did Lenborough in the dairy sector with their Daisy 102nd. What a wonderful record these two herds maintained.

This year the breed also gained the beef interbreed Championships at Alyth, Fife and Angus to name but three, which indicated that the breeders had got the message and might be on their way back. Then when Smithfield came around animals from Jim Norton of Blessington, Co. Wicklow, regional Secretary for Eire, took the reserve Dairy Shorthorn Breed Steer Championship after being 1st in the 21 month class and a 3rd award in the under 15 months class with two steers which were the product of the Irish Improvement Scheme. Irish exhibits had not been present for some years until he exhibited the previous year and gained a third award when Corbett Roper and Sons had yet again taken both the Champion and reserve at this event while promoting the breed as they so often did.

There were at least four sad losses to the breed with the passing of Harry Fraser of McDonald Fraser and Co.; also James Schofield the great exporter and member; Arthur Furneaux the past Society Secretary; Tom Chadwick the world renowned stockman for many years with the Histon herds, all of whom had contributed so much to the breed.

This year was also marked by a worrying financial situation for the Society due to the continued fall off in registrations and membership, as well inflation and depression in the country. A number of difficult decisions had to be taken, and there were many varying views which led to tensions. The two improvement schemes were going so well but still had much to do, also breeders expected services not only to continue but also to improve as several voices of discontent were being heard and these were growing in number. But services require money and time and the administration was being required to cut back. To add to the problems there had been ongoing discussions between both the Beef Society and the dairy sector as the former was very dissatisfied with certain administrative aspects and lack of publicity but they fully appreciated the benefits of Coates's Herd Book with its standing in the world. Sadly, disquiet was created during the discussions and it took some time to resolve but eventually it was decided that the Perth office would service the beef registrations and publish that section.

Interestingly, once the decision on this thorny issue had been taken, relations slowly improved and this was largely due to the relationships between the immediate past Presidents on both sides with their opposite numbers and those in the hot seat at the time. The Beef Shorthorn Society issued a statement recording the changes but stressed 'The change in policy will in no way detract from the existing close relationship between the two societies. On the contrary it is hoped that both Dairy and Beef will, by more specialised approach, gain considerable advantage from it and both will retain reciprocal rights of registration in their respective herd book sections.'

One idea to aid the financial problems at the time was that the herd book would be kept but not circulated, or produced in a different way. However the membership would not hear of any such suggestion, so they were printed in an economy format until the situation improved. Other matters coincided with the problem and so it was decided that the Society would move office and this would result in a further reduction in staff. Talks with the MMB were most satisfactory as they too coincided with resolutions for that organisation to assist minor numerical breeds so they agreed to take over large slices of the administrative responsibilities for the two improvement programmes, a huge relief for those concerned. The Balerno Group through the MMB had funded much of the previous development but that assistance was going to run down. Other reductions were achieved by the MMB decision that, as the research by Paul Hocking was just about at an end, he would be released; the other decision regarding future classification was resolved as John Bowen decided to become independent and offer the same service to members. Another drastic move was the sale of a number of paintings which the Society would not be able to house; they were offered for sale at very low prices; consideration was given to the sale of most of the Gold Cups which because of their value spent most of their life in bank vaults. This decision was deferred. Finally after dealing with a chicken and egg situation, it was decided that registration fees and membership fees should be raised. No more life members would be accepted and the membership fee rose to £10 and registrations to £3.50 for females and £5 for bulls both of which were affected by the new value added tax to a certain degree.

Another plan was suggested by Roger Osborne of the Cotley prefix, who, as Society President at this troubled time, was in a much hotter seat than he expected. He suggested a President's Royal Show Fund to enable the Society to have a continuing stand at the Royal Show and Dairy Event, participation in which was rightly considered expensive but essential. This was approved by council and was to become a matter of supreme importance in the next few years as will be seen.

Further it was agreed that the Dairy Shorthorn Journal, much valued both as publicity and information publication, would reluctantly have to go down from 4 issues to 2 per year and be in a more economic format; it would have a titular change to *The Shorthorn Journal*. There were also modernising structural changes to the number of committees that would be reduced by amalgamating the two experimental entities into a Research and Development Committee as their aims were so similar in many ways. This meant that there would be committees for Finance and Administration, Judges, a Dairy Shorthorn which would deal with matters that concerned the old show and sale, publicity, rules and discipline and publicity, and of course Council, reducing the structure from 8 to 5. Council delegates would reduce to 17 with 2 past Presidents entitled to attend. This last was invaluable to the reigning President to ensure continuity and advice.

Among all the doom and gloom there were a number of cheering events at home and abroad during the year as exports to China, of both 16 beef and 12 Dairy Shorthorns, were opened up giving yet more possibilities especially as China was developing a new breed and proposing to use the Shorthorn with their Mongolian Red breed as found in the North of China. There was another International Conference held in Australia which was a huge success. Australian Illawarra semen was available as well as the Willow Park consignments and on the Beef Shorthorn sector it was agreed that Maine Anjou could be used to assist in the improvement plans with the resultant animals admitted to the Herd Book but of course denoted. The Beef Shorthorn poll bull Pennan Neptune owned by Ardbennie now run by Jeremy Dewhurst had swept all before him winning the Supreme Championships at the Royal Highland, the Royal and the Great Yorkshire in 1977 as well as Perth and Alyth shows in 1976.

From Ireland the reports of their scheme were very favourable with 1,200 selected and 25 bulls available in A I and 11 approved for natural service. News from USA of a record-breaking sale (see the Irish Chapter) had a huge impact on Shorthorns on the worldwide scene; the breeding spread out from America and Canada to other continents and changed the Beef Shorthorn in those regions. Recorded at the time in the States as 'Deerpark type Shorthorns combine a growth rate matching Continental beef breeds with massive bone structure and a generous milk supply and without calving problems' they both caught the American imagination and subsequently 'nicked' with their previous breeding. At the sale down in Missouri the assorted consignment of stock was not all from Deerpark, but Ballingaranne, Castletroy and Salterstown breeding were forward. An average of $1,555 (£904) was reached for 52 sold of which 37 had Deerpark breeding in them. Top price of the sale was Shannon Magnificent at £6,400 and top female was Shannon Bee at £3,500, both bred by Kevin Culhane of Castletroy Limerick, in Eire.

At home the MMB, in response to complaints from breeders, had changed their bull selection procedures to accommodate the experimental schemes using incentives so that initially the joint Society and MMB committee met twice a year to consider selected registered bulls; later they considered every registered bull in case some bloodline had been overlooked and later still they also considered planned mating, again with incentives, to yet again improve the potential but at this stage they had to set up the process of considering the older proven bulls to select for putting to potential bull mothers. This had the advantage of ensuring that bloodlines did not get too narrow, as for example the quoted case of Histon Dairy Premier who had in fact died in 1964 but had well over 2,000 daughters here and the same number overseas with his breeding being in over 50% of the UK national herd, which was an incredible fact, but could prove serious when numbers were decreasing at such a rate. Each bull in the new scheme would have 750 doses taken and 30 would be stored for special nomination later and with provision for his breeder to receive 70 doses free for his own stock if required.

Maxton

On the performance front the **Maxton** herd of David Spalton had pulled off a major coup by winning the Interbreed Economic Milking Trials at the Dairy Event for the second successive year, 1976, with Oxhay Bates Duchess 12th. An amazing performance to be able to follow his success in management and selection, when Theale Barrington Duchess 87th took the award in **1975.** But in **1976** he really excelled as Maxton also took the breed Championship with Maxton Broom 12th, with his Oxhay Bates Duchess 12th reserve to Greaves Barbara 47th from the Milnes for the combined trials and inspection points award. Not content with this performance Maxton Graceful 4th succeeded in winning 1st in **1977** on both inspection and production and went with Maxton Bates Duchess 12 to win the Melvin and Shorthorn cups at the same event. This herd had been consistently successful almost from the start. Although the family had been with the breed since 1880 it was J.N. Spalton who actually turned to pedigree in 1942. He farmed with his sons Max and David in Derbyshire with the Highbarns herd using a number of useful bulls, including Theale and Berkswell breeding; then Ridgey Reality 3rd who sired David Spalton's second bull after he had married and set up the Maxton herd, first at Denby then at Lodge Farm, Church Broughton. He brought with him six cows and ten young stock from Highbarn and later acquired several heifers from the Theale herd. The first bull used was Bellmount Dalesman 7th who was followed by

*Maxton Snowqueen 22nd, winner of 6 championships including the Royal 1979
and the Dairy Event 1981.*

Highbarns Valiant Duke, then Swepstone Lord Bates and back to
Highbarns again for Darlington Prince. These, followed by others
including Hintonbank Dandy and Eathorpe Bellringer, with a number
of A I bulls, laid the base for a herd which achieved consistent success
in both the show ring and production and also provided bloodlines
for many other herds as well. One of the bulls, Maxton Red Alert, was
top of the 1974 bull progeny tests with a 400 day weight of 1,181lb
which was 109lb above the breed average.

Probably one of the outstanding results for the herd was to go on to
achieve wins at the dairy event five years out of six including in most
of these the interbreed production competitions with up to 65
competitors. In **1978** and **1979** they won with Maxton Barbara 17th
and in **1980** Maxton Caroline 8th was 2nd and Maxton Bates Duchess
12th was 3rd. Some critics might say these were only over a few days,
which of course is true, but when one considers the skill in selection,
competition and the consistency and the fact that these were mostly
with different animals it certainly must be a tribute to the management
and the stockman, in this case David Winnington, who has been with
the herd for many years and had been preceded by another long serving
expert Alex Shuttleworth.

The Maxton prefix has been prominent at many shows including
the Royal and even Perth and overseas as when the World Conference

was held in Canada in 1980 the Spaltons took a bull to the sale which followed the event at Calgary. Maxton Bold Crusader was placed male Champion and reserve overall Champion in the dual breed section and sold at the top price of the sale at $6,000 to Sandford Farms, Ontario. He had a weight of 1,322lb at 18 months. Originally David Spalton considered like several others that he did not need to expand into the blended scheme but being both curious and progressive he decided to 'test the water' and as always he succeeded in demonstrating his skill and selection as one of his acquisitions, Ormbridge Diana, bred by W.D. Oram sired by Branderlea Citation Topper and out of a Histon Dairy Premier dam, took yet another award in the interbreed economic trials at the Dairy Event in 1984. She took second place against 60 entries having calved her 9th calf a week before and took first on inspection in the senior cow class when her previous lactation was 9,711kg (2,388 lb) at 3.75%.

This herd has from the start also maintained a very productive bull beef unit showing very reasonable returns. Maxton cattle and semen have been exported to many overseas outlets: South Africa, Australia, Canada, New Zealand and of course Ireland to name a few. David Spalton served as President of the Society on two occasions – 1975/6 and then 10 years later again from 1985-87 – and judged at most principal shows in the UK including the Royal and the prestigious Burke Trophy interbreed as well as overseas, at the Royal in Melbourne, Australia, and the Rand Show in South Africa. He truly dedicated his life to his family and the breed and so it was no surprise when he was elected as a Life Vice-President in recognition of his immense contribution to the breed.

Amber

Another Derbyshire herd is the **Amber** herd at the historic Eddlestow Hall Farm at Ashover high above the surrounding countryside where Oliver Cromwell is reported to have stayed. Nowadays it is home to the Hole family in every sense of the word as the Holes (consisting of J. Hole and his family that included four sons, Walter, John, Joe and Bill all of whom were involved on the farm) moved in about 1953. Their herd had been started by the sons' grandfather early in the century but grading-up began in 1943 and the original bulls at that time were followed by Swepstone Lord Bates of Theale bloodlines, whose dam gave 2,146lb with her 3rd calf. Groby Desmond and Groby Dandy followed, the latter went to Hampshire cattle breeders after a spell in the herd and later came back to work on his granddaughters who proved a huge success. Amber Barrington King by Earlsoham Rose King 14th was in utero when the Holes bought Bellmount Barrington Duchess 14th, one of the few bought-in females. Some other bulls used were Eaves Fairy Gladiator, Orgreave Victory, Hinxhill Barrington Beau and Amber Keepsake Beau and from these the herd continued to grow. The steers or bull beef all being finished at home. Later Stockwood Lord Barrington 3rd was another very useful addition who was also made available to others on A I. Later there has been increasing use of blended bulls on A I all of which has resulted in the herd average of around 7,315kg at 3.94% and 3.28 protein for 108 cows. The herd has always achieved a very useful butterfat figure. A number of show wins have been achieved, one of their latest being with Amber Dainty Princess 67 who was interbreed Champion at Ashbourne 2003 as well as Champion heifer at the Royal and Bakewell shows. Previously they have had success at a number of county shows and the Scottish Dairy Show in 1962 and although, like Maxton, they were reticent to go down the blended road at first they eventually did so with great achievement.

1977 was also marked by the appointment of **Keith V. Cousins** as Secretary designate of the Society, a very unusual step caused by the circumstances that bought about a change of location for the offices and the impending retirement of Arthur Greenhaugh. Keith had been Secretary to the Red Poll Cattle Society and had worked as a livestock officer in Kenya; he also had managed the Cotswold Wildlife Park, so had excellent experience to benefit him as those before him for the rigours ahead! He oversaw the eventual move to a section of John Thornborrow's office in Priory Terrace, Leamington Spa, Warwickshire, and took over in January 1978 with a completely new staff. The CBIS(Cattle Breed Improvement Services) administration was taken over by B.W. Howe, who had his herd and farm at Sheffield Park, Uckfield, in Sussex. At this time the company had over 30 sires of varying breeds available. The experimental cattle became known officially as British Red and Whites and were becoming successful in their aims of high growth rates enabling calving to start at two years of age and to develop cattle with height, length and depth with the ability to achieve yields of at least 6,000kg at a minimum of 3.6% butterfat and 3.3 % protein. All registered cattle would carry the designation BRW and it had lately been approved that those with 50% Dairy Shorthorn blood or more could compete in show classes. The MMB were starting a bull of the day service that would include BRW bulls from contract matings; the Ministry had just sanctioned the import of semen from progeny tested Danish Red bulls so the scheme was moving on. It was evident that no matter if you agreed with the scheme or not there was a definite air of optimism coming back. The first bulls to be in the MMB plan were both pure and BRW. Twells Moss Trooper 9th Tonelea Best Man, Stowfield Red Roseman and Churchill Royal Chieftain, the last two being BRW bulls, with others of both sectors being considered.

On the Beef Shorthorn front the 1977 Perth sale had been very disappointing and the breed worldwide had lost one of its greatest legends in the death of Carlos Duggan from Argentina. His 100,000 acre ranch which had world-renowned herds of Herefords, Angus and Shorthorn had succeeded at every level and Carlos had judged in every principal cattle country – UK, Ireland, America, Canada, Australia, New Zealand, South Africa and naturally Argentina and other South American Counties such as Chile and Uruguay (a regular importer of stock from many of these especially the UK). His cattle had won the wonderful Palermo show grand Championship no less than 15 times with his Shorthorns and at least 6 with his Herefords; those who had visited his property will never forget the experience and his humour and hospitality. The Shorthorns were also famous as they carried on a part of the Sittyton herd and also that prefix.

The **1978** Perth sale was again not good although there was evidence of the benefit of change and the influence of overseas blood. The Champion Woodhead Monarch was by Weebollabolla Royal Commission as were several others in the top price bracket from Calrossie Turbine and Leviathan selling at 1,200 guineas and 1,100 guineas respectively and Baldowrie Convict from G. Rutherford sold at 1,100 guineas, all showing size potential. However the average was only £572 for 33 bulls. Baldowrie Convict had also been Champion at the Royal Highland.

Meat and Livestock Commission (MLC) figures were already proving interesting regarding the various improvement schemes being used to bring the Beef Shorthorn back to size. Because of the limited population one has to be guarded in the findings but they certainly indicated the trend:

1973-75   500 day weight average was 472 kg
1974-76   "   weight was 499kg+ 27
1975-77   "   weight was 511kg+12 total 39 kg
Weebollabolla Royal Commission 500 day calf weights 552 kg (16 in four herds)
dairy Shorthorn x
Beef Shorthorn

calves	100 day	200day	300day	400day	500day
(35 in three herds)					
(kg)	115	275	341	439	494
weight		+56	+33	+24	- 17
above breed average					
Maine Anjou x					
Beef Shorthorn	157	279	399	488	581
difference from average1975-77	+ 60	+91	+73	+70

Preliminary blended results of the first hybrid tests are illustrated below **showing each sire group on the Shorthorn for** the first three lactations as compiled by Paul Hocking

sire breed	no records	age months	milk lb	days	%fat	lb fat	% prtn	lb prtn
Lact 1								
D/Sthorn	2565	34	7736	296	3.64	281	3.32	263
R/Fr	562	30	8635	299	3.71	319	3.24	280
R/Hols	114	29	9742	300	3.57	347	3.15	304
R/Dane	83	30	8882	303	3.76	332	3.30	297
Lact 2								
D/Sthorn	1677	47	8694	287	3.56	310	3.33	294
R/Fr	355	43	9569	289	3.64	348	3.24	305
R/Hols	72	40	10544	296	3.61	385	3.26	351
R/Dane	49	44	9983	295	3.77.	377	3.30	344
Lact 3								
D/Sthrn	1007	59	9431	285	3.54	334	3.29	310
R/Fr	230	56	10871	290	3.61	392	3.23	348
R/Hols	10	51	11870	301	3.60	428	3.24	385
R/Dane	35	56	9934	291	3.79	376	3.33	372

Later results that include the Meuse Rhine Issel (MRI) and Simmental

BREED COMPARISONS				RECORDS WITH FAT%		
breed cross	sire numbers	group numbers	total wtg	milk kg	fat kg	fat %
RF X DS	46	31	382	+618	+24	+.12
RH X DS	5	3	94	+1189	+44	+.05
DR X DS	11	6	67	+384	+19	+.19
MR X DS	6	4	44	+313	+20	+.35
SM X DS	12	4	27	+112	+14	+.36
DS X RF X DS	14	1	24	+462	+16	+.04
RFXDSX(RFXDS	2	1	19	+635	+29	+.22
RF X RF X DS	23	2	50	+694	+30	+.16
RF X RF	74	6	142	+743	+30	+.08

BREED AVERAGES						
sire and dam	no.	age mth	milk kg	days	fat%	fat kg
DS X DS	3467	33.8	3250	296	3.65	128
RF X DS	705	30.4	3946	299	3.69	145
RH X DS	157	29.0	4465	301	3.60	161
DR X DS	129	29.8	3895	300	3.82	148
MR X DS	65	28.3	3442	297	3.90	134
SM X DS	39	29.8	3319	295	3.87	129
DSXRFXDS	30	30.1	3639	292	3.53	128
RF XRFXDS	63	30.8	4057	298	3.75	152
RF X RF	207	31.0	4000	301	3.75	149

The table below is not conclusive for MRI or Simmental as they were only recent introductions to the evaluations.

sire no	wtg total	milk kg	ptn kg	ptn %	ptn kg +fat
		RECORDS WITH PROTEIN % E			
33	149	+668	+20	+.O5	+44
4	69	+1076	+31	+.11	+75
7	15	+474	+22	+.10	+41
6	37	+264	+12	+.09	+33
3	19	+180	+9	+.06	+22
6	12	+449	+13	-.06	+29
20	9	+453	+18	+.07	+46
2	36	+626	+22	+.06	+52
27	31	+570	+20	+.05	+50

no prt	prot%	prot kg
12111	3.32	119
275	3.24	129
101	3.17	140
23	3.38	135
53	3.38	114
27	3.35	111
13	3.11	103
45	3.26	134
44	3.21	128

These last 14 were taken on 3 farms

In **1979** the Perth figures were improved at an average of £749 for 41 bulls with a top of 2,600 guineas for Watt Taylor's reserve supreme Champion Pennan Tiger, a significant purchase by W.P. Bruce Ltd whose stock was to have a massive influence in the very near future. Uppermill paid 2,200 guineas for Dungarthill Captive. The Supreme Champion was W.F. Ferguson's Newark Security by Chapelton Juryman, sold to one of the enthusiastic Orkney breeders, T. Linklater. The other high price was from Calrossie with a Weebollabolla son Calrossie Mount that sold for 2,300 guineas. Fred McWilliam, judge for the event, a third generation Shorthorn breeder and judge all round the world who had managed the Edellyn herd for T.F. Wilson in USA and then went to Australia to run the South Boorook herd for J.Allen, commented, 'The present day breeders will ruin the Shorthorn as they are trying to compete with the Angus as the butcher's beast. They are and should be the Improvers not the terminal sire. During my time overseas I have been returning from time to time and watched the decline in size and length and with it the popularity but this time I notice a change that is dramatic. There is no point in blaming those who have gone before they bred for the type demanded. The loudest critics have been those who have done nothing about it. The dedicated improvers have been too busy to bother making useless sarcastic remarks in public. The Argentinian has faced the same problem and are now making great progress with the use of the Lincoln Red. '

One of the progressive herds of the time was the **Pennan** herd of Watt Taylor Ltd; they in fact had almost 'sewn up' the Highland Show, as their Pennan Neptune took the Championship in 1977. P. Sovereign took it in 1978, P. Wyvis in 1981 and P. Windsor in 1982 and '83. P. Windsor was also top price bull in Perth in 1981 at 2,200 guineas when sold to Uppermill; P. Vulcan had been top price in 1980 when sold to Major John Gibb for his comparatively new forward looking Glenisla herd. P. Tiger had been reserve Champion at Perth in 1979 and sold for the top price of 2,600 guineas so the herd was really benefiting from its policies as was the breed. Obviously changes would themselves be slow and perhaps it would be a slow task to bring the buyer back to the previous high regard held by the breed, especially now when there were so many breeds to pick from. Every farmer used to say their father had Shorthorns but the generation was moving on and so the younger generation yet had to be convinced.

Two of the herds dispersed in 1979 were retirement sales: one was the Kimble herd of the Robarts family when the milking portion was dispersed and it was the 1977 Royal Show Champion Kimble Rose 68th that made the day as she sold for 1,000 guineas, a figure not reached

Pennan Windsor, a fine example of this herd, Royal Highland Show Champion 1982 and 1983.

for a Dairy Shorthorn for over 30 years, selling to Jim Collins from Yorkshire. Definitely a breeder's sale after all their successes and the average was £498 for 42 cows and heifers averaged £454. The second retirement sale, held on the same day, was of the **Huxley** herd of Harry Prince who had lost his original herd founded in 1943 with foot and mouth in 1967. The second herd was founded soon after with the purchase of the remainder of the famous Kelmscott herd of the Hobbs family and this probably contributed to the reasonable average achieved of £378 for cows and £382 at the sale for heifers with established breeders being the main purchasers. Harry was not exactly retiring but turning to beef cattle for a so-called easier life. Another established herd, that of Pride and Clarke, was also to achieve a reasonable trade with a top of 480 guineas for Downview Kirklevington 37th to T.A. Rose who bought several. This sale was due to the sale of their farm and the average was £355 for 39 cows with 10 heifers averaging £367. The Irish trade was improving probably as a result of the scheme and the American interest, turning the trade around so D. Cororan experienced an excellent trade for his Ballyhar herd that averaged £443 for cows and £336 for heifers. At home the Crewe Show and sale reflected an improved interest with the average of £384 for cows and £345 for heifers with the Champion Orgreave Rosette 6th fetching the top price of 500 guineas; the reserve Champion Maxton Silversmith was bought by the Bold brothers for their herd right on the Derby Hills but not far from the Maxton home.

Pennan Neptune, Supreme at the Royal Highland, the Royal Show and the Great Yorkshire.

In 1978/9 the Society had in the circumstances taken a very brave step as the council had decided to turn the President's Royal Show Fund into **The President's Permanent Building Fund** with Archie Smith-Maxwell as its Chairman. The fund was to maintain not only a presence for the few days of shows but to be for the permanent administration of the society's affairs. This was intended to be nearly all funded by member subscription through private and regional donations. Many would consider this a 'pipe dream' with the decreased membership but the response was extraordinary. Donations came from every corner of the UK and Ireland from members past and present and associated businesses all showing immense faith in the future. Several members donated stock to be sold to help the fund and the auctioneers agreed not to take commission for their sale, another generous move. The hope was to have it completed for the 1980 Royal Show.

With the shrinking national herd the main sales for dairy were now in Crewe or Yeovil in spring or autumn, apart from reduction or dispersals, and on the beef sector the Perth Sale was virtually the main event each year in this period; although successful sales were still held at Inverness, the 'Cream' was generally accepted as being at Perth. In 1979 for the Crewe sale there was a problem as there had been a suspect foot and mouth outbreak virtually on the day which thankfully subsequently was diagnosed as swine fever, so in the event it was allowed to proceed but buyers were conspicuous by their absence. Eventually 18 cows sold at £469 average, heifers £367 average and bulls £595, all of which were an improvement on the previous sale so it was not all bad. Gateshayes Barrington Airdrie from Gilbert Withers in Devon sold to T.H. Golledge in Somerset for 1,000 guineas but they came a long way to do it! The Champion from L. Kenning and Sons of Wappenbury near Leamington was Wappenbury Phyllis 25th, sold to Jim Collins. He had recently created a record by selling on his purchase of Kimble Rose 68 for £2,000 to Jim Norton of Baltiboys, Blessington, Eire, beating the previous Dairy Shorthorn record of 1,500 guineas for Brackenhurst Cerise Barton in 1943.

Gilbert Withers went on to have one of his dispersals at the Yeovil Spring sale and Gateshayes cattle took most of the prizes including the Championship which sold at 800 guineas for G.Barrington Duchess 103rd; his cattle averaged £571 and the remainder averaged £444. Five calves and a heifer were sold in a 50/50 sale towards the Building Fund. Later in the year there was a shared sale between Orgreave, Woodcall and the heifers from the dispersed Kimble herd and in this seven animals from Orgreave made over £1,000 with the sale attracting much interest from Ireland and even Canada. The principal prices were 1,050 guineas for Orgreave Lady Laura 53 to Mr Charles Epps – a buy that he was never to regret – and 1,000 guineas paid by him for a bull Orgreave Royal Waterloo; another bull from the same Landmark herd was purchased by D. Spalton also for 1,000 guineas and two further young bulls, Ark Royal and Royal Lancer, were purchased by Mrs P. Fegan for her Moyglare herd in Eire.

Averages were: Orgreave £367 for 14 cows, £435 for 44 heifers, £832 for 4 bulls. Kimble £572 for 9 heifers and Woodcall £270 for 13 heifers.

Two other dispersals were later in this year; one owing to ill health was the **Mickle** herd of T.T. Hewson which although founded in 1941 contained some of the best blood going back to start of the century and beyond. It had won many awards and contained a number of prizewinning cattle with stock being sold to a number of herds, both beef and dairy, to improve scale and size. In the case of the former the Cadzows and Hendersons were the most prominent of these. Cattle were also exported, notably Mickle Rose King, who won the Rand Show in South Africa in both 1955 and 1956. Probably the most noted winner in the herd was Mickle Telluria who won over 20 Championships and was reserve Champion at the 1949 Royal as well as breeding a number of daughters with high butterfats, none below 4%. A stud sire, Townend Prosperity, became one of the best show bulls of his time winning at the Royal, the Great Yorkshire and the Royal Highland where he was supreme 3 times and 5 times male Champion. This dispersal sale was again at an unfortunate time and the potential was not appreciated with an average of £371 for 31 cows although the young stock was relatively better sold with calves selling to average £263. The top price cow was Mickle Waterloo Lady 3rd at 560 guineas.

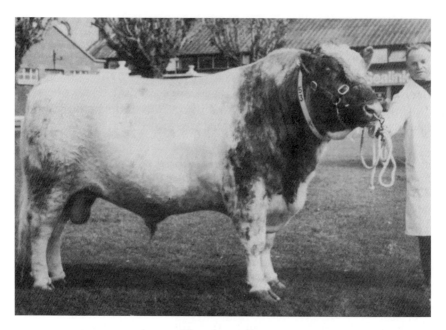

Kinaghmore Roy

The other sale was a retirement sale of a herd belonging to Misses Mckerness and Stiven from Essex, where hardly any dairying was practised in the county at this time. Established in 1957, the **Kirven** herd average was £351 for 31 cows with the top to a herd changing breed, Kenreuther Estates purchased Kirven Pepper at 460 guineas.

The Royal Dublin Show this year, as in most years, was an interesting tussle between the two types of animal for the premier award, but this year it was even more so as the eventual supreme went to a son of the famous Deerpark Leader 4th, Kinaghmore Roy from Jim Norton who had a weight gain of 3.9lb per day, more than any other breed at the event. He weighed 13 3/4 cwt at 13 months and went on to make a massive sire. Reserve to him was a classically bred Domville Grand Duke from Col. Watson's Ballingarrane herd and they also supplied the female Champion, Jennie Deans 100th, a renowned family in this herd.

The Royal Show at Stoneleigh also provided interesting Champions with Dunscar Cavalier from J. Hill and Co. winning for the second year and Eathorpe Dainty 56th as female Champion for the dairy section and the beef being, as mentioned, the Weebollabolla son, Baldowrie Convict, standing 149cm tall, further demonstrating the increasing height progress of this sector. The female award went to Uppermill Flossy Flush.

Undoubtedly the severe shock this year for all concerned, and most of all for his family of course, was the sudden death of Keith Cousins who had taken over as Secretary at a crucial time, establishing the office with an entirely new staff. He achieved so much in such a short time: improving relationships, coping with a mammoth change in the society's fortunes and working closely with the members to restore confidence as well as picking up all the threads of connections and normal work this job entails, he negotiated the organisation of fund raising and planning for the new building. The fund at the time of his death stood at over £32,000, a magnificent response.

Two other breed characters were lost to the breed in the year: John Cumber, who had achieved so much with the Theale herd not only with Shorthorns but also with Shire horses and Angus cattle. He contributed to agriculture as a whole through many organisations with which he became involved. The other was John Nickalls of Plumpton Agricultural College in Sussex where as well as his teaching he developed one of the highest yielding progressive Dairy Shorthorn herds in the South of England and was, like John Cumber, involved in many associated organisations.

One of the later sales in the year was a retirement sale of another 'great' in Shorthorn history, the retirement of Mr Webb at 80 from dairying; he was selling the remnants of the renown Streetly herd. This was another breeder's sale and the top price was for Streetly Wild Queen 60th at 980 guineas; averages were 56 cows at £414.16, served heifers at £325, 33 maiden heifers at £169, 4 bulls at £442.

1980 was a memorable year in so many respects, firstly as it marked my appointment to replace Keith Cousins as Secretary, which was quite a change for the Society and me! Firstly I had to catch up with the inevitable backlog caused by his loss and also the fast developing plans for the finalising of the new building as well as making contact with the membership and all those connected with the business. In a way I was fortunate, as a number of the latter were known to me in my previous life of farming with pedigree cattle, and breed society committee work, all cut short by an accident that caused me to look elsewhere for a crust! The staff could not have been more helpful and patient with the sudden inevitable changes all of which were greatly assisted by the then President Leslie V. Thomas and his predecessor Roger Osborne, both of whom then and thereafter were in constant touch with advice, explanation and assistance with continuity. My first sale was the retirement sale of Brigadier and Mrs Acland whose **Eccelin** herd was one of the first to join the BRW scheme.

The herd was founded in 1943 and subsequently enlarged when the Brigadier retired in 1946, providing a number of families such as Swallowtails, Magpies, Pleasants and Roses, Annies and Ednas from a variety of herds; once the BRW decision was taken a number of routes were taken: to go with Meuse Rhine Issel(MRI) as well as young bulls in the new Young Bull Proving Scheme. The herd had been successful in a number of shows and competitions. The Brigadier had been President in 1962/63 but had been on Council for many years as well as being involved with a number of agricultural organisations and in fact had received a Prince of Wales award for his many works for the industry so the sale was one of sadness, but also great interest as it was the first involving BRW cattle. The sale attracted a lot of interest with buyers from all over Britain despite bad weather.

Sale averages were: pure Shorthorn £394 with a top of 460 guineas and BRW cattle 437 guineas. MRI were 455 guineas

The Royal Show was again a major event in the history of the Society as **Her Royal Highness Princess Anne** was invited to open the finished new offices. What a day for her and the Society, as she had already carried out ten of the twelve official duties she was to perform at the show, all in atrocious weather conditions, before she officially declared the building open before a packed crowd of members and onlookers. She was not to know then that to ease the workload on her Majesty The Queen she would eventually take over as Patron of the Breed to continue the much-valued Royal Patronage of the Society almost since its origins.

The Champions at this event were Orgreave Valiant, a fine example of a Dairy Shorthorn, and Champion Gateshayes Barrington Duchess 103rd, a very correct female exhibited by S.M. James of the Glanhirwen herd, one of the foremost in Wales; he had acquired Duchess at the Gateshayes dispersal the year before.

The beef Champion was Woodhead President, appropriately named by the Hendersons, as their current President W. McGowan exhibited him! President was sired by Mandalong Super Elephant and it was extraordinary and illuminating how many winners at shows and sales were sired by the imported sires from Australia and Canada in these few years, all enforcing this change in policy but sadly it was to be some time before any major new herds were to be established. Again it was a good year for Fingask as their two-year old heifer by the same sire had won the female Championship at the Royal Highland. McGowan's M.S. Elephant had also sired the top price bull at Perth – Pennan Vulcan who was purchased by Major Gibb for Glenisla at 2,200 guineas and the supreme Champion at this event Uppermill Fyne from Miss Durno again, also had the same sire. Thirty-six bulls averaged £930, an increase of £225, so things were definitely improving.

Talk of show winners reminds me again that in many ways this does not give altogether a fair picture as relatively few breeders exhibit their stock, owing to a number of factors, especially today when it is so expensive on time and labour when all are cut to the bone in these respects. Also naturally there are a number who do not wish to and others who consider it is unnecessary and these members are all just as important to the future of a breed as they are keeping the strains going, or perhaps more importantly the Shorthorns are keeping them going! Farming has always been a hard way of earning a crust, but it has also been a highly pleasing and satisfying way of doing so although the stresses are severe at times. Stockbreeding can be soul destroying but it can also provide a huge sense of satisfaction and those involved are so fortunate in their way of life, despite how it feels when things are not going right as often it takes a considerable time to correct. The constant task of trying to improve is always present but in this instance the history can only be recorded by the performances in the field and the public acceptance, or not, of what the breed provides.

Several examples of non showing herds can be quoted and some of the most pleasing of this category are those herds owned and run by the **Camphill Trust,** an organisation founded on the principles of Dr Rudolph Steiner for the benefit of people with learning disabilities and the physically handicapped where communities are formed and live as families but each individual can express his or her potential and prove both to themselves and the world outside what can be achieved. Many of these centres have grown almost into villages such as at Hollywood in Northern Ireland or Danby near Whitby. The Trust movement was founded in around 1939 under the guidance of Dr Konig, an Austrian. A number of communities were set up around the world including Scotland, England and Ireland, most of which have farms which, although supervised, involve the patient or client as they are called today, with the day-to-day work both as a therapy and a work ethic. Their **Botton** Shorthorns play a very important role on these farms as their docility and ease of handling enable the client to develop confidence and an affinity with animals that is a well known therapy, so breeders can be proud of being able to contribute to such an undertaking. Some of these community farms do show occasionally but not often, as again when they do it is a therapy to enable their clients to participate.

There are of course prison farms like Wymott with the prefix **Colonywymott** at Leyland in Lancashire where the same therapy proves of benefit and several of the prisons have Shorthorn herds as there are often a number of people involved, changing quite often and the Shorthorn temperament is able to cope better with both the variation and inexperience of those involved. Furthermore at the other end of the spectrum several colleges including Harrow School had the breed for the same reasons of multiple involvement. Other examples are large units such as at **Newbold** in Monmouth were the Long family farm a large unit of some 300 milkers with minimum labour and a very low cost system where there is not often time for showing but they entered into the BRW scheme where they found improved and a more economic performance over their black and whites. A third example is the **Forcett** herd near Richmond, Yorkshire, established in 1946 by Col. Waller and currently owned and farmed by his grandson James Heathcote. Founded with Gainford and Caperby breeding, the herd has developed with the aid of carefully chosen sires, first Aske Wildfire, then Gainford Red Banner, Glympton Wild Duke, then back to Gainford Rudolph that their renowned Wild Daisy family came from, then Gainford Rostral who only stayed a while, to be followed by Deansbiggin Royal Guard and Blytham Barrington Pioneer, then Swepstone Wild Lord 2nd and a number of the Young Bull Proving scheme sires, all of whom ensured that this herd won many herd competition awards at breed and county level. They also maintained high average yields with commercial management. From the early days the herd was supervised by George Stockdale to whom great credit was given by his employers, but where in recent times the labour situation had prevented showing; but excellent quality cattle have continued to be produced and the families have always been much sought after at sales. Today's agricultural policies ensure that so many just do not have the time to spare even if they wished to, as it is not only time away but also hours of preparation.

This was the year of the third International Conference held in Calgary, Canada, where Maxton Crusader stole the sale event with top price and prize, as buyers were anxious to acquire the new bloodlines with such a quality sire.

The autumn Perth Sale was another eye opener as again the overseas bloodlines topped the prices: another Pennan bull, Victor by Mandalong Super Elephant, secured a bid of 2,800 guineas after gaining a second rosette. Mr Campbell Graham of Auchaneck, an Angus breeder who was to play such an important part very shortly, bought Otterington Pilgrim by the same sire for 2,400 guineas and W.P. Bruce gained the supreme with Balmyle Rumpus and also the reserve supreme award with Balmyle Robert, both by Burton Dickler and both from Maine Anjou cows. This again demonstrated the future trend but the average was disappointingly down owing to one or two that again let the side down.

The following year the Champion Newark Frosty Fog by the Royal Commission sire, bred by Mrs M.Walker, sold to the Scottish Milk Board for the top price of 2,200 guineas with the reserve supreme from Chapleton Rambler by Calare McCorquodale fetching only 1,050 guineas but the 3rd prize bull by the Mandalong sire went to Uppermill at 2,200 guineas for Pennan Windsor; the female trophy went to W. Mcgowan with his Canadian sired Fingask Brawith Bud by Scotsdale Havelock. A little later in the year the Baldowrie herd was dispersed in the retirement sale for past President G. Rutherford when again the Maine Anjou (MA) preference was evident with averages at £479 for 33 Shorthorn and £504 89 for the Maine Anjou, although the increase may well have been to secure some of the MA bloodlines. **1981** was another great year for Miss Durno's **Uppermill** herd when Robert Minty won the herdsman of the year award at the Royal Highland as well as having won the interbreed beef bull award with Pennan Wyvis who was standing 146.5cm at the rump. Not content with this the breed team was made up entirely from Uppermill and they created a record by winning the interbreed beef award against 14 other breeds. No breed had ever won this competition with all their team coming from one herd.

Pennan Wyvis went on to achieve the top price at the Autumn Perth event when the Henderson brothers bought him for 2,800 guineas. The Champion was Balmyle Scotch Mist who was weighed in at 80kg above the breed average and eventually sold for 1,900 guineas to Uppermill. Balmyle Silver lining gave Bill Bruce the double as he gained the reserve supreme weighing 102kg above breed average and selling for 2,000 guineas; the sale average was £1,054 for 20 bulls, thus breaking the '£1,000 barrier'. The females sold well also as two made 800 guineas: Pennan Broadhooks Astrix 2nd the female Champion and Flossy Bud from Uppermill helping the average of £592. Recent MLC figures provided encouraging reading

bulls two year averages 1979/81			heifers two year averages 1979 /81		
age (days)	no	weight (kg)	no		weight (kg)
200	73	233	25		188
300	92	328	65		252
400	122	427	81		324
500	102	502	24		373

weights at 400 days	bulls	heifers
1968/70	409	274
1974/76	416	275
1980/81	427	324

Obviously there was a way to go but the major point was that the increases in weight and size had not altered the ease of calving.

In **1982** the beef Society took the unusual step of circulating their buyers to ascertain their intended use of stock purchases and their preferences. This was owing to the substantial weight for age increases with a view to deciding how far to go to suit the buyer. The results showed that 64% were buying for suckler herds; 34% were buying to produce herd replacements; 24% were buying with the intent of a top

Uppermill Centenary group

crossing sire and 43% were going to do both; 72% were very happy with the market for Shorthorn cross heifers; 69% considered the modern Shorthorn to be the correct size and 77% considered the display of weights and heights of bulls to be helpful; approx 50% said they were willing to pay over £1,500 for a bull.

1982 was also the centenary year for the Durno's Uppermill herd and it was only too obvious that they were still on top form since the 1882 origins; since 1948 they had won no less than 7 Royal Highland Championships, 8 at the English Royal, 5 Perth Bull Sales and 5 at Turriff with exports to at least 7 countries all demonstrating the enormous skills and dedication of the Durno family and the stockmen concerned through good and bad times. One must also recognise the Marr family who ran the farm before this time but the current herd although it came to Uppermill in 1916 it had been founded as the Jackstown herd in 1882.

Sadly this year marked the death of Ronald Henderson, DSO,MBE, TD. Ronnie, as he was known, was a huge influence on all who knew him and the breed as well.

Around this time it was decided that in order to be able to run an efficient office with full time staffing, holiday and sickness relief and reasonable salaries, etc, the Stoneleigh office could provide secretariat services for other organisations who were not at the time able to provide accommodation. The Irish Draught Horse Society and the Rare Breeds Survival Trust both came to the building so it became a hive of industry and history had repeated itself. Prior to this decision the Society administration had received a further knock as Mrs Conway, the Secretaries Assistant, had suffered a stroke and was forced to retire, which had again emphasised the vulnerability of a small-staffed organisation. Fortunately Mrs Hilda Powell who had been on the staff during the days at Market Harborough was re-recruited and so provided invaluable continuity and a link with the past.

Spectacular results had been achieved by the beef sector of the breed with improved prices and weight gains as demonstrated by about +27 kg at 400 days and +34 kg at 500 days in the years between 1970 to 1981; even the media agreed the Shorthorn was the most improved beef breed in the UK. This had thankfully been reflected in higher prices and averages indicating the return of interest from the commercial buyer but still membership remained low. The spring Perth Show and Sale had provided a Champion from the Hendersons for the fourth time: Newton Timothy by Mandalong Super Elephant (I wish they had shorter names!). But it was John Gibb's Glenisla herd that produced the top price of 1,800 guineas for Glenisla Sun Rise by Chapelton Leander that again helped to produce a high average at £999 for 31 bulls. The females also sold well at £553 for 9. Champion here was again an Uppermill, Broadhooks Bloe selling at 800 guineas.

The Dairy Shorthorns were also experiencing improved demand and the Crewe autumn sale achieved the **highest averages ever recorded to date** at £616 for cows £592 for in milk heifers, 548 for in calf heifers and £501 for bulls. The Championship here went to the Hillmans with Stockwood Wild Queen 24th selling at the top price £780; L.V.B. Thomas gained the male Champion and reserve female Champion with Drisgol Renown selling at £700; and Belladonna 57th selling at 650 guineas. The 3rd Elite sale with its high entry classification was held at Stoneleigh and won by Glenby Beauty 44th from almost local H.S .Johnson and Sons. Top price here went to the **Stowfield** herd of Henry Teverson for his BRW Flora Berry 2nd.

Later in the season this herd held an open day which was attended by a huge crowd of members and those from other breeds as since the start of the experimental project Henry had put the theory in to practice with remarkable skill and success. It was also a tremendous demonstration as cattle were split into the various breed groups involved in the schemes, including the beef aspects as well. The herd was founded in 1948 on pedigree lines although there had been a non-pedigree herd of Shorthorn and Lincoln Red for a number of years before. Not being impressed by the progress made, apart from the incredible performance of progeny from Histon Dairy Premier of which there were some 50 head, but conscious of the problem of so many going back to the same size, mentioned earlier, Henry began to experiment and was at the forefront of the experimental scheme starting from a low of 4,224kg at 3.4%. In 1975 he raised the output to 6,484kg at 3.89% by 1980 and always stressed that the yields were not forced or uneconomic. By 1984 the figures had reached 6,879 kg at 3.63% with 3.27% protein with a combined weight of fat and protein of up to 490kg. All under the quota situation with its restraints, this was for 87 milkers and no less than 34 cows in the herd yielded over 8,000kg and also bearing in mind that heifers were regularly calved at two years of age.

Furthermore because of the scheme, in which he had so much faith, he had used a variety of breed sires in order to find out for himself. He also decided to show, to advertise the scheme and the potential, particularly in production classes, securing breed Champion at both the Royal Show and the Dairy Event in 1986 with five different first prizes in the former and four in the latter.

Such a talented man, actor, a broadcaster and authority adviser to the BBC, writer and commentator as well as an innovative farmer it was a terrible shock when in 1985 while filming a production for the breed and just having commented at the Bath and West, he was stuck down by a brain tumour and died. This was not only a tragedy for the Society but also of course for his family and this was emphasised by the eventual dispersal sale which took place at a time when there were many serious uncertainties with the quota system and buyers were very unwilling to risk purchasing in case it affected them. So this unique herd which would have been and should have been appreciated, sold at very low prices for what was the fruit of all his work as the herd was just about at its peak. Nevertheless some remarkable animals were dispersed around to demonstrate what could be achieved. After serving on Council and Chairing the Experimental and breed development committee for many years he had been elected President from 1980 to 1982.

Such was the uptake of this type of breeding that the MMB marketed 5 BRW sires and 13 Shorthorn, CBIS marketed 5 BRW and Dairy Shorthorn breeders also marketed 9 Shorthorns indicating an increasing demand for both sectors especially as several individual breeders were also selling semen as well. The most popular of these was Meadowhaven Prides Starr from Australia whose progeny was looking very promising. His ICC figures at +396Kg milk +21.4 kg B/F and +14.9kg protein were a great sales incentive.

Two significant new events added to the calendar this year, the first of which was one that became a regular annual at the Royal showground; known as BEEF 82, it followed the increasing trend towards specialist interest events. Down in the South West the Bath and West Show Society held the first of another specialist event, the South West Dairy Event that at first was greeted as just another show especially as it came at the end of a long season; but it quickly became a major event in the circuit. 1982 was the second of this show and it completed a fantastic year for one of the prominent herds with the **Tonelea** prefix, owned by Roy and Wendy Whittle of Milverton, Somerset. They had won the Royal Show Championship with Tonelea Fairmaid 18th. This event was won with a daughter, Tonelea Fairmaid 34th, against very strong competition, giving the herd a huge boost as they had won nearly all the local shows as well as the Royal this year including the Devon County and the Royal Bath and West show earlier in the year, as well as being reserve Champion at the first South West Dairy event the previous year. All this without the judges realising that it was the 25th anniversary of their coming to their farm and their silver wedding anniversary as well! This herd had been founded in 1957 from a portion of his father's **Tonevale** herd which was later very successfully carried on by Roy's brother Jack. Tonelea had used a number of fortunate sires including Calstone Lord Cactus, Stokeleycross General premium, Gateshayes Dairy Premier and Streetly Lord York and the herd has been consistently in the forefront supplying bulls to the Young Bull Proving Scheme: Tonelea Best Man2nd and 3rd. Roy Whittle, later joined by his son Arthur, was to be elected President in 1997 after many years on the council.

Mention has been made in several places about the good fortune the Society had in its Presidents and their calibre, combined with the tremendous dedication they have given, both to the Society itself and the associated Beef Shorthorn Society. Few members may have realised that they have carried out this sometimes very difficult task and position with considerable travel without recompense and often at considerable inconvenience to themselves. An excellent example of this was Col. S. Watson MBE, MA, owner of the Ballingarrane herd in Eire, who took the office in 1982: a man of humour and many accomplishments with a distinguished war record, an author of around eight books, a broadcaster, and a financial expert but also dedicated to his estate and cattle. The Society was also fortunate in that he was elected treasurer through what was to become a period of recovery; with his beneficial contacts and expertise he was also able to ensure an improved state of the Society's finances.

They were substantially helped by an anonymous donor who undertook to donate funds over a period to assist towards schemes designed to avoid both a further decline but also to aid the recovery of the breed, by council approved schemes of assistance with publicity such as show travel mileage allowance to help with demonstrating the improvements that were being achieved. They also assisted with the establishment of an officially monitored herd to prove and establish the claims made.

The latter was established at the Cambridge University Farms that had in fact also got a well established **Cantab** herd which was involved with the experimental breeding virtually from the start if not earlier. It was founded around 1923 and later graded up, but when John Brookes became farms director in 1959 the herd was 'up-dated' and a number of pedigree cattle were bought in at a variety of dispersal sales. In 1965 it was decided that they should embark on an experimental plan using Red Friesian bulls on a section of the herd with the object of assessing what improvements could be made on both yields and growth rates. The latter, like a number of farms in that region, were producing finished beef from dairy herds fed on root by-products. The first results were encouraging with steers finishing two months earlier and yields being around 130 gallons above their contemporaries'. They later joined in the scheme and were major contributors of facts and information but 50% were maintained pure to enable comparisons on identical management. On the retirement of John Brookes, his successor, Prof. Alistair Steele-Bodger, fully endorsed the work and also the afore mentioned monitored herd to run along side the existing unit for further evaluation and demonstration both to the students and the world at large. Many Cantab families became prominent in the scheme, notably the Frieda families, and they also did a lot of MRI and Simmental evaluation but while the MRI seemed to blend in well, the Simmental was really only successful in respect of the beef work. This was one of the surprises to the geneticists as the lines used were mainly from Swiss dairying lines and a number of breeders expected better results from this particular involvement. Some, like the Barlow family from Preston, found they blended exceptionally well in their **Littlewood** herd that had been established for many years, initially with Northern Dairy Shorthorns.

One of the steps taken in the early '80s was the introduction of **Special Members** to Council as it was considered that in these critical times it would be a huge asset to have the thinking and skills of those members who had special interests or could offer special services which might be missed if one had to wait for the established system of council representation. So it was agreed that there would be an immediate intake of 6 with the proviso of a regular retirement of a rota of 2 in each period; to this they added that the past presidents representation would change from 2 back to 4 so that there was adequate continuity of advice and experience. A further step was the selling of 4 of the 5 Gold cups and their replacement with medallions that would act as a permanent reminder for those successful in this competition.

1982/3 saw the reduction, then the dispersal, of the Moyglare herd in Maynooth, Eire, owned by Mrs Pamela Fegan who had done so much in a comparatively short time for the breed on both sides of the water but particularly in Eire. This had been caused by several factors but principally owing to the ill health of John Farrell, the herd manager who had done so much to make this herd remarkable. At the reduction the cattle attracted much interest selling to 530 guineas and later at the dispersal 22 cows averaged 596 guineas selling to a top of 870 guineas and the bull Moyglare Observer to Ballingarrane Estate for 600 guineas. Calves were selling to a top of 500 guineas. Twenty heifers averaged 492 guineas and a number of new units were established. Around this time there was also sale of bullocks bred by John Maloney of Highfield fame in Eire which went to slaughter with a killing out to average 67lb per hundredweight, far above continentals at the time in that region, having been raised at the National Stud at Kildare and finished to around 13.1 cwt, again demonstrating their return to popularity.

1983 was the year when Hinxhill Duchess 82nd broke the **world record for butterfat** giving 8,727lb of fat in 11 lactations with a milk yield of 203,885lb. She had also won the Society Gold Cup for six years in succession for Charles Epps of Munsley, Ledbury, Herefordshire, who had also won the National Dairy Herds competition Harold Jackson Trophy from 1978 to 1980 continuously. The **Ashperton** herd founded in 1948 on Hastoe and Iford lines starting in the latter with Iford Tulip 9th that went on to win 10 championships. By 1960 the herd was averaging 11,061lb at 4.05% fat. Among bulls used were Hinxhill Superior 6th and Effarem Elegant Duke who produced a number of promising progeny, then Orgreave Valiant out of the Orgreave Lady Laura 25th of whom both Charles Epps and her breeder John Hill were so proud, then Orgreave Waterloo followed with his own Ashperton Lord Premier all of which ensured the herd being consistently in the awards at shows and in national herd competitions and the average by then was 5,329kgs at 3.92% for 63 cows and 11 heifers.

The elite sale that year ensured that there was not a cup or trophy that had not been won by Richard Roper's Lenborough herd and been engraved with their title! This year they exhibited for the first time at this event, securing the Championship and both the two top prices with first their winner Lenborough Spot 96th who fetched 1,300 guineas and then their Tulip 331st at 1,000 guineas, demonstrating also the length of some of their families. The average was 763 guineas for cows and 618 guineas for heifers in calf. The event was followed the next year by Lenborough again topping the sale with their Pansy 270th reaching 1,250 guineas; the Championship went to Mrs G.R.H.Smith's Oxton Vain Lucy 42nd. Averages this time were £754 for cows and £604 for heifers. The shows and sales at Crewe were showing steady improvement in both stock and prices but prices throughout the industry were still fairly conservative as there was so much uncertainty with regard to the future. The sale saw a top price for a bull of 1,800 guineas for Maxton Mossybank : the highest priced bull since 1952. He was only $9 \frac{1}{2}$ months old with an outstanding pedigree being from an 8,000 kg dam with over 4% and sired by the then famous Twells Moss Trooper 4th; he was destined to become a great sire himself for his purchaser, C. Royle from Dunham Massey, nr Altringham. His herd, **Dunham**, was founded in 1947 starting with ten cows and a wedding present from his brother of a bull from the Fylde herd of J.B. Silcock, Fylde Forrester 13th. This bull went back to Hastoe breeding. Then like so many of the top herds over the years he used Iford breeding, but it was not until quite a long time later that the herd went fully pedigree. In 1970 when the herd moved to Home farm at Dunham Massey they bought 16 animals from the Hathershaw Herd in Ilkley, Yorkshire; the herd expanded to 60 head but now is approximately 120 milkers.

Over the years this herd has gained a great reputation for quality and yields and this is demonstrated by the fact that despite not showing much except at local or Society shows and sales they have won over 14 Gold Cup Awards and have over 100 '50 ton cows' to date. They have been area herd winners on a regular basis and today's average is around 6,980 kg at 3.91%.

Many bulls have been used including Hinton Bank Dandy, Hadnock Ullyses 2nd, a series of Maxton sires including Bow Tie, Mossybank, Cleric, Edward, Butler, Ireby Presto, Deenwood Kirklevinton King, Dunham Resolution and Wild King; then Kyle Resolution, Winbrook Max and Hooton Fair Achievement. All to date providing excellent stock and uniformity. More recently there has been a move into the blended sector but there has also been a desire to keep at least 75% pure blood lines. The Royles have bought in only about 24 females in the 58 years and recently commented that during the bad times for the breed, theirs was the only Shorthorn herd in the county of Cheshire; now there are more than ten. This has been another very promising pointer to the expansion and success but no doubt also to the quality and consistency of their stock and the management of it.

From the beef aspect the figures below indicated the results of the dairy BRW scheme tests on six breed sires on cereal based beef production systems

Sire breed	Adjusted weight, days				
	100	200	300	400	500
Dairy Shorthorn	103	199	308	407	451
Red Friesian	98	208	316	423	462
Red Holstein	111	218	342	446	512
Danish Red	109	223	348	468	454
MRI	107	210	327	424	474
Simmental	117	228	356	477	570

1983 was the year the Beef Society changed their secretary: Tom Lang and his wife Barbara retired after seeing many changes in the breed's fortunes. Their contribution had been considerable. This happened at a time when the Perth Hunt and the Highland Cattle Society also decided to look at other options for their administration and so the Beef Shorthorns decided to move from York Place, where they had been since 1949, to space in the Aberdeen Angus office still in

Perth at Kings Road. The successor to this post was Mrs Barbara McDonald who took over in the November having had agricultural and accountancy experience.

The 119th Spring Perth Show and Sale was judged this time by W.P. Bruce of the Balmyle herd, which prevented him exhibiting; his cattle had contributed much to the breed in recent years in demonstrating bold steps by his use of the Maine Anjou in the herd with great success and were to achieve almost the top price of the day on this occasion with Balmyle Time Bomb who sold to Messrs James Biggar for 3,000 guineas and his second bull, Balmyle Ton Up, was very close at 2,800 guineas. Top price went to Messrs James Durno, as Uppermill had become: Uppermill Baronet, who was reserve Champion, sold for 3,100 guineas. They also bred the Champion, Uppermill Brandy, by Pennan Wyvis, the Mandalong Super Elephant bred bull that sold for 2,200 guineas to Ardbennie Farms. The average was £1,199, another increase with 31 bulls forward with females selling to a top of 480 guineas.

The 1983 Royal Highland was won by another Pennan bull: the massive Windsor, again from Uppermill; reserve to him was Balmyle Universe and the Balmyle stock again came up trumps with Balmyle Universe next winning the Interbreed Beef Recorded class against 30 others from 9 breeds in the weight for age competition combined with conformation. Not content with this Balmyle Tessa 4th was to receive the female Championship as well! To add salt into some others' wounds, Balmyle Scotch Mist won the Royal Show for Messrs James Durno. This **Balmyle** herd was founded in 1972 with the purchase of 120 Beef Shorthorn, Dairy Shorthorn and Maine Anjou animals, the first bull being Burnton Dickler a reserve Perth Champion, as was the next, Pennan Tiger. The herd had incredible success in very short time as Bill Bruce seemed to have hit just the right combination; he freely admitted he had used severe culling to achieve his viable animal, retaining the easy calving ability of the breed and the temperament and milk but improving the weight conversion. This herd was to continue in the limelight in the next few years leading up to a reduction in 1986; this brought great credit also to the skills of Friar Thompson, the stockman, who always managed to bring out his stock at 'twelve o'clock' (on top form) as indeed all skilled stockman have the gift and experience so to do. There was also a draft sale this year (1983) of 38 females selling to a top of 740 guineas for Balmyle Tessa 8th where a number of new breeders found some of this popular breeding. Over the previous years this herd had achieved champions at the October sales from 1979 to 1985 continuously and again in 1987 and had enjoyed the highest prices there in 1981,'82,'84,'85,'87 and '88 they had also been Reserve Champion at the February event from 1985 to 1989 as well as gaining the highest price or second from 1983 to 1989. A superb

Balmyle Warpath while at Uppermill.

record for such a young herd.

Sadly following the death of Ronnie Henderson the dispersal of the Newton and Woodhead herds took place toward the end of the year to a top of 1,000 guineas for Woodhead Crocus to W. McGowan. Cows sold to average 664 guineas, bulls 655 guineas, cows with calves at foot 752 guineas to a large crowd of buyers.

To review the BRWS scheme to this date for the dairy section I could do no better than to summarise the paper given by Henry Teverson to the Cambridge Cattle Breeders Conference, when they honoured him by their request that he report on this, the most innovative programme for a breed ever undertaken, at their renowned annual event. Firstly he outlined the scheme and then went on to report on its progress explaining the performance of Histon Dairy Premier who had the highest rating of any bull in any breed in his contemporary Comparisons (ICC) with a plus 150 on over 1,000 daughters; as a consequence there were very many of his progeny in the breed which was extremely dangerous. That is why, in the scheme, every bull is limited to 750 doses in order that no bloodline would be over used or restricted. In the '60s the breed only required 250,000 doses (approximately half the population) and this was being filled with a few old bulls without a progeny tested concept; this not only reduced the breed bloodlines but progress was almost nil while other breeds were forging ahead. The scheme, up to **1984**, had been very successful but over $^2/_3$rd of the breed remained 'pure'; those same breeders, urged on by the competition, were also making serious steps at improvement.

An unorthodox approach was made in 1977 to remove all old proven sires from general use and to ensure the whole available semen was from tested selected sires: 10-15 bulls would receive a meaningful progeny test. An extraordinary prospect for what was now a very small breed. Initially only three sons of any sire were tested. Once progeny records were available, the best were used on the best cows available to breed the next generation of bulls for test. The idea was that the speediest progress genetically would be made by testing as many bulls as possible with maximum selection pressure through the sires and dams.

The experiment required breeders to put the breed ahead of their individual prestige, which was expecting an awful lot. They were asked to make their top cows available and put them to programmed sires and then offer any resulting bull for testing. Furthermore when using semen they were asked not to nominate more than 40 cows to any one bull. The principal officer of the MMB, David Bright, monitored the programme with Dr Paul Hocken and by 1984 49 bulls were involved, 40 pure and 9 BRWS. The scheme was also supported by a classification scheme by the linear method, so results were soon to be expected. In September of that year the scheme was at a critical level and at a low ebb as top cow identification was proving a problem: as well as having top performance, they were subject to being of VG or excellent classification; added to this they were expected to have a minimum production of 500kg of fat and protein in at least one lactation. A further problem was that only 50% of Shorthorn breeders were or would use A I at that time. Anyway financial incentives were offered starting at £300 and 70 doses were offered for each A Licence. This was later raised to £500 for a grade A bull.

Since this lecture the figures have altered significantly but almost secretively, as a number of breeders were loath to disclose that they were testing the programme but when herd books were issued all was revealed!

As mentioned earlier, Henry Teverson went far beyond the necessary request and for 7 years he had submitted $^3/_4$ of his herd to young bulls with only the top 20% going to proven sires. This achieved the highest yields ever recorded in a Shorthorn type herd, averaging 6,921kg(1,522 galls) for cows; two-year-old heifers averaged 5,961 kg (1,311 galls) with one quarter of his herd achieving bull mother status (yields meeting the requirements for a bull mother).

The Crewe Show and sale this year included a part of the **Ormbridge** herd for Mr and Mrs W. Oram from Norfolk, who were forced to give

Ormbridge Diana: just calved her 9th calf a week before and was 2nd in interbreed economic trials dairy event 1984.

up their herd. Owing to severe transport problems their stock arrived in a pitiful condition but after sterling work by their fellow breeders through the night, most of the cattle were able to be offered which was both a tribute to the helpers and to the Orams as they had been one of the most successful herds of the blended type. Their cattle sold to 800 guineas and averaged £624 for cows, £ 511 for heifers. The Show and Sale stock averaged £570 for cows and £546 for heifers with a top of 1,000 guineas for Drisgol Waterloo Drummer who was exported to South Africa for one of the breed's greatest enthusiasts in that country, Fred Dell. A few years later we were able to view this bull and his progeny and they certainly proved Drummer a very reasonable buy. The female Champion and reserve at the aforementioned sale were awarded to the Oxton Herd of Mrs G.R.H. Smith for Oxton Wild Eyes 399th and Oxton Lady Annetta 23rd, the former selling for 780 guineas and the latter 830 guineas; there were a large number of new buyers which was again encouraging.

Just prior to this one of the most well known herds was dispersed before a huge crowd: the **Stockwood** herd of the Hillman Brothers, who were ardent 'purists'. Buyers came from all over the UK and Ireland and several records were re-written: 1,600 guineas was paid by several West Country herd owners, amongst whom was R.D. Doggrell for Stockwood Lily 40th, the highest then at auction for a UK female, and her calf for 500 guineas. Stockwood Baroness 38th sold to the new herd of Mrs E.A. Kuiper for 1,050 guineas. The stock bull Stockwood Dignity by Wreay Barrington Premier 3rd who had done a fine task in this herd went to Richard Roper's Lenborough herd at 1,500 guineas. It had been a very considerable time since so many animals made over the 1,000 guinea mark. Stockwood Digitalis 141st sold for 1,100 guineas to the Whittle's Tonelea herd and yet another, Digitalis 185, went west to another recent comer to the breed, W. Brown. Another bull by the same sire sold at 1,100 guineas to the Amber herd, as referred to earlier, and was due to be heard of much more in the future – Stockwood Lord Barrington 3rd.

The 1984 World Conference was held in Kentucky, USA. Their Show and Sale at the Louisville Stadium demonstrated their upstanding clean style, partially helped by the Irish bloodlines input; Deerpark Leader 13th sired their junior Champion, and also the reserve to him. It was interesting again to see that although the types of Shorthorn varied according to needs, neither of the changed breeding programmes had resulted in any increase in calving problems. The breed reigns supreme in this respect.

1985 Perth sales produced a much improved average of £1,443 with prices going up to 4,300 guineas for the supreme Champion Balmyle Wrangler, a massive prospect weighing in at 955kg, which was 218 kg above breed average at 500 days and standing 146 cm; he was at that time the heaviest Shorthorn bull ever recorded by MLC. The reserve Champion was Balmyle Woodstock who sold for 4,200 guineas.

This prefix was again supreme at the Royal Show with Balmyle Warpath now owned by Messrs James Durno; he went on to become reserve supreme interbreed beef bull at this event. Uppermill made it a double with their Rothes Just winning the breed female Championship.

The dairy year started with mixed results at their Spring Show with better quality but lower averages as the quota situation was still not resolved. The Hole family had a very successful day as they won both the supreme and reserve Champions with Amber Lucina 11th and Princess Alice 2nd respectively and the male award went to Maxton Viscount whose dam was the dairy event trials winner Maxton Bates Duchess 3rd. The average was very conservative at £520.

A further trial for the breed was set up at Seale-Hayne Agricultural College, Newton Abbot in Devon, again with the aid of an anonymous sponsor, to evaluate the performance of pure Dairy Shorthorns steers alongside Hereford x Friesian steers; all were to be off grass and fed a complete diet with 30 of each being split into replicate groups and fed on an ad lib basis to ascertain consumption, conversion and carcass statistics.

The shows and sales were a mixed bunch on the dairy side with the dispersal of what was then the oldest herd in the book, mentioned in the early stages of this book, Orfold of the Luckin family, founded in 1899. It had not been shown for a number of years but contained the largest concentration of Hastoe breeding still extant, but had suffered badly in difficult weather conditions that year, so consequently did not reach a favourable average, 68 cows at £396 and heifers at £465. However the purchasers would be certain that their cattle would improve. Regional sales in the west and north east were getting better results with excellent cattle being available, and the north east had in recent years experimented with sales on host farms with success. This year the host was the famous Winton House home of G.A. Dent and Son where so many northern dairy achievements had been experienced. They had also played a very important role with their Dairy Shorthorn stock and the event attracted large crowds from both this country and overseas. The Champion was Villabrook Ladygrove 18th with reserve Wreay Rosebud 19th both reaching the top bid of 900 guineas and both going to Tom Ripley of the Hauxwell herd. The average was £531 for cows and £563 for heifers for a full catalogue. The **Villabrook** herd, founded in 1956 by Harry Lancaster just outside Preston, demonstrated what could be achieved on a limited capital and limited land but loads of enthusiasm; it would be very hard to achieve this today. Founded on a county council holding with three cows, Inglewood Grey 3rd, Townend Juno and Deansbeggin Lady Rose with the later addition of Gallwin Bryteyes 2nd and Gallwin Wildeyes Beauty, the herd was built up by Harry Lancaster and his family to a highly efficient size of around 65 cows on 58 acres with 14 acres rented elsewhere, incorporated a milk round marketing about 150-200 gallons a day. Mainly using A I sires in the early days, such as Orma Barrington Supreme, Orma Wild Dairyman and Calstone Lord Cactus, they achieved an average of around 5,422kg at 3.8% over 10 years. One of those foundation cows, Inglewood Grey 3rd, was to achieve fame by winning the regional Gold cup with three yields averaging 16,243lb at 3.88% and a top of 21,055lb at 3.9%; she followed these with a further 20,000lb yield, later to become a 100,000lb cow winning the Gold cup in the region no less than four consecutive years. She was also to breed a number of championship progeny including Villabrook Lord Grey who went on to be purchased at 550 guineas by the Northern Ireland Ministry for A I and must have been one of their cheapest buys as he was reported as still going strong at 16 years of age! Favourite families were Strawberry, Wild Eyes, Lady Rose, Ladygrove, Fillpail, Whitesocks and Cowslip. Another Lord Grey 3 progeny was Villabrook White Ensign who won the Championship at the Royal Lancashire show before leaving a number of very useful progeny, but it must not be thought that this was a one cow herd as there were a number of 100,000lb cows which space will not allow me to detail. However the Lancasters, for Harry was always insistent that Mary and their three sons shared in the credit, always believed and supported the Young Bull Proving Scheme so a variety of sires were used including another of their breeding, Villabrook Stockman 2nd, out of Southleigh Cowslip 45th who gave 58,150kg in her lifetime of 12 lactations. Harry served on Council for a number of years before becoming President in 1993-95.

Another popular family herd was dispersed in this year – the **Woodcall** prefix founded in 1951 as a pedigree unit although it had been going for a few years before. The herd was graded up by Sid and Cherry Calwood and their Aster, Buttercup, Lilac, Iris and Tulip lines continued through the life of the herd but like several others they went to Hastoe blood to find good udder quality and correctness. Others were added from Ladygate, Yattendon and Beaconhurst herds with bulls Berkswell Imperial,Whatcote Lord York and Illington Brocade but one of the most influential was Pearlake Lord Barrington and another was Orgreave Foggathorpe Fashion followed by a series of further Orgreave sires including Dramatic and Barrington Triumph. This herd did not show much except at the Royal and dairy events and it was at the latter in 1966 when Woodcall Burrows 6th won 1st inspect and 3rd in the milking trials and reserve breed Champion following this up as Champion and Supreme Champion All Breeds the following year. Unfortunately the herd was struck with brucellosis in 1968 so that it took till 1972 for them to become accredited again. The retirement sale average was £487 for cows and £415 for heifers with a top of 700 guineas for Woodcall Ada 5th to the Maxton herd. A further long established herd was dispersed owing to ill health, the **Kinsell** herd of John Bartlett in the West Country, which became a pedigree unit in 1959 but was founded originally in 1910. They sold to 620 guineas and the average was similar at £415 for cows and £461 for heifers.

In 1985 over in Ireland the bull **Ballingarrane Belgold** completed a unique performance in **winning his 3rd Cork Championship** at the Cork show; he then won the interbreed as well having also won the Royal Dublin Championship for four successive years, then went on to win Mullingar Championship as well. All this was also a great tribute to the herd manager, George Fennell, who passed away as I was writing this book.

Breed Champion at the 1985 Royal Show in the dairy section was R.D. Doggrell and Sons' Chicklade Pansy 61st; the male award went to W.F. Moy with Churchfarm Dandy. This was the first Championship for the **Chicklade** herd from Wiltshire that had been established around 1946 when Reg and Ray Doggerell joined forces with £100 capital, first on Manor Farm, Stolbridge, Dorset, then expanded to include Holden Farm, East Knoyle, Wiltshire, around 1966. They split the herd with 100 milkers and 130 followers going to Holden. For several years a succession of bulls from the Stourhead herd were used, possibly the best being Stourhead Marksman who was followed by Harding Baronet, Tuxwell Wild Pretender, Calstone Lucky Draw and Desert Ranger then later a number of Twells, Gateshayes, Wreay and Stockwood sires from the Young Bull Proving Scheme. At this time they did not show much but won a number of herd and progeny competitions while the herd was steadily increasing. Management of the farm was by no means easy as a major trunk road dissected the area near the buildings which stood at the bottom of a steep hill with considerable risk to man and beast sometimes twice a day against ever increasing traffic! The partnership was dissolved in 1970 and by 1975 Reg Doggrell's son Henry had joined the partnership and showing increased. As well as the Royal Champion in 1985 they had the Champion at the South West dairy event in 1987 and at the Bath and West in 1987 and 1988 and reserve in 1991. With 153 cows they achieved averages of 5665kg.

The Perth autumn sale saw a return to Calrossie for its Champion in Royal Banner with the reserve to Balmyle Xcetera; they had continued success for their senior sire Balmyle Scorpio but, because of fodder shortages, averages were down at £1,021. There was however a good trade for the small Dairy Shorthorn contingent led by Parton Promoter, again over breed average weight by 56kg, out of the Greaves Vera 52 who had yields around 6000kg. He sold at 1,100 guineas. This sale included the Ardbennie dispersal, a herd that had achieved so much, for some time under the care of the skilled stockman Sandy Law; it was founded in 1959 and had used a number of innovative sires. Their highest price was for A. Pauline Daisy for 1,600 guineas to Glenisla with two others selling to over 1,100 guineas: A. Flossy Rose and A. Pauline Nanat 1,150 guineas. Uppermill Brandy went down to East Grinstead, Sussex, to work in the new herd of D.E. Sandys at 1,000 guineas. The Dipple herd of the Late Miss Brown was also dispersed that day.

Sadly **1986** was to be a year of a number of much respected herds selling through the death or illness of their owners and these would leave a considerable gap both in the progress and standing of the breed and breeders. However to work in some sort of chronological sequence: the Perth Show and Sale, the 122nd, provided a really excellent show of bulls to be won by an outstanding sire prospect, Chapleton Xile by Balmyle Timebomb out of Chapleton Princess R13; at 1 year and 11 months he stood 150.5cm and weighed 965 kg. He was to go on and do great things for his purchaser Messrs James Durno (this was the trading company of Mary Durno!) of Uppermill who gave 2,300 guineas. Reserve to him was Balmyle Express from W.P. Bruce who was an older bull at 2 years of age with a height of 153.5 cm and weight

Ballingarrane Belgold

Moyglare President, sold in Perth 1978

Burke beef trophy winners 1993: Balmyle Crackle, bred by W. Bruce and Flossy Freta, bred by Messrs James Durno

Burke dairy trophy winners 1989: Drisgol Mabel 7th and Drisgol Rose 47th, both bred by L.V.B. Thomas.

of 950 kg who was also do great things in the Glenisla herd of Major John Gibb who gave 5,200 guineas, the highest price for 12 years against stiff competition. The eventual average was £1,287 for 19 bulls sold and the females sold to a top of 950 guineas for an Uppermill heifer, Sybil Blythesome, after she took the female Championship. One of the satisfying factors in the increase in height and scale was not only the retention of the ease of calving but also almost as important, the correctness of leg and durability of the hoof which might have been so easy to lose in such an exercise.

The 1986 World Conference was held in Argentina, in Buenos Aires, delayed by the Falkland conflict and in fact so close to the end of it that many were worried by our possible reception, totally unnecessarily as it turned out as our welcome from every quarter was extraordinary. The event was based around their wonderful Palermo show which is a once in a lifetime experience. The show lasts for two to three weeks, as does the Australian Royal Show although the number of cattle forward is far less than our Royal Show, and being such a large country everything is done on such a huge scale; for example we visited their Linears Market where stock is sold for home and export with some 20,000 cattle, 5,000 pigs and 1,000 sheep going through *every day* with stock coming in overnight. Selling starts at 7am and the market is cleared and cleaned by 3.30 pm. With a country of 30 million people and 50 million cattle the scope is incredible. The supreme Champion this year was RPS Tribune 82nd from Oregon so on this occasion the locals lost out. Our tours around were fascinating as we could view the effects of so many years of British imports. They were in the process of changing their cattle type as well and in their case they were using a large amount of Lincoln Red breeding to gain size but this at that time was bringing its problems no doubt by now resolved by the introduction of American and Australian bloodlines. The World Council President changed from Robin Halse of South Africa who had presided for 12 years travelling around the world many times to further the breed; in his place was Pendril Gunningham of Argentina.

Back in Britain the first of the dairy dispersals was the Villabrook herd to be sold due to the declining health of Harry Lancaster to a top of 1,000 guineas for V. Merrymaid and an average of £602. I regret having to use this method of reporting progress or the lack of it, but it seems the fairest way in limited space, but there was a quote once that 'if your head is in the oven and your butt is in the refrigerator your condition is average' which does not quite describe your plight!

Following this was the dispersal of the **Spetchley** herd which had been eliminated a few years before by foot and mouth and rebuilt. They had been pure breeders but had tried the blended scheme and it was one of these that was the top bid for Spetchley Duchess Gwynne

11th who was by a bull who was to have a major success in the breed, Newnham Accolade, one of the Red Friesian influences; she sold for 700 guineas but the average was only £424, certainly not due to the poor quality of the stock but probably to the fact that it had not been officially recorded for some years.

The third dispersal was due to the sudden passing of Henry Teverson referred to earlier; it occurred in a period of ridiculous uncertainty for dairy farmers where quotas were being imposed to limit a farmer's production. Such quotas were being bought and sold in order that some farmers could continue with their type of production and others were giving up or going to lower cost methods. Also levels of such prices were uncertain but one thing was certain: it was a particularly bad time for Shorthorn producers after their huge efforts to remould their cattle to be more competitive, especially as the government was being so vague regarding the future requirements and indeed what the quota was to be based on. All farmers were unnecessarily 'floundering' at this point, many were leaving the industry and to emphasise the point for example even Dairy A I dropped by over a quarter of a million in the first year. All values were changing, in 1945 it took the produce of .7 (note the decimal) cows to pay for 1 acre and in 1984 it took that of 2.8 cows. However, to return to the sale: 885 guineas was the top bid for Stowfield Red Rust 4 by the Shaw Bros from Derby who also gave 850 guineas for S. Favourite Berry. An extraordinarily low average was achieved at £437.

The next sadness was the **sale of the Lenborough herd** following the death of Richard Roper who had contributed so much in so many ways to the breed. His continued desire for excellence and purity within his herd made his estate an example. As one would expect there was a huge turnout of over 600 people and records were broken despite the economic climate, **the 1984 record of 1600 guineas was shattered** when Andrew Orsler of the Orchardhome prefix paid 2,000 guineas for Lenborough Tulip 336th and Andrew Timbury paid the same for Lenborough Pansy 302; it was again beaten when the competition ensured that A. Orsler paid £2,800 for Lenborough Dubbie 218th with a very young heifer calf at foot. From a large catalogue the eventual average was £598 for cows and £555 for served heifers. Cattle sold to every part of the country.

Later in the year another sale for health reasons was that of the **Eathorpe** herd for Graham and Jean Robson of Marton near Rugby, again supported by a large gathering, with cattle going far and wide, the top price being paid by D. McKeon from Sligo, Ireland, who gave 950 guineas for E. Fanny 105th who went on to win a number of championships in that country. She contributed to the average of 605 guineas for cows and 528 guineas for heifers. It was ironic that this prefix was to be heard in two further contexts this year, once when Eathorpe Bellringer 6th won the Male Championship at the Royal Norfolk for J.P. Wyatt of Twells prefix and then later in 1986 when **Eathorpe Anne 21st achieved the lifetime yield record having given 215,246lb of milk and 7,708lb butterfat and 6,578lb protein with 15 calves,** most of them in the ownership of Andrew Orsler of Orchardhome prefix. R.H. Robson, who turned to pedigree status when he decided to go for TB attestation, established the Eathorpe herd in 1947. He purchased from several sources to establish what was a herd of sizeable dairy-like cattle of families of notably Dainty, Clementine and Fanny lines from Stokelycross Clementine 61, Maplewell Dainty 3rd and Churchill Fanny 92nd, added to which a number of animals came from Drisgol, Crava, Glanhirwen and Tonevale herds before using bulls from the Young Bull Proving Scheme. One of the most beneficial strains he bought was Seckington Darlington Airdrie from John Arnold. Quite recently the herd used blended bulls to great effect. Local shows, which naturally included the Royal, had yielded a number of awards including Royal Champion in 1979 with E. Dainty 56th then E. Anne 21st as above who was also a 1st there. Many awards have been achieved in herd competitions having been leading herd in Warwickshire for 10 successive years and won 1st and 3rd in the 1985 dairy event milking trials. Yields were on a steady annual increase to 5,963kg at 3.72% and 3.38% protein at the time of the sale.

At this point it is important to recognise that owing to the large number of dairy herds compared with beef there are bound to be a larger number of the former in this review than beef particularly when the beef herds had fallen in numbers during the time before the revival, especially at this period which had been the lowest. With the improved acceptance of the type there was a growing number of breeders returning or coming into the book. However the current state of the breed was indicated by the fact that this sector, **the Beef Shorthorn, was accepted on to the Rare Breed Survival Trust lists of concern in 1987.**

The Doggrells' Chicklade herd had also held a reduction sale which established some new herds; the top price went to a flying herd (one that buys cows in milk and sells at the end of lactation) further west where A.J. Goaman kept a top quality lot of Shorthorn cattle but sadly although he often bought high quality, high priced cattle they were never available to continue to show their capabilities of breeding. He gave 690 guineas for Chicklade Ruby 109, the average being 465 guineas, similar to the autumn sale at Crewe where Oxton Wildeyes 420 achieved both the Championship for Mrs Smith as well as the top price of 700 guineas. The autumn Perth sale was a repeat for the dual herd of the Hewsons as again they topped the prices with Parton Dandy, who fetched not only top dairy but also top of the day at 1,900 guineas, a previous winner at both Penrith and Cumberland shows and with a 4% yielding dam and by Goodwick Royal Emperor; he was purchased by the Scottish Department for their bull stud. The top price female at this event had been generously donated by W. Anderson to the sale for a raffle and fetched 700 guineas after the winner decided to take the sale price rather than the heifer. Champion Beef Shorthorn this day was the last Dewhurst bull to be sold, Ardbennie Champagne, who fetched 1,800 guineas.

Further losses to the breed were in the passing of a large number of personalities who had also given so much to the Shorthorn in their time: one of them was Jack D. Webb, who had served on Council and been President; his Streetly herd had made a huge impact over a number of years.

Also regretted were Capt.N. Milne Harrop,MBE, another President and past Council member and owner of the Gwersyllt herd in Wales, and C.A. Hayward, who had served on Council and been Treasurer for a number of years during some of the critical times. Starting his agricultural life as the son of a butcher with one cow and 14 acres, his farming enterprise rapidly expanded to over 1,000 acres where he ran two herds: one Friesian and one Shorthorn. His **Hooton** Shorthorn Herd was founded around 1951 on Hastoe and Chivers lines; his originals came from Ellanby and Moundsmere, he then added some from Amershill and Histon including H. Musical Bouquet 8th that gave 86,795lb with 7 calves and was on going. One of his early bulls, Histon General Gwynne, was also a show success followed by a son, Hooton Musical Duke. Others included Hastoe Lord Dukedom 5th who was line bred to Musical Bouquet, then Hinxhill Grand Beau and Histon Dairy Premier and Henshallbrook Premier Supreme and a number of bulls from the Young Bull Proving Scheme. This herd rapidly developed into one of both merit and achievement: in 1960 Hooton Lily Fair 3rd won the female Championship at Lincoln and in the late '60s the herd won 4 out of 5 consecutive progeny groups at the Royal Show and 3 consecutive daughters of Grand Beau yielded 20,638lb, 16303lb and 16781lb, all at 4.3%BF and 3.2 protein. Hooton Duchess 19 was first in the in milk classes at the Royal Show in 1969,1970 and 1971, yielding 16,492lb at 4.3% in 1973 as well as being supreme Champion at the Royal with Hooton Lily Fair 23rd.

They won 6 supremes, 5 reserve Champions, 6 female Champions and 5 reserve female Champions in 9 major shows as well as a host of other awards including 21 challenge certificates. They continued in 1974 winning 6 firsts and 2 seconds at the Royal Show alone. By 1976 their average was 12,852lb at 3.67%. The H.Lily Fair family have certainly proved their worth over the years with Lily Fair 85th Champion at the Royal in 1991 and 1992 with an average over 9 lactations of 9,245kg at 3.43%. Lily Fair 134 was junior and reserve Champion at the 1999 Royal as well as reserve heifer interbreed with a first lactation of 7, 413kg at 4.09% and 3.24 protein. H. Lily Fair 111th and 109th were reserve pairs for the Royal interbreed 1995 and Lily Fair 111 Champion at the Royal 1995, followed by Lily Fair 111th again but with Lily Fair 115th being reserve pair interbreed at the 1996 Royal. With Lily Fair 115th being reserve Champion at this same event while also giving a yield of 6,048kg at 3.15% with her 1st lactation, what a phenomenal record for consistency and achievement; it illustrates how quickly favourite and profitable families multiply.

This family have had more than their fair share of difficulties but over the years these have seemed to bring and keep them together which was always the concept of Arthur Hayward. With Geoffrey Smith he was a passionate advocate of the Swedish Red as the way forward during the discussions on the breed improvement as it was (A) Red and (B) was 72% Shorthorn in its origins, the rest being Ayrshire and their own Herrgard and Smaland breeds; the problem at the time had been leucosis in their national herd which was why our ministry was loath to grant a licence to import. Although the herd was pure initially they have succeeded in the blending scheme, again by disciplined breeding which some of those participating did not practise. So the herd continues today with a herd average of 8,070kg at 4.40% BF and 3.2% protein with an enviable family partnership of John, Anne, Christopher and Mathew and they remain very much 'in the game' as further results will demonstrate.

All the herd losses in this year made it, to quote our Queen 'an annus horribilis' in a breed that had suffered such a reduction and was in the middle of a recovery. Among normal retirements and changes in farming policy there will always be a turnover but there was a dreadful loss yet to come in the death of Crawford Perkins and his son, David, both dying from carbon monoxide gas poisoning when in a grain silo; one was overcome and the other attempted to save him. Their **Hadnock** herd near Moreton on Lugg, Hereford, had been founded as long ago as 1879 in Monmouth and had become well known for their Flash, Fairy, Kirklevington and Ringlet families (one of which is pictured in the Irish section, p. 74, after being sold at a very high price in those days). The herd was dispersed in 1943 when Crawford was in the services but re-formed on his demobilisation with the old lines gathered from a number of sources adding Lady Barringtons, Spring Flowers and Wildeyes families but it was from one of the original Flash lines that his bull Hadnock Famous 6th was to come and make a name for himself before going into A I. His dam was a 100,000lb cow H. Flash 37th. Other sires included Stukeley Imperialist and Lord Craggs. The herd won many awards at county shows and attained a herd average of 11,563lb for cows and 9,609lb for heifers. They also had a very effective but somewhat unusual method of marketing their milk as they sold a very large proportion of their output through 12 vending machines in Hereford City. Bravely his wife and daughter carried on the herd after the accident.

1986/7 were the years when the Society office was able to come into the 20th century! A legacy from Richard Roper enabled the office to become computerised with all that entailed in the conversion of the pedigrees to the wonders of modern science. The office also had several changes as Mrs Powell semi-retired after a total of 17 years and the accountant Ken Pitt, who had also deputised as secretary during the interregnum between the passing of K.Cousins and J. Wood–Robert's appointment, retired. One further achievement was the completion of two breed videos both to publicise the cattle and to provide an insight for visitors to the forthcoming World Conference in 1989. This project had been started with Henry Teverson as commentator so his work lives on both in the cattle and in these publicity items.

John D. Thornborrow was also honoured for his considerable services to the breed by accepting the office of Honorary Vice President. The other administrative change was that David Bright, who was retiring from the MMB, had agreed to assist the Society with their breeding programme, a tremendous bonus with his experienced and unbiased input which in some degree helped to fill the void that had been created.

The Perth sales were honoured by the presence of Her Majesty the Queen Mother on an unofficial visit although gracing the sale as Patron of the Aberdeen Angus Society celebrating their 50th Anniversary. In the Shorthorn rings the Champion was Balmyle Yardstick and the reserve was Chapleton Yorker; the top price went to Major Gibb with Glenisla Warlord selling for 2,600 guineas to contribute to an average of £1,283 for 15. The beef 'thunder' this year was stolen by Uppermill's Chapelton Xile who took the Championship at the Royal Highland and then the reserve overall. He repeated this at the Royal Show when there were a total of 1,200 beef entries. He and Rothes Just from Uppermill, the breed reserve Champion, were the reserve winners of the Burke Trophy.

The Dairy Champion came from the successful herd of Andrew Orsler with his Orchardhome Anne 12th.

In the autumn Calrossie had another draft sale, this time in Inverness, selling 21 at an average of £716 with a top of 1,200 guineas; this left them with a much reduced pedigree herd, but with a commercial herd at around 100 head. The autumn Perth event was judged by James Playfair Hannay, who awarded the Championship to Balmyle Zeus and later backed his judgement by buying him at 2,000 guineas but not before he had placed his stable mate Balmyle Zig Zag as reserve. He too sold at 2,000 guineas and the average for a very few bulls sold, 9, was an average of £1,178.

This year a return to Carlisle as a venue was tried for a local herd dispersal, the old established Kinmount herd; despite a very poor Friesian sale preceding it, this one met a good demand with buyers coming from Scotland to the south with a top of 1,000 guineas for Kinmount Golden Plum 6th but an average of £475 possibly affected by the Stock Exchange problems of that time.

In the autumn another Dairy Shorthorn dispersal bought about by retirement was that of the Eype herd down in Dorset where possibly the stock exchange problem again affected the sale but the cattle met a fairly consistent trade with a top of 660 guineas and an average of £498.

The next few years were very eventful for the breed and also in the agricultural field and as always it was the Perth Show and sale that came first in the year; although there were not many forward, the quality was considered the best for many years. But the prices hardly reflected this although the market was fairly buoyant for all breeds with Charolais and Angus having top prices of 18,000 and 15,000 guineas. The Shorthorns were not so fortunate and their Champion was in fact undersold at 3,600 guineas for Balmyle Zenith; Balmyle achieved the double with Balmyle Zephyr going into the reserve Champion place selling to the Orkneys for 2,800 guineas. This was also a triumph for the stockman, Friar Thomson, who won the Herdsman's Trophy outright after 3 successive wins, a feat seldom achieved and of course it was a great achievement for the bull's owner Bill Bruce. The average for the day was £1,461 and the Dairy Shorthorns averaged 717 guineas selling to a top of 950 guineas. At the AGM held customarily during this event Miss Mary Durno accepted the invitation to become the Honorary Patron of the Beef Shorthorn Society in recognition of her magnificent efforts and support for the breed over many years.

In the May of **1988 the Royal Agricultural Society of England (RASE) celebrated their 150th Anniversary** as it was on May 9th that the Royal Charter was granted all those years ago, although the concept had been formed at a dinner in London in December 1837 at the Smithfield Club. However it was on May 9th, 1988, at the Whitbread Porter Tun Rooms in Chigwell Street, London, that over 600 guests sat down in the company of Her Royal Highness Princess Anne to mark the occasion; just as it was all those years ago, all the food and wines – but not the champagne! – were produced in Britain. This included the roast sirloin which was Shorthorn supplied from stock that traced back to the first Shorthorn Herd book, from J.P. Wyatt's **Twells** herd at

Twells Moss Trooper 4th

Snetterton, Norfolk.

This herd was founded in 1921 when the family came up to Norfolk from Devon with non-pedigree cattle; in 1936 Joe Wyatt's father presented him with 20 Shorthorns and hired the farm to start him off and Stokelycross Lord Norfolk 23rd was appropriately purchased to start the grading-up process and produced several winners in the classes for grading that were at a number of shows of the day, coupled with excellent yields. Fothering Baron Rose worked in well following him but Joe Wyatt was of the opinion that the Stokelycross lines were the ones to follow to provide the large deep cows he considered were needed. So a series of their bulls were used including Marquis Barrington 4th, S. Thunder 11th, S. Lord Thorndale 2nd, S. Royal Norfolk and S. Drum Major, before partially using A I bulls like Histon Dairy Premier and Redrice Senator Beau, as well as using some of his own breeding. The Clementine family had bred extremely well at Twells producing a number of 100,000lb cows. Hastoe breeding was also involved with the purchase of Hastoe Veracity 16th. Further families have been Darlington, Nursemaid and Thornedale, all having success in the pail as well as shows including Smithfield and other fat stock shows as the policy was always to fatten out surplus females and steers. The farm is on some of the thinnest land in Norfolk which emphasises the skill in maintaining such large framed cattle and producing genes like the Famous Twells Moss Trooper 4 who has been mentioned several times before as producing top weights and also excellent milk figures to top the leagues. To visit this herd one is struck by the consistent type and temperament where cattle decide to co-operate by staying behind a piece of baler twine rather than trying out the road! Also by the large amount of vegetable waste such as carrots, from a nearby canning factory, that make such economic feed. Exports have been made to Australia, Columbia, Bogota, and it was interesting when we were in New Zealand, visiting what was possibly the largest Dairy Shorthorn herd in the world at that time, the Dibbles at Tauhei Morrinsville, we could easily pick out the Twells Moss Trooper 4 daughters, so dominant are his genes. In the year of this review, 1988, the Twells herd took both male and female Championships at their Norfolk show.

Sales in the dairy sector got off to a bad start this year with a cancelled event at the Crewe spring date owing to poor entries, the first ever; but a series of reduction or dispersal sales made up for it later where the averages were approximately the same at Newbold reduction (£511); Amber reduction (£612), Mainfold dispersal (£660) but the outstanding one was the Gateshayes final dispersal, when Gilbert Withers at 74 had finally decided to retire permanently; cows averaged £801 and heifers £778 and with 11 lots selling at over 800 guineas and a top of 1,150 guineas for Gateshayes Wildeyes 29th bought locally by R.F. Collins from Honiton. Again the North-West regional show and sale hosted by the Dent family was a success with a consistent trade to average £634 for cows and £683 for heifers with Villabrook Ladygrove 14th as Champion but Red Rosette with a Belgian Blue calf from the same herd was the top bid at 950 guineas. The autumn Crewe sale made partial amends with a catalogue of 91 and a Champion in Drisgol Daisy's Sovereign 10th selling at 900 guineas and a much improved average at £597 for cows and £562 for heifers.

The year was also marked **probably by the largest private breed importation:** the current President of the Beef Shorthorn Society J. Campbell Graham bought in a shipment that included 51 females and 3 bulls from Alberta, Canada, having recently also imported Scotsdale Tradition to his Drymen herd. An effort to substantially widen the gene pool. Two other recent importations had been Egmont Exuberant from Tasmania by Major Gibb of Glenisla and Glenford Pacesetter and River Acres Talcott Joyful from Saskatchewan, Canada, by James Playfair Hannay of Tofts so the overseas bloodlines were really boosted in this country. Overseas in Australia Haddon Rig Success had smashed all records at their Dubbo event when he was sold for $34,000 so things were also on the move abroad but we still had a way to go!

The Royal Show provided a remarkable double this year for a herd that had built up from one cow and a gifted calf as a spare time hobby, to one of the foremost dairy herds of the era by Mr and Mrs Andrew Orsler and their **Orchardhome** herd from near Leighton Buzzard,

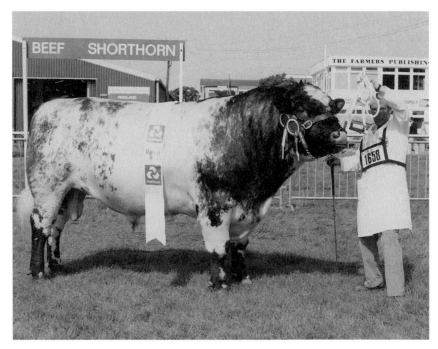

Scotsdale Tradition.

Aylesbury. It was to become a remarkable year for them as well. Their cow Orchardhome Annie 12th had won the Royal Show Championship in 1987 and this year they did it again with the same cow with a larger entry. The male Champion was Twells Barrington Dandy from the last reviewed herd but owned and exhibited by local exhibitors L. Kenning and Sons. The Orchardhome herd went on to also win the Dairy Show at Stoneleigh with Orchardhome Millicent and reserve to her was Orchardhome Lady Walton 70th from the same herd; not satisfied with that they went on to win the dairy event in the south west with Orchardhome Nellie 15th who went on to also win the Royal and Three Counties in 1990. This herd was founded in 1965 while Andrew was a milk recorder but he obviously had a gifted understanding that guided his aims and ambitions as he built his outstanding herd with a Hastoe and Hinxhill base using such sires as Orgreave Mandate and Orfold Double Magnum as well as choice selections from the A I bulls including Meadowhaven Pride Starr and then some of his own breeding including Orchardhome Anchor. The aim was not only to be show winners as he also broke world records after his purchase of Eathorpe Anne 21st mentioned earlier. This herd also had one of the few polled dairy lines, the first being O. Petunia, a grade up cow who produced over 100 tonnes of milk with 15 calves as well as producing polled progeny including O. Poldark, who in turn produced two polled sons O.

Drednought and Walpole. They built up this herd to have an average of 6,265kg at 3.79% B fat and 3.43% protein but sadly this herd was to be dispersed in 1992 having won the National Gold Cup four times as well as countless herd competitions. All this achievement was built up from nothing when the whole industry was going through difficult times.

11. The '90s

Slightly outside the period, 1989 was such a milestone and landmark it really needs to start this chapter or have one of its own! It was the National Celebration of British Food and Farming, the 100th year of the Ministry of Agriculture and 150th year anniversary of the Royal Highland Agricultural Society and Show and as an addition we were hosting the World Conference. Furthermore the Perth Bull Show and Sale was to close before moving to the new site of a huge new agricultural centre just off the motorway the following spring so a number of people were apprehensive of the loss of atmosphere.

The spring sale was a definite turning point for the breed as the averages showed an excellent increase of £455 up on bulls that averaged £1,916, females were up £315 at £1,029 with Champion Balmyle Apache selling at 3,100 guineas but the top price was Uppermill Burt at 3,200 guineas to Col. Dewhurst of Dungarthill whose heifer Dungarthill Crocus Alpha had won the female Championship.

A new record was set up later in the year when the Upsall herd of the Hon. Gerald Turton and the Otterington herd of Miss Furness held a joint reduction sale with one of the largest consignments since the '50s. **The female record** for auction was shattered when **Venitia Sapphire of Upsall was sold at 2,800 guineas** to Campbell Graham of Drymen who also purchased 12 others. A new herd which was also due for great success was boosted when M. Abrahams of Ripon purchased 7 lots to add to his Newfield herd. The average was 525 guineas for heifers from Upsall and 669 guineas for cows with calves from Otterington.

Tables were published by the MLC showing the comparative weight increases at 400 days for the main breeds showing progress made with an outstanding increase for Beef Shorthorn heifers

Breed change	Avg bulls 1987/8(kg)	Increase change since 1974 (kg)	Avg heifers 1987/8	Increase since 1974 (kg)
Angus	458	+ 74	337	+58
B.Shorthorn	455	+39	355	+80
Charolais	615	+61	447	+28
Hereford	463	+38	343	+48
Limousin	533	+83	394	+39
Lincoln Red	501	-10	342	+5
Simmental	591	+61	423	+21
Maine Anjou	564	N/C	343	N/C

As well as these figures the MMB published figures that demonstrated that the **Dairy Shorthorn had made the greatest improvement of any dairy breed in the last 10 years with an increase of 795kg of milk and 63kg of fat and protein.** This confirmed that the efforts were being rewarded.

Shorthorns were selling well in Ireland as their cattle were coming back into demand with an in-calf heifer making 1,350 guineas in a mixed draft sale from Kevin Culhane of Limerick, with an average of 1,000 guineas; optimism was returning. The RDS show had more Shorthorn entries than for many years at 46 and the Champion came from one of the smaller herd keen members, Jerome Smith, with his senior bull bred by S.J. Kelly from Dungannon, Caulfield Golden Fog. The reserve was from E. and G. Carter from Sligo with an Eathorpe cow Goodie 15th. The Balmoral Winter Fair had been won by another Northern Irish cow, Whitefalls Waterloo Rose 4th, a ten-year-old who also demonstrated economic longevity being in front of an entry of 220 dairy cattle; it was a double for her breeder Ken Workman as he had also won the Championship at the Spring Show. There was also a heifer sold during a mixed draft sale for Kevin Culhane at Limerick going for 1,350 guineas.

On the mainland at the spring Perth show and sale there was a distinct improvement in the averages with bulls up £455 at £1,916, up £315 for females at £1,029. The top price of 3,200 guineas was for Uppermill Burt purchased by Col. Dewhurst whose Dungarthill Crocus Alpha had secured the female Championship. The male Championship was awarded to Balmyle Apache who fetched 3,100 guineas.

Later in the year there was a Beef Shorthorn production sale held jointly between the Hon. G. Turton's Upsall herd and that of Miss Furness's Otterington herd making up one of the largest consignments for several years. A new female **record price at auction** was set when J. Campbell Graham paid **2,800 guineas** for Venitia Sapphire of Upsall and then he went on to purchase a total of 12 animals. The next principal numerical purchaser, M. Abrahams of Ripon, increased his comparatively new herd by 7 lots. The sale averages were: maiden heifers from Upsall 525 guineas; cows and calves from Otterington 669 guineas and their maiden heifers 422 guineas.

The World Conference was coming ever nearer, but just before it a dispersal sale was held near Leyburn, N. Yorkshire, for Tom Ripley's **Hauxwell** herd as he had decided to emigrate to Canada. This herd had developed into one of the premier herds from 1972 when on his 20th birthday he started with Forcett Rosy 34th. From then on, with great support from his father, who had a prominent Friesian herd, he continued to build up a very choice breeding herd as he had inherited his father's eye for good cattle. Using a number of young bulls from the scheme and also Meadowhaven Prides Starr who he favoured, he managed to achieve a continuing average of 5,842kg with 3.49% butterfat and 3.25% protein for the previous 12 years, no doubt in fierce but friendly competition with his father! The sale was attended by a huge crowd including some early visitors to the conference and over 100 buyers were on the books by the end of the day for some 200 plus lots, although the family had retained some youngstock to found their new herd. Top of the day was Hauxwell Dairyman 2nd going at 1,100 guineas to the Teasdales well known Brafell herd. There were a number of 1,000 guinea buyers to finalise the average at 760 guineas for cows and calved heifers, 727 guineas for served heifers and 517 guineas for maiden heifers with bulls at 483 guineas. They set up in Prince Edward Island, Nova Scotia, and achieved much the same success before having to sell up again with evidently a large crowd from Canada and USA when their top price H. Miss Molly sold at $5,500. Their skills were much missed on both sides of the water.

After the Hauxwell dispersal it was time for the World Conference, attended by over 150 delegates from all continents as well as from the UK. This was in Edinburgh and timed around the Royal Highland Show. Dairy Shorthorn classes had been restored after many years and were judged by the previous world president Robin Halse, who chose as his Champion Stowfield Royal Kathleen 3rd, bred by H. Teverson but now owned and shown by G.A and D.W. Dent. Chapleton Xile won the Beef Shorthorn Championship classes and went on to win the Interbreed Supreme Beef Championship having been reserve for it on his previous outing two years before. What a performance again from Uppermill. The conference delegates then went on tours of UK herds and those in Ireland attending two large open days, one at Drymen hosted by the Beef President, J. Campbell Graham, and the other hosted by Kevin Culhane in Limerick, Ireland, where they saw examples of the Irish cattle whose fame had spread like wildfire around the world. Both tours then gathered at the Royal Show in Warwickshire where there were over 70 entries, a huge effort from exhibitors. In the dairy sector Roy Whittle of Tonelea chose as his reserve Champion Eathorpe Bellringer 6th but his supreme Champion was Drisgol Mabel 7th. She was later joined with Drisgol Rose 74th as the pair that went on to win the dairy Burke trophy against all breeds (see colour picture between pages 224/5), an amazing triumph for Leslie Thomas who was presented with the trophy by Her Majesty the Queen. What a way to celebrate the end of the World Conference and the Year of Food and Farming.

The **Drisgol** herd was founded by J.B. Thomas, Leslie's father, in West Wales in 1944 with the purchase of Beechwood Dewdrop 2nd from the Reading sales; she went on to found one of the large families in the herd. The next prominent family was started from the purchase of Graemes Belladonna 2nd. Then a bull, Illington Marksman 3rd, was to make a major impact on both his progeny and the show ring winning over 30 championships. Other purchases followed, such as Thrimby Lottie 8th and Holmscales Belle 3rd who was the founder of the Daisy family. Marksman was followed by Illington Speculation 5th from the same herd who went on to win 50 championships, then Snotterton Primrose Gift who was not a show bull but produced ten sons sold at Reading and produced a number of good milkers. Leslie took over the management in 1955, helped always by his wife Megan. Their herdsman Tony Williams also ably assisted them for 40 years.

They then bought from a herd from which several other successful herds had started, Inglewood. They bought Waterloo 6th, who started his Waterloo family to add to the Bella, Daisy, Dewdrop and Belladonnas. Among the most prominent bulls that followed were Drisgol Daisy's Baronet to great effect then Cleeve Barrington Duke 2nd, Stockwood Gay Lad 5th and Drisgol Waterloo King, all ensuring that the Drisgol average had climbed to 11,351lb at 3.71 % by 1963. In 1969 they achieved a double, winning both the Championships at the Royal with Drisgol Dairyman 2nd and D. Duchess 2nd. They also won 5 out 6 Championships at the Society shows and sales and had won over 200 Championships among their prizes since 1955. They also raised their average in 1993 to 6,018kg at 3.98% BF and 3.3% protein. In recent years some use had been made of the blended programme with great effect. Leslie was President of the Society in 1979/80 and later was also President of the Limousin Society, having also developed a very successful herd of that breed in recent years.

A consistent winner during the dairy events, the **Rodway** herd of Graham Madeley near Telford continued their winning achievements in 1989, having won the Melvin Cup for production and inspection three years in a row. This year their Rodway Tiny 105th was Champion on inspection and Rodway Tiny 87th secured her third successive win in the production classes at the Stoneleigh event and they also took both the Champion and reserve at the Bath and West event with Rodway Barrington Duchess 4th winning the senior cow and Rodway Floral Duchess the junior section. These were no mean achievements especially as the original Rodway herd established around 1937 in the name of J.A.C. Madeley and Sons had been eliminated by foot and mouth disease in 1967. It was re-founded on cattle purchased from the Swanford and Agden dispersals, also later the Wendest herd, and used the sire Streetly Count Gwynne and then Specialist; more recently Graham, as well as very successfully re-establishing the herd along blended principles, was one of the first to follow the organic methods of production to increase his milk sales price.

The autumn show and sale at Crewe was another triumph for Drisgol, who gained top price and the Championship with Drisgol Mabel 10th raising bids to 1,100 guineas and their Drisgol 52nd won the reserve Champion award. The male supreme was Weaverdale Oxford for Graham Pattinson and averages were again well up at 745 guineas (580) for cows, 763 guineas (639) for heifers in milk and 723 guineas (562) for heifers in calf (bracketed figures are the previous averages).

The dairy year drew to a close after being an incredible one, but as always, there were losses in herd dispersals and members passing away. This year saw two very senior breeders lost – G. Blake at 94 of the Kingsley prefix, whose cow Musical had broken the world record in 1975; also J.S. Chivers at 97 who had done so much for the breed including acting as President in 1952/3 and being on council for a number of years as well as running the Chivers Company and their herds. It is true that old age goes with the Shorthorn breeders as well as their cows!

The beef year ended on a sad note, as it was the last at the historic Perth Caledonian Road town site and also because it included the dispersal of the Dungarthill herd, started in 1949, which had achieved considerable successes. It was on an upbeat note so far as trade was concerned when progeny of the winning bull Chapelton Xile won both the male and female Champions both from Uppermill with Lodge and Lovely Luce respectively but it was the reserve Champions that topped the prices with W. McGowan's Fingask Zodiac selling at 3,800 guineas and Glenisla Lovely Gazelle selling at 1,300 guineas, the bulls averaging 1,699 guineas and the females 1,067 guineas. The Dungarthill herd steadily traded up to a top of 1,600 guineas for Dungarthill Ury Maid 9th.

One other development was a visit by a delegation to ascertain if the Norwegian Red breed, again with a Shorthorn percentage in its make up, would be an additional breed to consider in the blended programme. A number of other breeds had also been suggested as they had a very interesting national breeding programme with a herd of 280,000, compared with our Shorthorn herd in the UK herd, from which they selected 400 bulls annually for initial testing and from which they made their final selection. The Norwegian Red concept had grown from an amalgam of 2 or 3 breeds. Subsequently, although there was a limited take up, it was not generally accepted, as our breeders did not wish to lose their standard of conformation. However because of the number of red breeds that were being tried the Shorthorn Society decided to set up another register, named **the Red and White Register** , so that again these breeds could be recorded and assessed that would accept any red breed animal so long as its pedigree was known. It was still a fact that there were more red breed cattle throughout the world than black and there was a school of thought that breeds in this country might follow the Norwegian concept of an amalgam and, as one prominent geneticist said, 'that was how the Shorthorn was founded, so introducing new genes should not be viewed as a betrayal of trust, but a failure to grasp the opportunities, that might be.'

Visits were also made to view the Danish Red and also the Normande breed from France at this time as although the various breeds needed to be investigated it was established very early on that there was no point in developing and emulating the Holstein-Friesian. The desirable objective was to create a viable and competitive alternative, but also retain the well established Shorthorn advantages. Following the memorable year one would assume things would slow down but the interest was steadily rebuilding; although still at an early stage, the atmosphere at sales and shows was much more positive and hopeful. It is a shame in some ways that in a book of this type one can not expand more on the shows and other occasions especially as the general improvement of type and the increased interest of potential customers and new members was marked as both the beef and dairy developed their varying improvement methods. That created an element of friendly competition with exhibits at events like the specialised annual beef event held by National Cattle Breeders or the 'European' dairy event as that had become, and down at the south west dairy event as well as later the Welsh dairy event by the exhibition of the 'Improved Shorthorn'. But it was bound to take time, as both the breeders and the buyers were going to take some convincing that it was here to stay.

There were however a number of questions still unanswered. On the beef side, what level of Maine Anjou should be desired? And when should the book be closed again? And on the dairy side it was already becoming clear to the blended breeders that to achieve a beast that was not just relying on hybrid vigour it was vital to instil some discipline in one's breeding policy, as one would be in danger of finishing up with a mongrel if one just kept introducing new blood, and not going back to one's roots in order to achieve some consistency. Several had discovered that for some, the first introduction was great, the second was good, but the third was in many cases a big step back with shelly animals that did not have the same properties, so it came back to stockmanship and culling. There was also a danger of the increased popularity resulting in indiscriminate rearing. Any breed that expands rapidly runs the risk of falling into the trap of popularity with increased prices and this temptation decreases selection. However this stage had not quite been reached and only time could tell, but the advantage of such a previous enforced decline had been that it necessitated vicious culling of the less productive elements, although a number of useful blood lines had been lost by them being crossed to Friesians, etc.

1990 was variously affected nationally by weather conditions creating shortages of fodder in some areas and also by the media focus on the **Bovine Spongiform Encephalopathy(BSE)** incidents in a very few cattle which had worryingly occurred since 1985. It was similar to scrapie in sheep but could also effect humans and although steps had been taken to avoid cross infection by regulations on processing methods, it was evident that there was a considerable time lag before the disease manifested itself so there was uncertainty in the consumer's mind, resulting in a reduced demand for meat products. The disease affects the nervous system and particularly the brain and it was subsequently thought the cause was due to the long established practise of feeding meat and bone meal that had not been sufficiently heat treated, so this product was banned, but because of the time the problem took to manifest itself, there was considerable loss of confidence; therefore a policy of animals for the food chain being no older than 30 months was introduced and certain parts of offal were also banned. Furthermore there was uncertainty at this time as to the possibility of the mother passing the problem down to its calf.

The fact that there was depression meant that buyers were wary, which was not surprising; despite this the Perth event was a good one for Major Gibb of Glenisla as he gained the two top prices and the Championship with his bulls Glenisla Borodino, the Champion, that fetched 4,000 guineas and G. Archer that reached 2,000 guineas. Uppermill gained most of the other principal awards: Reserve Supreme, Junior Champion and Reserve with U. Sandon and U. Sadler and female Champion with their Lovely Loot. The dairy bull Parton Ranger who had been Champion in that section at the Royal Highland, sold for 1,400 guineas.

Although the **Glenisla** estate had been in the family for three or four generations it was not until 1972 that Major John Gibb founded his herd based on purchases from Uppermill, Dungarthill and Pennan and it was from the latter that his first heifer was purchased out of Perth market as he had been inspired by the late Ronnie Henderson's efforts to improve size. Then some dairy dual type were added, bought from Maxton and Beechdale and others, as well as from Newton Hall; eventually he turned toward the Maine Anjou lines with the purchases of lines from the Rutherfords at Baldowrie and then to Balmyle Xpress from W. Bruce purchased in 1986 for 5,200 guineas, the top price of any breed that Perth week. Once these lines were established, the decision was taken to seek overseas pure lines through semen and stock from Canada, Australia and Tasmania using such bulls as Cactus Flat

Lord Lovat judging in the street at Perth's Caledonian Road Market.

Stardust, Diamond Xerxes and Dakota 2nd, Downsview Roan Mist and Egmount Exuberant, at the same time using mainly naturally polled stock. Some ten differing lines were involved and the combinations all resulted in the stock being regularly sought after at sales. It was during the early '90s that the herd established a regular consignment of around 20/25 females on an annual basis to the autumn Perth sales, as well as his bulls. From small beginnings, this herd established a regular and eager regular group of buyers who appreciated the strong commercial value of this type. Major Gibb was elected President of the Beef Society in 1986-1988 and after being a World council delegate from 1982 was elected World Council President in 1998.

One of the surprises in 1990 was the dispersal of the Balmyle herd that had established their family lines such as Wanda, Irene, Greta, Katie, Phantasy and Gypsy from dairy lines as well as the beef lines. Naturally there was huge interest after their successes at bull sales in recent years, resulting in an average of over 3,000 guineas for all their bulls sold. The top price of this sale was for a B. Tessa, who traced back to a Twells Moss Rose family as well as her Maine Anjou bloodlines: she and her heifer calf made 2,000 guineas. This sale also had consignments in from Glenisla, Parkfield and Flawcraig and followed the autumn bull sale. Many of the Balmyle animals were in calf to B. Xpress who had been bought back from Glenisla. The two bulls averaged 755 guineas; 25 cows averaged 1,022 guineas; 9 in-calf heifers averaged 1,000 guineas and 17 maiden heifers 796 guineas: in a depressed agricultural climate that was exceedingly good. The Glenisla heifers averaged 510 guineas for 6; Parkfield 575 guineas; Flawcraig's 2 cows with calves averaged 675 guineas.

On the dairy side there were three blended dispersals, all selling in a very depressed market: one, Swinfen, averaged £531; another, Titsey, (owing to the death of Tom Okey, a breeder dedicated to the scheme from the start in the south east) finished at £509, although they sold to a top of 1,050 guineas and their heifers sold better at £550. The third was the remnants of the Northease herd near Lewes that sold to average £595 for heifers and £584 for cows. Another sad day was the dispersal of the renowned Gainford pure-bred herd in the north where prices were a little better with 7 animals selling over the 1,000 guineas to a top of 1,500 guineas for Gainford Bessie.

Dairy events were more encouraging; here G. Madeley took both the Champion and reserve at Stoneleigh with Rodway Floral Duchess and Marie respectively. G.Long of Newbold, who for a time exhibited regularly at such events, won the three-day trials with Newbold Gwen 11. Rodway Floral Duchess had won the south west event in 1989, she was by Cotley Crusader and this year it was the Cotley Crusader team that won the group award at that event and Cotley Erin that was the Champion, making it a great event for G.H. Osborne and Son; in fact Erin was due to repeat the achievement the following year.

It was also a good year for the Orchardhome herd of Andrew and Gill Orsler. At the Royal Show their O. Nellie 15th was a worthy Champion giving them their third Royal in a row and Nellie had also won 3 Championships in 3 outings that season. It was also an Orchardhome female that won the RDS show in Dublin when Orchardhome Florrie 4th took the supreme award for Ballingarrane Estate making it a year to remember for the Orslers.

This was the first year since the inception of the show that dairy bulls were not shown at the Royal Show as a result of health and safety regulations. These were to get worse for such events with the increase in insurance cover following the new blame culture that was developing. Although the turnout was very low in this sector this year the Beef Shorthorn Champion was a win for an overseas bull, Glenford Pacesetter, imported by Playfair Farms; the female award went to Uppermill with Secret Sheba.

A decision had been taken to move the Society Dairy Shows and Sales to the Chelford Market premises of Frank R. Marshall in Cheshire; John Thornborrow would continue to run the event as the Society

Balmyle Crackle

Auctioneer. The sale was not a very good start in that venue as many farmers were over milk quota but it was again a Drisgol heifer, Waterloo 52nd, who gained the Championship and the male award went to C. Royle's Dunham Crispin, as did the reserve with Moss Tracker. Waterloo 52nd was the top price at 850 guineas and the average was £572 for cows and £727 for in milk heifers.

1991 was a cold start at Perth and agriculture was again in a depressed state; cattle exports were slowed right down by the BSE so a poor trade was expected but the spring sale was better than hoped with an average of 1,653 guineas; females at 850 guineas was reasonable. The Champion was a great example of the breed, Balmyle Crackle, who sold to a farming butcher, John Doughty, in Leicester who had recently added a Shorthorn herd to his Angus. He gave 4,000 guineas against stiff competition to secure this bull. The only dairy bull forward was from Hewsons of Parton, who have both dairy and Whitebred Shorthorns; this was Tycoon, who fetched 1,000 guineas.

One of the dairy dispersals that year that drew interest from all parts of the UK and Ireland was the Ashperton herd of Charles Epps. His 'pure', in the accepted sense, Shorthorn cattle had broken many production records and won many herd competitions as well as Gold Cup awards at least 12 times. The herd, based originally on Hastoe breeding, carried on through the Lady Laura family from Orgreave which had done well for him. On this occasion it was another of his lines that fetched the top bid for a female – A. Sybil 83rd sold for 1,300 guineas and her calf made 620 guineas in the females; it was Ashperton Laura's Masterpiece the bull that fetched the top bull price on the day going to a recently formed herd in Wales of P. Houseman for 1,500 guineas. The average was £683 for cows, £642 for heifers.

Influential breeding on the dairy side was to be imported into the country by the importation of Kingsdale Peri's Champ from the USA. His figures of + 760 milk +35 butterfat and+28 protein with 1,024 eligible daughters were very enticing, as was the fact that his dam had been all American Champion three times and had yields of 17,500 lb. He would also mean fresh bloodlines. It was also interesting to notice around the shows in the UK that at a number of them the interbreed Champions were once again going to beef and Dairy Shorthorns; while shows are by no means everything to go by, what it demonstrated was that the breed was once again being recognised for its potential when at least 14 shows were won in this way, also it was a great advertisement to onlookers. Furthermore, sales were being attended by more and more commercial as well as pedigree buyers and although, because of the national market, the prices were not huge, the trend indicated that the breed was returning to favour. Three other dispersals caused by retirement, going out of milk or emigrating were held for very commercially run low-cost herds of long standing: the Cadhay herd in Devon, the Crawshaw near Preston and the Oakthwaite herd in the Lake District were all well attended with prices up to 820 guineas and good averages, despite the continuing gloom in the industry. There were excellent genetic index bloodlines for those staying in the trade, particularly the Oakthwaite herd, established in 1951, as an example where a number of top CGI cows had been identified despite the low cost input; cattle sold from here were always regarded as having high potential.

It was becoming harder and harder for anyone to go into the industry especially a young person as they not only needed to acquire stock and land they also had to buy quota. To add to the problem the national dairy herd was still falling from 1975 when there were 3,400,000 dairy cows to 1991 when there were 2,583,000 cows and 1,694,000 beef cows.

With more widespread computer skills and growing technology there were increasing genetic evaluations coupled with many abbreviations such as

PIN –Profit Indices that indicated financial potential

CGI- Cow genetic Indices

PTA- Predicted Transmitting Ability for the production capability of the progeny

EBV- estimated breeding value

ICC-improved contemporary comparison

to name but a few. It was becoming increasingly evident that some people were chasing index numbers to sell stock, but to such an extent that messages were coming from USA, for example, that the animals so bred were deteriorating in quality and longevity, particularly in the Holstein which, although giving much milk, was not lasting and had many weaknesses – in legs and feet for example. There is also one more I will quote which is BLUP, which is Best Linear Unbiased Prediction, which analyses all known relatives including sons, daughters, uncles, aunts, grandparents, etc, to calculate the expected performance due to its genetic makeup; from it you can ascertain the growth or milking ability compared with contemporaries so that it can be assessed to a large extent genetically, separating that aspect apart from the food input influence. All these aides are useful if used as a guide and not as a 'religion'! Farmers must retain their stockmanship and also have realistic costs of production and one of the aides to this is productive longevity. Much earlier I referred to the performance of a bull in certain herds being also very much dependent on the quality of the females put to him; today that still applies but there is the additional aid of all the genetic indicators above as well as A I and embryo transplants. The sixth and maybe seventh sense of the stockman or herd manager is just as important when it comes to the final selections as day-to-day care and management. The sadness today is that commercial pressures put so much stress on time that these vital aspects may be overlooked.

Back to 1991! The Royal Highland Champion dairy animal was Brafell Lady Waterloo 41st for the Teasdales in front of a much improved quality turnout with Newbold Premier Topper all the way from Monmouth for C. Long and Son. The beef Championship went to the Gibbs' Glenisla Druid who won over the female Champion, Uppermill's Flossy Freta, who was to come into her own again later. The same herd had the reserve female with Lovely Laurel and they also bred the reserve male, Uppermill Rio, although he was owned and shown by an up and coming herd, **Loch Awe** of Mr and Mrs C. D. Coombs. This herd was only founded in 1984 with dual purpose type Shorthorns from herds such as Twells, Maxton and others combined with purchases from Balmyle. They had started with a bull, Uppermill Fleet, and then Fitties Champ, that was a Maine Anjou, then back to Uppermill Rio, then Balmyle Zephyr who they had purchased from a herd in Orkney. After these they went to use the Canadian Banner Instant Royal and were to build up to a herd of some 120 cows later and another polled herd with the prefix **Dunsyre**.

It is not feasible to record every major event in this detail but as we get more up to date with the recovery there is inevitably more detail and as the industry became more intense the same thing applies, so certain events stand out. That year's Royal Show comes to mind as the previous year's Royal Show Holstein Champion was the current year's Holstein Friesian Champion; although she was a grand example of a cow, this seemed like midsummer madness: the critics of the Shorthorn programmes had little to complain about if this was how the industry was going. In the Shorthorn sector the dairy class Champion was again from the Hooton herd – Lily Fair 85th – with Drisgol Delila 33rd as the reserve. In the beef Uppermill Lang was awarded the sash and the reserve female Champion was again from Uppermill – Lovely Laurel . In the dairy event it was again a triumph for the Madeleys with Rodway Tiny 110th with Orchardhome Nellie 15th reserve Champion. Recording these events, one is aware how often the major winners manage year after year to produce the animal for the event and also to suit a variety of judges; for many years in the beef sector they have appointed as judges both breeders of experience not only from this breed but others as well and also herd managers at their shows and sales, always assuming they have been approved to officiate by their respective societies of course. In the dairy sector it was also noticeable that judges went for the animal rather than being selective as to the blending or established breeding type.

Through thick and thin the same herds have continued to be at the top of the line and in the dairy sector one such herd was the **Cotley** herd of the Osborne family in Wiltshire, whose Cotley Erin 13th repeated her success of the previous year at the south-west dairy event, winning the Championship. The same herd had achieved the Championship at the Bath and West Show with another of this family, Erin 15th this time. Then they were one of those who achieved interbreed success when their team took the interbreed group of three award at this show. The present owner's father, Garnett Osborne, had founded this herd in 1929 when he started grading up but sadly it was destroyed in 1937 with foot and mouth disease; he then started buying in pedigree stock from the Kingham and other sales as well as 10 from the Swepstone herd and the **Stourhead** herd. This prestigious herd at Stourbridge also in Wiltshire was noted for its productive longevity and consistency with an average yield of 9,859lb. From here Garnett purchased his first memorable sire, Stourhead Mogul, who was to be the first of several. As long ago as 1950, with 120 milkers, they had exported to many countries including Ireland.

Later Garnett Osborne used a number of Swepstone sires including S. Lord Foggathorpe 10th, S. Wild King 3rd, S. Lord Bates 2nd, then Almer Cavalier and Calstone Lord Cactus. Some of the early successful families were Lass, Lilian and Graceful Lady, and the herd continued to multiply, winning many awards until in 1955 it was about 400 head with some 120 milking and all surplus males fattened to about 8 cwt.

Cotley Anne 40th, Supreme Champion at the 2000 Royal Show and Reserve Champion at the 2002 Royal Show.

So the herd was split into two units, one at Haytsbury and one at Manor Farm, Tytherington. The herds were consistently winning prizes at countless shows and sales such as the Yeovil regional events, which at its height had entries of around 200 head, and most of the local area shows, always assisted by their herdsman Percy Bond who was with the family for around 40 years. By the late '60s their averages were around 9,850lb with 3.73% butterfat and there were around 10, 100,000lb cows in the herd with notable families added to those above, such as Melody, Lady Barrington, Anne, Duchess, and the Erins which had come from George Maundrell's Calstone herd and were to be the start of the Crusader bulls that bought more accolades to the Osbornes.

Around the early '70s Roger Osborne, who had taken over now for some years, decided to take his herd down the blended route and used semen from the red and white bull Newnham Accolade that was being used in the Churchill herd. This sire really transformed the size, type and conformation as well as the production, being an enviable example of what could be achieved, again by judicious and disciplined involvement, in the scheme. The average rose to around 7,842kg at 3.9% butterfat and 3.39 protein for around 100 cows and 6,115kg at 4.2% butterfat and 3.47% protein for heifers at the time of the sale through retirement in 2002: but we are not quite there yet! In these years some of the other bulls or semen used were Cotley Sundowner 4th, Crusader, Chieftain, Winbrook Royal Event and King Henry, Kayl MP Spellbound, Marleycote Cosmonaut, and others in the Young Bull Scheme.

Sales later in the year demonstrated more interest: at Chelford the Drisgol herd gained another double with the female and male Championships going to D. Delila 35th and D. Daphne's Prospect respectively, both taking the top bids of 1,000 guineas which contributed to a healthy increase of averages to 724 guineas for cows and 788 guineas for calved heifers. Perth was also improved with the Royal Show winner Uppermill Lang selling very reasonably at 1,700 guineas; the Champion on this day was Uppermill Rambo and averages had increased to 1,365 guineas; however the day was made when the female Champion Fingask Lancaster Colleen sold at 1,200 guineas for the McGowans, followed by a consignment from Major Gibb of Glenisla. This chosen selection of 20-30 from Major Gibb was to become a regular event at each September sale. They sold to a top of 1,000 guineas and an average of 681 guineas.

In the Society this year Mrs McDonald left the Beef Shorthorn Society and their council eventually decided to return their administration to the Stoneleigh office with myself as their Secretary. This was a considerable step and it meant that the whole of the Society was administered under one roof once more as was the World Shorthorn Council which gave the organisation much more scope at home and throughout the world. The journal would also cover both sections of the breed so any enquiry could receive both sectors in one cover and any query could be dealt with from the same staff especially as a number of breeders kept both beef and dairy stock. A further administrative change was made in the production of the herd book to follow members' wishes and also to change the layout so that it could be sent in a loose leaf format; for example, if a beef or dairy member required only their specific section they could have it or any other combination. It also meant that the Society needed only produce the number required rather than storing vast quantities that might or might not be needed, thus saving on printing costs.

In **1992** some more figures came through from the MLC for Beef Shorthorn Bulls (all in kg).

	1970	1978	1991	Increase 1970-1991
100 days	112	133	149	+37
200 days	214	234	265	+51
300 days	312	314	373	+61
400 days500 days	400	404	490	+90
	488	496	595	+107

the same figure equivalent for heifers

	1970	1978	1991	Increase 1970-199
100 days	110	116	136	+26
200 days	201	217	222	+21
300 days	246	279	305	+59
400 days	274	287	374	+100
500 days	317	358	421	+104

These demonstrate quite clearly the success of the Beef Shorthorn improvement programme and why buyers were returning.

1992 was marked by a number of Dairy Shorthorn sales of importance as well as the World Conference in New Zealand. It was interesting not only to see the superb country and farming but also to learn that the breed in both sectors was universally expanding its share of the market, also that improved prices were being received. It was also the time when Pendril Gunningham retired as World President after holding that position since 1986 and Ross Procter of Ontario, Canada, partner in the Bodmin herd, was elected in his place.

The first of the sales mentioned was a dispersal of the long established **Wappenbury** herd, founded in 1905 near Leamington Spa in Warwickshire, initially under the **Debdale** prefix and then changing to Wappenbury when the brothers Joe and Cyril Kenning took over from their father. This herd was noted for the scale and quality of its pure-bred Shorthorns. Sought after lines were established, such as Rosettes, Greenleaf, Springfly, Primula, Wildeyes, Contessa and Foggathorpe that had between them won a number of prizes and herd competitions including Champions at the show and sales and the Royal show. Attended by over 400 people, the sale set a high standard for the year as many were after these productive pure lines. The top price of the day was for W. Contessa 34th who realised 1,020 guineas, selling to A. Goaman from West Devon who was a major purchaser. The average was £842 for cows and £691 for in-calf heifers and £515 for maiden heifers and calves.

The next was a record-breaking sale for the Orslers of Orchardhome, reviewed earlier, founded in 1965; they consistently produced prize and production winners in recent years having even won the most recent dairy event with their **Orchardhome Maude 6th** and the three day trials with O. Florrie. It was the former **with her calf that set the record when they realised 3,150 guineas.** A major purchaser was R.W. Swales from Yorkshire, returning to the breed after some time, who bought 23 lots; several also went over to Ireland and the top of these was O. Barrington Duchess 17th to D. Mckeon of Sligo. The average was £1,107 for cows and calved heifers, £765 for served heifers and £592 for maiden heifers.

The third major sale was a reduction for the Chicklade herd of the Doggrell family who had been helped for forty years by their herdsman Derrick Whatley down in Wiltshire. They had been successful exhibitors at shows throughout the West Country and the Royal and dairy events. One of these families achieved the top price of 1,500 guineas for C. Duchess 14th, but it was the number of high priced animals that marked the quality of those forward before a crowd of some 500 people as 30 lots made over 900 guineas, with cattle again going all over the UK. The Doggrells also generously donated to their region the proceeds of a well bred yearling bull : it raised 550 guineas. The averages were 967 guineas for cows, 908 guineas for calved heifers but close-to-calving heifers averaged 1,036 guineas and bulls 708 guineas.

The dairy sector had a good year all round as at their spring show and sale at Chelford the heifer average was one of the highest ever at £830. Champion at the event was Maxton Darling 52 that was sold to Northern Ireland. Trade was again fast in the autumn sale with no less than 18 sales over 1,000 guineas, with a top of 1,500 guineas, again from R.W. Swales to set an average of £1,060 for cows in milk; £1,179 for heifers in milk; £1,028 for heifers in calf. The winners on the day were very much the Pattinsons of Weaverdale as they achieved Champion and reserve with W. Nobby 40th and Nigger 47th.

In the Beef Shorthorn sales the spring event was again a good result with an average of £1,937, an increase of over £350; their Senior Champion, Balmyle Dinkum, junior and overall reserve Champion, Chapleton Dakota, respectively fetched the top prices of 3,000 and 4,000 guineas. Dinkum was the last bull from that herd.

1993 produced some very good statistics for Irish progeny overseas in the USA where the Irish bulls had achieved so much. That they had continued to do so was evident in the analysis of their bull list with 450 bulls in the senior list. Ninety-seven were direct Irish sires that showed that the trait leaders in no less than four traits were the Irish sires. In the birth weight 'M and S Culhane', sired by Highfield Highler 204th, led the field. In the weaning weight a Deerpark Leader 13th sired animal was the leader – H.P. Bandwalker – and he was also the yearling weight leader and in fact 3rd and 4th places were also Irish. In the balance traits the highest average on all traits was Deerpark Leader 13th who had also sired the winner A.F. Paramount. In the junior section 12 out of 159 had direct Irish sires. Later in the year 2000 Deerpark leader 13th was still the leading sire with 587 daughters contributing to his continued success and quoted by the US Shorthorn Association as being 'one of the top breeding bulls in the 20th century'. The surprising market figures for the UK were that 51% of our beef came from the dairy herds, 28% from the beef herds and the rest came from cull cows. Selling through supermarkets in 1980 had been 20%

but in 1991 it was 42%; the conventional butcher was really losing out
and this often meant that the beef from the supermarket was not hung
long enough therefore the flavour and tenderness was impaired so
consumers lost interest. However it was hopeful at this stage that an
association with one of the supermarket leaders could be negotiated,
to market branded Shorthorn beef but the handicap was still the
comparatively small numbers in the UK to enable regular supplies.

A very new breeder, Alan Wass, who farmed land in Scotland and
Norfolk with a Beef Shorthorn herd, won the spring Perth event with
his **Derryage** Excalibur, but it was the reserve Champion, Uppermill
Bounder by Banner Instant Royal, who topped the sale at 3,400 guineas;
later in the season he was to win the Championship at the Royal
Highland. Bulls at Perth averaged £1,689. The autumn sale showed a
better average at 1,793 guineas with a top price of 2,500 guineas for the
junior Champion Uppermill Rotary. The Champion was Loch Awe Eros
who raised 2,100 guineas for the Coombs and again the females from
Glenisla met a ready trade averaging 1,263 guineas with a top of 2,300
guineas for Glenisla Foxglove Flake a record price for a yearling. There
had been sales of Beef Shorthorns at the annual show and sale for the
Rare Breeds Survival Trust at Stoneleigh before, but this year there
was a special offering and demonstration by Bob Howard of **Trunley**
prefix near Bramley in Surrey who with D. Sandys of Richmond had
done much in that area to promote the breed, although having
comparatively recently started their herds. Bob Howard had consigned
around 24 of various breeding and ages to the event, some having been
his foundation stock and it was one of these that fetched the top bid at
2,500 guineas and his stock averaged 1,420 guineas but it was one of
the other exhibitors John Dunlop whose bull Tarrant Endeavour who
not only took the breed Championship, but went on to win the
interbreed Championship as well.

The Royal Show was a great event this year and the judge Mervin
Lennie from Orkney was privileged with one of the best shows for
some time. He eventually gave the male and supreme Championship
to Balmyle Crackle for John Doughty in front of Banner Instant Royal
from Uppermill but he gave the female award to their Flossy Freta and
placed her as reserve supreme. Later in a thrilling contest they made
up the pair that was interbreed supreme for the Burke trophy and Miss
Durno was presented with the coveted award by Her Royal Highness
Queen Sophia of Spain, before an attendance 26,000 people. The Beef
Shorthorn Teams won in 1962-59-56 and 1954 when the Shorthorns
created a record that still stands by winning both the dairy and the
beef cups. Someone made the interesting comment on the performance
that when it was first won by the breed there were 10 dairy breeds and
9 beef eligible, but this year there were 8 dairy breeds and **20** beef

eligible. Quite an increase but it also emphasises how the competition for the market had increased as well, nevertheless a remarkable achievement from a breed that had shrunk so low in numbers to be able to come up with such a quality pair.

The dairy winner at this event was Orchardhome Maude 6th again; although Charles Epps now owned her, he allowed Andrew Orsler to show her again for old times' sake! This time the show was judged by Lloyd Peters from Australia so there could not have been any pre sighting of this consistent winner; he picked the Doggerell's Chicklade Strawberry as his reserve.

In the sales, records were broken when the Chelford show and sale was held: the Spaltons' Maxton Lady Hermione 53rd was sold at the sale after the show for 2,800 guineas, the highest ever paid at a Society show and sale, paid by J. and G. Whalley. The Champion of the show was Winbrooke Vi 36th from the Dents herd and she fetched the second highest price at 1,800 guineas; reserve female Champion was Bilbro Blush Rose from H.P. Jackson but the show reserve Champion was awarded to the bull Amber Royal Ringlet who was sold to A. Ritson for 1,700 guineas. Cattle were certainly in demand as the average also set a record at £1,120 for cows in milk; £1,276 for cows in calf; £ 1,257 for heifers in milk; £1,374 for heifers in calf; bulls £1,351 and therefore an overall average of 1,302 guineas.

Two old-established herds were dispersed, one giving up milk production: the **Birchfield** herd founded in 1949, of Stuart Elliott in the Peak District where once more there was excellent genetic material available as they had used such sires as Hodder Ruby King, Swepstone Bates Duke 8th, Eaves Fairy Gladiator and Wreay Wild Premier 3rd as well as their own B. Furbelow Boy. The average of £1,116 was for 49 cows, with a top of 1,450 guineas for B. Lady Furbelow 197th. The other herd was the **Hintonbank** herd, founded in 1924 by Mrs J.Alsop; she did not believe in showing but her herd was often top of the Shropshire herds also with very high butterfats; later the herd was run by her daughter Mrs J. Hutchinson Smith with her family. They specialised in Cheshire Blue cheese production obtaining many awards. Early bulls used were from Iford , Northease and Drisgol herds; later they used bulls from the Young Bull Proving Scheme and their own Hintonbank Dandy who became one of the successful sires. They then went into the blended scheme but went towards the Holstein. There was also a reduction sale for the Rodway herd of the Madeley family whose cattle were also appreciated with a top of 1,750 guineas for Rodway Red Rose 12th; the average was 1,309 guineas for heifers and 1,086 guineas for cows.

Mention above of **Winbrook** at Winton reminds me that the prefix was started after George Dent's father sold the famous Brook herd of

Winbrook Royal Kathleen 2

Northern Dairy Shorthorns and was continued by George Dent and later his son David; in around 1965 the herd sale averaged 95 guineas for 53 cows and 53 guineas for 30 heifers. There were four sons: George, Arthur, Christopher and William. George had gone to Winton in around 1960, starting up with a number of cows from Brook and anyone that doubted that NDS cows could not yield much would be proved very wrong when they read the NDS chapter and also when they read the Brook and Winbrook herd figures. In an upland situation Alice, Ruth, Queenie, Gill and other descendants produced averages of 9,262lb in 1964 with fats at 3.7%. The herd won many herd competitions and had great successes at local and county shows, supreme at Cumberland with W. Alice 2nd, Westmorland with W. Jill and W. Dairymaid 2nd at the Great Yorkshire show. Several Winbrook sires had gone into A I including W. Midnight in Northern Ireland. However around the time of the Stowfield dispersal they decided they needed some more size and their purchase of Stowfield Royal Kathleen 3rd at the Stowfield Sale ensured that the prefix stayed in the public eye with consistent wins at many more local and national events; they had the champion herd in the north west region in 1991,1992,1993 and 1994 with very correct stock and a production average of 5,937kg at 4.04% for 35 cows and 5,029kg at 4.05% for heifers. Tragically they were one of those hit by foot and mouth but fortunately had a group of heifers on some away land that provided some of a restart.

When mentioning the Dent family, so many have been involved with the breed over the years, but in such a record I could not overlook the **Kaberfold** herd, started in 1919 by W.J. Dent, and continued by J.B. Dent from 1951. Prior to this the herd had been non-pedigree and altogether there will have been five generations of Dents concerned in this herd. More recently the herd has been line bred to Kaberfold Cascade and among the progeny have been K. Royal Casket 1,2,and 3, K. Epigram, K. Prince, K. Viscount 1 and 2 and K. Rosette Hero. The herd has won countless interbreed competitions and prizes at many shows including winning the Penrith Show and Sale two years in succession. In 1949 with six animals they won six major awards including the male and female Championships as well as winning the Lowther Trophy Outright with a pair.

Another similar long family connection (as well as using some of this breeding) is the **Strickley** herd of the Robinsons of Strickley near Kendal; they have four generations connected with the herd which, although started as non-pedigree, graded up from 1916. They were the first herd in Westmorland to milk record and the 3rd to go accredited. The first notable sire was Janie's Warrior who really stamped his mark and created a consistent type, one of which won the interbreed at the London Dairy Show in 1938 – Strickley Maggie 11th. This sire was followed by Kabberfold sires and then Stockwood Gay Lad came and in turn came Hodder Ruby Prince, who had a stiff leg through injury and had to have a special licence, but left some excellent stock. Then a son, Strickley Play Boy, later Drisgol Waterloo Comet and Tyas Lord Barrington. Then came a change in direction with the Australian Illawarra Meadowhaven Pride's Starr that Willie Robinson and a syndicate bought in. After this there was an introduction of Meusse Rhine Issel bloodlines that coincided with a health breakdown eventually diagnosed as a copper and selenium problem coincident with ostertagia worms (it never rains but it pours); once diagnosed, the herd made a rapid recovery to ensure their stock and well known Daisy, Peggy and Janet families were again in demand.

1994 was a very eventful year after an atrocious spring, and for the dairy industry (again with hindsight), it was an atrocious year as the **Milk Marketing Board was wound up** as a marketing organisation although there was a continuing organisation to deal with National Milk Records that took the latter wording as its title. The MMB was considered to be a monopoly. It had grown into a large civil service type organisation with the accompanying bureaucracy but it had provided very essential stability in the market. However after the first year without it, when the dairies and supermarkets vied for everyone's business with splendid offers, the market developed into a cut-throat price war with dairies unable to sustain these offers and the producer

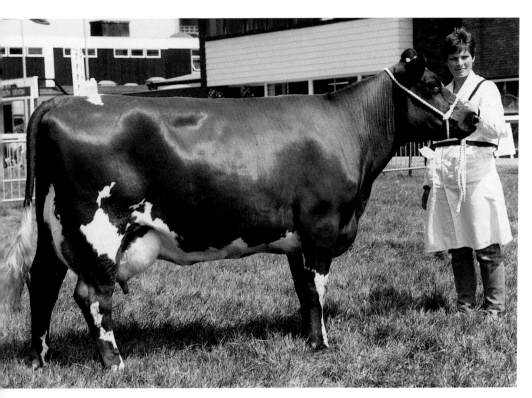

Stowfield Favourite Berry: Champion at the Royal Norfolk 1985.

Chapelton Xile Supreme Interbreed Champion 1989 at the Royal Highland and Supreme at the Royal Show

Orchardhome Maud 6th

The Croxton Park herd at pasture.

Rantonall Joy 16th

Winbrook Vi 24

A dairy class at the Royal Show in 1989.

Kaberfold Barrington

prices cut to uneconomic levels. Many had made considerable capital investments in order to expand.

One of the results from the Society's point of view was that they needed to found a company to ensure the marketing of Shorthorn semen and the continuation of the Young Bull Supply Scheme that had improved status of both the sections of the breed. It coincided with the end of the CBIS Company, which had both purchased bulls and semen but more recently had only marketed semen. So the council formed **RED CATTLE GENETICS (STONELEIGH) LTD** as the trading arm of the society with directors elected. The organisation became known as RCG. Their first chairman was John Hayward of the Hooton herd, and the directors were coincidentally elected from both the blended and pure sectors of the breed. The company would market both pure and blended semen and negotiate contracts with the breeders. The Society office would deal with the administration and the Society Secretary would hold the same office for this company. The government had also decided that a bureau of records should be set up to record all data for all breeds and herds so that they had an accurate record of the national herd health status as the BSE issue had raised a number of issues.

There were a number of dispersal and reduction sales in both sectors this year as well as the usual Society sales; all showed increasing

Tofts Romany

averages, some of which were due to the apparently increased interest in dairying. Obviously that did not affect the Perth sales, the first of which averaged a pleasing 2,015 guineas with the supreme Champion and reserve coming once again from Uppermill with U. Larch and U. Leslie respectively. The same herd achieved the top price of 3,200 guineas with their bull U.Lister. Chapelton Fulcrum also reached the same figure for the Biggars, being sold to the Scottish Milk Board. Such a success for the Uppermill herd was a fitting marker for Miss Durno as she was awarded the OBE that year in recognition of her services to agriculture not only to the breed but also her work as a Director of the Royal Highland Show.

Later in the year there was a combined reduction of the a number of herds including the Newfield herd from Ripon, the Tofts herd from Kelso and the Bromborough that was dispersing and Upsall that acted as hosts. The sale was held in a climate of lowered beef prices but reasonable averages were achieved: Upsall £1,446; Tofts £1,114; Newfield £1,486; and Bromborough £1,136. Top of the sale came Lavender Cassa of Upsall from Upsall at 2,600 guineas.

The **Tofts** herd was established in 1980 by the Playfair Hannays, who already had a top Angus herd. They had acquired foundation animals from Newton, Parkfield, Winbrook and Twells herds and combined these with a dash of Maine Anjou, and Canadian breeding through the sires that included Balmyle Zeus and his brother Zephyr and Glenford Pacesetter. As well as producing bulls for suckler herds, they intended to produce excellent cows for the same purpose with their own Angus females. It was to be their Tofts Romany that was to be reserve Champion at the Royal Show in 1994 and go on into a remarkable career winning the Championship at the same event in 1995 and also the Royal Highland for his new owners Messers James Biggar of Chapelton. This bull was a good example of how the various sectors of the breed could be brought together to produce what was required as he had the accepted Beef Shorthorn strains in company with dairy and northern dairy and Maine Anjou bloodlines in his pedigree as well. He also proved to be a great producer of quality stock.

Newfield was founded in 1987 from Chapelton, Fingask, Glenisla and Uppermill, as well as the entire remaining Otterington herd in 1991 after Miss Furness's death. This herd was making rapid strides for M. Abrahams under the management of Ray Sanderson. Bulls included Chapelton Eclipse and Newfield Colonel. The **Bromborough** herd was a small pedigree unit within a very large commercial one that worked a Continental sire onto Shorthorn cross dams.

The dairy sector, after a slow start at their spring event, had an incredible year; their summer sale, as it had become, although not achieving a record breaker with the high price certainly did so when one counted up over 40 lots selling over 1,000 guineas. The male Champion Maxton Sailor by David Spalton's outstanding sire Maxton Mossybank raised 1,500 guineas, going to a new herd in Wales. The female Champion, Rantonall Goldie by the American sire Kingsdale Peris Champ, was from the pure-breeding Rantonall herd of John and David Winnington; R. Jewell by their latest sire Hooton Fair Resolve from the same herd, who had not been shown, realised £1,800, also going to another Welsh herd of Mr and Mrs J.E. Willis. The average on the day was £1,234 overall for quite an increased entry.

The noted Drisgol herd held a sale marking the retirement of Leslie and his wife Megan, before their son Simeon took over to continue the winning herd. A crowd of over 500 people including top black and white breeders were present to see another **record fall with D. Mabel 13th selling at 3,000 guineas the highest ever paid for a Dairy Shorthorn at auction:** this was paid by J.C. Hayward of the Hooton prefix. She was out of D. Mabel 7th who had won 20 Championships as well as being part of the Burke trophy team; Mabel 13th had herself been 2nd at this year's Royal. D. Sibella 63rd was another sold at a high price of 2,100 guineas and D. Bella 24th, who had been first at the Royal and Champion at the Royal Welsh, was 2,000 guineas. Calves were also reaching high figures with Mabel 7th's son D. Best Man, at three months of age, sold at 1,000 guineas. At the end 20 had sold over 1,000 guineas and all contributed to the average of £1,172 overall.

Retaining the sales in one group has meant that the Royal shows have been left till towards the end. At the Royal Dublin, although there were several major prefixes in the winners, the successful exhibitors were mainly from the smaller herds. Dermot Cahill from the Dovea A I centre, who had done so much to encourage the breed during the improvement scheme, was the judge on the day. The Champion was the bull Tierquillan Enda, owned by J. O'Connor, whose Nohaval herd had been established for quite a time. His family had not registered for some years until the improvement scheme, then had become enthusiastic again, building an excellent herd. The Champion female was a Ballingarrane cow Lottie from the herd of P.J. and Carmel Kelly. The groups were won by the McKeons from Sligo whose cow Carrowhubbock Fanny 9th went on to the Royal Ulster to gain reserve Champion and the Flanagans who also had an Angus herd. They won both of the junior heifer classes so nearly every one had success! But the quality of the event was failing and indicated that it would soon not get support, which was tragic after so many years of being a major event in the Irish calendar. It was getting harder and harder to get to the venue, with the congestion in the city. The Royal Welsh went to Drisgol Bella and the Royal Highland to Balmyle Crackle with Fingask Bergerac as reserve. The English Royal was a repeat success for Orchardhome Maude 6th, with another Chicklade heifer, Flower 4th, as reserve to her. In the beef Balmyle Crackle won again and Flossy Freta repeated the same success winning the females, this time with her calf. I have extended this round-up as it was **the 50th anniversary of the regions** that had done so much to support the breed by their membership involvement, and to publicise it by their shows and sales and open days, all of which generated local interest as well as interchange of ideas, problems and cattle.

The autumn Perth Sale supreme was awarded to M. Abraham's Newfield Gambler, making it the first time for many years that an English bull had won this honour; the reserve went to the junior reserve Uppermill Rebel. In the females it was a 21st birthday present to Catriona Gibb: Folda Glenisla Rosebud took that Championship and nearly topped the bidding at 2,000 guineas, but it was her father's Glenisla Duchess H6 that eventually gained the top with a bid of 3,100 guineas. A number of new buyers were forward to produce an average for bulls of 2,188 guineas; females were 1,245 guineas

1995: Perth was considered to have the best turnout for many years, with the Champion cup going to Uppermill Ling, who sold for 3,600 guineas; but the top price was another from the same herd, U. Bews at 4,400 guineas, with the reserve being Newfield Hannibal. The average continued its upward trend at £2,356.

The World Conference was held this year in South Africa where we were able to see the results of many years of exports, particularly from Churchill, Gainford, Maxton, Drisgol, Uppermill and Winbrook in recent years as well of course as their own cattle. Judge of the dairy

Newfield Colonel

cattle and their equivalent to the Burke trophy was our David Spalton who was privileged, with his wife, Lynda, to meet their President Mr de Klerk.

The **Parkfield** herd of Roly Fraser from Scone was one of those dispersed and had an average of 1,028 guineas for cows and calves and 1,050 for heifers with calves, and a top of 1,500 guineas for P. Rosewood Pink and 12 selling at over the 1,000 guineas.

There was a shortage of keep when the **Newfield** herd near Ripon held a combined open day and reduction sale. Cattle sold around the UK including the Isle of Man and reached a top of 1,650 guineas – for N. Augusta sold with her calf – but it was a year of several dispersals of Dairy Shorthorns; most were old- established ones due to death or retirement, but they happened to be of the pure-bred type in the majority. The **Groby** herd that had been owned by Mr and Mrs F. Morris had been founded in 1940 and experienced considerable success during the ensuing years, managed for them successively by J.W. Tweddle and Leslie Mellor. Their first sire Netherscale Wild Marmion sired 11 Champions and over 50 prize winners. A later bull, Groby Brigadier, sold to Islip breeding centre for 2,000 guineas having won the Championship at the Society show and Sale. A number of high-priced sales from the herd also won many herd competitions. Exports included animals to South Africa, Kenya, Argentina, Ireland and Argentina. Another major success in more recent times was their bull Groby Dandy. The sale was at short notice but the quality of the stock ensured a ready trade with maiden heifers reaching 1,300 guineas and calves 400 guineas. G. Dorothy 117th sold to the top at 1,400 guineas and the averages were: cows £796; heifers £674; maiden heifers £692.

The next sale was that of Miss R.Aldridge who was retiring after being dedicated to the pure breed with her **Eaves** herd, founded in 1948 with one cow on a smallholding. That cow was Evenhill Fairy 19th, who went on to become a 100,000lb cow and have around 30 of her descendants in the eventual sale. The Fairy family extended to almost 200. Later moving farms, the herd developed with many of the well known pure lines, among others Orgreave, Orfold, Amber, Lenborough and Stokelycross in which Miss Aldridge had great faith, and this was borne out by her stock. One of her many successful animals was Eaves Fairy Gladiator who had a considerable influence on the breed as he went on to Amber and Birchfield herds. Many of the bulls used included those on the young bull list, such as Twells Moss Trooper 4th and Heather King 15th, Maxton Mossybank and High Society, Tonelea Commander and Ratby Rupert and Villabrook Merryman. Showing was not generally practised but a number of herd competitions had been won. Management was strictly commercial and since the quotas, they were not even 'steamed up' (fed up with concentrates before calving) but the average yields were 6,585kg at 3.77% Bf and 3.13% protein at the time of sale when a large company gathered. Again stock went throughout the UK. Eaves Fairy 166th was the top price at 1,850 guineas, so the original Fairy was a good investment! There were a number selling over the 1,000 guineas to finish at an average of £987 for cows and £883 for served heifers and even calves reached £730 despite the national climate that was somewhat subdued at the time as well as the tropical summer being experienced, making keep short.

The other well known herd sale was that of Frank Moy who was retiring after a long association with the breed. His **Churchfarm** herd in the Cotswolds found a ready demand with a top bid of 2,000 guineas to secure C. Blush Rose 7th, sold to the Willis family from Wales. A further Blush Rose was sold at 1,550 guineas, then her month-old heifer calf was sold to a long established breeder, W.S.J. Pugh, who paid 920 guineas. One of the features of the pure-bred sales was the high calf price to those who did not wish to see these valuable lines die out. The average finished at 849 guineas for cows; 957 guineas for heifers.

The grass shortage and the quota situation meant that farmers could not realise the potential of their stock and so a large number of all breeds were for sale. It also had some effect on the joint reduction sale of the Cotley and Chicklade herds in the West Country but a number of new Shorthorn buyers ensured a steady demand to obtain these well bred cattle with potential. Averages similar to those at Churchfarm were achieved: £989 for the Cotley cows and £940 for the Chicklade entry.

In the Society sales **a record was broken again**, this time the sale was at Carlisle, for Winbrook Jill from the Dents when the Davies family from St Clear, nr Dyfed, who had been supporting sales for a while to form a Shorthorn herd alongside their Friesians, **paid 3,200 guineas** for this Champion, being underbid by another recent Shorthorn herd owner from Northern Ireland. The Chelford events were another success for the Winningtons of Ranton with their Rantonall herd when their R. Songstress 11th gained the Championship and sold for 1,350 guineas but the top price was for Hooton Lily Fair 110th who fetched 1,600 guineas to a telephone bid from N.Ireland which were definitely looking for English breeding. Rantonall repeated their winning streak in the autumn when they again gained the Championship, this time with their young bull R. Director. The female Championship was again from the Dents of Winbrook by the same sire Maxton Edward, W.Tulip 2nd that later fetched 2,000 guineas to S. Girven of N.Ireland.

This was definitely a good year for both Hooton and Rantonall as they were also Champions at the Royal Show when Hooton Lily Fair 111th was supreme and Rantonall Dainty Princess E.T. was reserve to her. H. Lily Fair 111th teamed up with her relation H. Lily Fair 109 to win reserve Champion in the Interbreed Dairy Burke competition and then a little later H. Lily Fair 109 went on to Harrogate to gain the Championship at the Great Yorkshire. What a successful year for these two herds and the breed. The **Rantonall** herd was registered by W. J. and D. Winnington in 1978 although the family had bred Shorthorns for around 44 years before this. They graded up from their original stock using bulls such as Garnedd Llewellyn from J. Perry and added stock from Stockwood, Lenborough, Hauxwell, Orgreave, Wappenbury, Woodcall and Streetly and it was from here that Streetly Waterloo Rose 39th bred them their first major successful sire Rantonall Prince Roseman and several sons of his were used.

A son of Maxton High Society, Maxton Vesper bred several type daughters and much use was made of the Young Bull Proving Scheme animals alongside bulls of their own prefix such as R.Allan, Barnabas, Heartthrob, Dainty Prince, Pure Joy Lord Nelson, Mark and others; in recent times Hooton Fair Resolve has produced outstanding stock. The main female lines have been Joy, Echo, Waterloo Rose, Nellie, Burrows, Susanna, Nellie, Maysay, Lady Serene, Di and Wild Queen. The herd has been noted for longevity allowing sale of several young stock and more mature animals including recently ten to Ireland.

The Perth autumn sale was a sad occasion as it included the last of the Calrossie pedigree herd but even then they broke another record, when **the female Calrossie Amber**, who was in-calf to one of the best bulls in USA, Sutherland Titleist, sold to Major J.Gibb of Glenisla at **3,600 guineas**: **the highest price for a Beef Shorthorn female at auction.**

Rantonall Pansy 6th, Echo 9th, Joy 16th

The Calrossie females sold to average 1,680 guineas for cows with calves, 1,300 guineas for cows in calf, heifers in calf 2,633 guineas, and maiden heifers 1,050 guineas. In the main event Alan Wass had an excellent day gaining both the Championships with Derryage Hannibal and Gypsy 3rd respectively, the latter gained the top female price at 1,600 guineas.

Although this is the up-to-date record of the breed's progress it might be fitting to recall that this year was the 100th anniversary of the death of Amos Cruikshank, who, as recalled in the early chapters, did so much for the breed both at home and abroad, exporting to many countries. It was also the bi-centenary of the death of Robert Bakewell who in effect revolutionised the breeding principles of the world; I wonder what he would have made of the two breeding policies of today's breeders.

At the start of **1996** detail was circulated from a recent veterinary symposium when it was reported that well over 25% of the national herd was experiencing foot problems, most of which required foot trimming. Some of this was caused by modern husbandry method problems such as feeding, yarding or standing in slurry but it was a horrific and expensive statistic, more likely caused by foot and leg angles as well as hoof make-up. This problem hardly affected the breed, as foot trimming in both sectors of the Shorthorn breed is almost unknown owing to the excellent structure of the breed in this respect.

Sales got off to a difficult start with dreadful weather conditions preventing some stock and buyers from attending so the average of 1,966 guineas for 20 bulls was reasonable, especially as the quality remained good. The Champion at Perth came from a young herd,

Moncreiffe John by Fingask Bergerac that went on to fetch 6,200 guineas, the highest price at the event for 30 years for a Shorthorn bull. He was purchased by Alan Wass who had the reserve Champion Derryage Jackpot. This herd, only founded in 1990, had quickly won considerable success with 2 supreme Champions and 2 reserve Champions as well as Champion and reserve female at this event. The autumn event was also won by a young herd, Loch Awe Jack Flash for the Coombs, but the industry was really worried by the effects of the BSE crisis mentioned earlier that made the increased average a very welcome statistic at 2,345 guineas. Uppermill Rogie reached the top price at 3,700 guineas. There was quite an offering of females from 6 vendors who were selling some 34 animals; this could have been too many in the depressed situation, but in the end they need not have worried as there were eager buyers. There are two female sections in this sale, one for led stock and the other free running (or hopefully walking!). This year Glenisla had the Champion in G. Waterloo Zola. But it was an unled heifer that raised the top price, Glenbrae Broadhooks Kizzy from J. Nelson of N. Ireland, whose herd was also developing quite fast, received 1,600 guineas.

Over in Eire it was a sad day when Kevin Culhane sold his world famous **Castletroy** herd through ill health. It contained unique bloodlines of the Irish strain that had done so much for the USA Shorthorns. The stock, which had never received supplementary feeding, attracted a huge crowd of over 600 from all Ireland, Scotland and Ireland. Top price of the day was for C. Freda 2nd who raised 1,720 guineas selling to Michael Quane of Deerpark who purchased several lots; the largest buyer was Lord Harrington buying 7 for his developing new herd. A young May calf sold at 1,400 guineas to Sam McCullum in the North who also purchased several lots. The average for cows in calf was 828 guineas; heifers in calf 1,262 guineas; maiden heifers 900 guineas; bull calves 523 guineas; heifer calves 632 guineas, not including a cow and calf that raised 960 guineas for the Irish charity donating funds to Uganda. One of the pleasing aspects of this time, both in Ireland and the mainland, was the evidence of new herds being set up despite the trends in the industry. One could again consider that breeders were returning to the breed.

In the January of the year a small delegation was invited to the Orkneys, an area where the Shorthorn played a very important part of the islands' economies; but because of the distance and transportation costs it is not a feasible proposition to run a herd with the object of selling breeding stock to the mainland. The number of Shorthorn herds is quite considerable especially as the islands are so exposed, so a number of them have come to the mainland for suitable sires. Contrary to general belief several of the farms are quite large and with a total headage of around 30,000 head of cattle and units extending to as much as 1,600 acres, the cattle business is very important. M. Lennie of Nearhouse, S. Scarth of Cavan, E. Flett of Hurtiso, Black of Toab, Sinclair of Lucknow, Robertson of Brunthouse, Stanger of Birsay and many others are some of those breeders who show stock at their Orkney show and raise stock for local needs or the slaughterhouse on the island as it developed its own market brand for the Orkney meat, Orkney Gold, that sends both lamb and beef products to the mainland particularly to the south and London.

Towards the end of the year Beef Shorthorn won the overall breeds supreme for the fourth time since they had been put on the organisation's list in 1986, at the Rare Breeds Survival Trust show. This was held for many years at Stoneleigh on the Royal showground (more recently at Melton Mowbray). Before two judges this year Trunley Lavender Damsel 17th, bred by Bob Howard and owned and shown by the Wymott Prison farms, won this award; she eventually sold at 1,150 guineas, being one of the highest prices for all the breeds on the day.

1997 was a difficult year despite a healthy increase in the breed sale average at the Perth sales (2,562 guineas with a top of 5,200 guineas for the Champion Uppermill Grant and 2, 700 guineas for their female Champion Lovely Lash, giving them a great day) and an excellent demand for females despite the considerable depression in both sectors of the industry with the cumulative effects of the BSE crisis. This had been handled with panic and media hype, so had resulted in huge unnecessary slaughter and an over-reaction from customers. There was no denying the horrors of the disease in humans and animals but over reactionary safeguards had been installed. There had been 164,381 animals diagnosed with the problem. A further 195,485 suspects were slaughtered as well as 1,056,877 slaughtered in the 30 months' scheme in 9 months. Scientists had predicted that provided they were correct in their suspicions as to the cause there would be a falling off in the incidence and it was beginning to look as though they were correct. In the mean time to this date there had been 60 human cases, which of course was 60 too many, but it was said that the risk was such that it was 60 times more likely that one would be struck by lightning. At the same time there had been 60,000 cases of women dying through cancer brought on by smoking. 1,200,000 animals had also been slaughtered in the cohort scheme (where there has been contact) but still the media kept the 'scare' publicity and this, coupled with the slaughter schemes and the decline in consumption, created a severe downturn in both sectors of the industry. Livestock prices in general had taken a dive but with the decline in incidents it was hoped that public consumption would gradually return.

On to more positive things: **1997 was the 175th anniversary of the Coates's Herd Book** and as the President of that year, Graham Madeley confirmed the improvement schemes had all proved successful and demand was returning on both sides of the water. In N. Ireland they had been staging coloured breed sales which had proved very beneficial; for two years they had attracted great interest both from buyers and sellers, so much so that a number of English breeders had been invited to enter stock. Herds like Maxton were in demand; their prefix had again come to the fore by their winning the interbreed award in the three-day trials at the European Dairy event with Maxton Ada. Winbrook and Hooton had also been much sought after. They had repeated their previous year's win as H. Musical Bouquet 28th had gained the Championship and highest price 1,760 guineas on that occasion, but it was in fact Hooton Lily Fair 117th that gained the top price of 1,700 guineas and their H. Fairy Duchess 19th was reserve Champion. Champion of the day went to a local breeder, K. Boyes, with his Pennygate Pansy who sold at 1,100 guineas. With these achievements it was looking as if J. Hayward would need to start a herd in Ireland to meet the demand! There was another mixed sale further south at Carrick on Shannon where the Champion, a yearling heifer Lavelly Lady Jane, reached 1,800 guineas and a bull, Rynn Luke bred by B. and N. Faughnan, sold at 1,700 guineas. This trend continued in to the south when J. Moloney sold his renowned Highfield herd near Limerick which had so many achievements in recent years. This stock had, as mentioned, made such an impact overseas and had been bred for scope, bone and size, also used to survive and thrive on an all grass, no concentrate diet, with any line that could not produce on this system being culled. To see these cattle grow and gain in the spring had to be seen to be believed. Like at the Culhane sale, huge interest was evident in the very large crowd to see the top price of 2,100 guineas being paid by Lord Harrington, again a major purchaser, for H. Strawberry. They had already seen a young February calf, H. Fury, sold at 1,900 guineas (3x his dam) to Michael Quane for Deerpark. The eventual averages were: cows with heifer calves 1,681 guineas; cows with bull calves 1,844 guineas; heifers in calf 1,050 guineas; cows in calf 808 guineas.

Over in England one of the increasingly popular events that had been held for three years was the calf show for younger members. For many years of the decline sadly there had not been many young members and as I said sometime earlier there were too many single breeders! However things were now changing and those young enthusiasts were also very aware of the dangers in getting their stock over fat, after years of it being drummed into them, so several of those young members in the north east had got together with their parents and created very successful events, keenly attended, organising preparation, showing and handling classes. One of those families participating and organising was the Collins family from Dewsbury, Yorkshire. Ian Collins was later to win the national intermediate judging competition that culminated at the European dairy event in 1998. He was later honoured by being invited to judge in South Africa at their Royal Show, demonstrating effectively the success of the calf shows that initiate such skill and interest. The family's **Churchroyd** herd is one that had been winning more and more in herd competitions and shows and this year they pulled off the dairy Championship at the Royal Show with Churchroyd Bronte Wildeyes 9th; not content with that they also carried off the same award at the Great Yorkshire with the same young cow. Reserve at the Royal was another Cotley cow, C. Anne 35th, and in the Beef Shorthorn ring it was a repeat for Balmyle Crackle with Glenisla Pauline Daisy 3rd winning the female Championship after just a few weeks before being Champion at the Royal Highland Show.

Mention a moment ago of the younger members reminds me that one of the most pleasing happenings was that two colleges had also decided they would reintroduce Dairy Shorthorns to their herds for the benefit of the students – Reaseheath in Cheshire and also Brackenhurst in Nottinghamshire (so that famous old prefix of that name was revived). The autumn sale at Chelford was in some ways a sad occasion as it was to be the last that **John Thornborrow was to act as Society auctioneer before his retirement bringing to and end over 100 years** of his family firm's association with the breed. He had been running the event at this market of Marshall and company now since 1990 with their close co-operation and it was Glyn Williams who took over specific responsibility for his company from then on as Marshalls were appointed as the Society auctioneers. The Champion and reserve awards on this day went to Maxton with their M. Graceful 34th and M. Lady Jane 4th and the male award by a well bred bull, Winbrook Max from the Dents. The top price was 1,400 guineas for Graceful and averages of : cows 686 guineas and heifers 686 guineas were achieved.

The **1998** Perth sales were marred by the passing of Miss Mary Durno, OBE, who had for so many years been a major personality not only with her Uppermill herd but in Scottish agriculture as a whole and known throughout the world. However it was learned with relief that the Uppermill Shorthorns would be continuing under the management of her nephew Stuart Durno, so that very long connection with the breed would continue. To prove it the herd won the female Championship at this event with their Rothes Menna. The male Championship went to Loch Awe Lysander by an Australian sire Belmore Uptown, selling at 4,000 guineas but the top price of 4,400 guineas went to Chapelton Landmark. The sale price of all breeds was down but the Shorthorn females, including a further reduction from the Tofts herd, were eagerly sought and it was Tofts Holly H12 that topped the bids at 1,700 guineas. The autumn sale was held again in a very depressed atmosphere and again it was a long established herd that gained the Championship with Chapelton Landmark by Tofts Romany; another noted herd, Fingask, gained the reserve award with their F. McCracken, the female Champion being Glenisla Foxglove Flake L10.

The World Conference was held in eastern Australia this year and, as one might expect, it was largely beef orientated. Everything there is done on a huge scale with vast acreages and numbers of cattle. Feedlots holding 40,000 head of Shorthorns and more stretch literally farther than the eye can see; it showed us how important the industry is to their country and how involved the breed is with that industry. The scale was further emphasised when, among others, we visited the home of the Weebollabolla herds of the Munro family that covered an area one and a half times the size of Scotland and the herd was again over 40,000 head. It made our average beef and dairy herds of 60-70 head seem like toys, but it also emphasised the importance of structural correctness in both the dairy and beef strains of the breed.

Back at home it was these attributes that were drawing producers back to the breed; at sales the commercial buyer was having to study his economics closely owing to the state of the industry, but of course the numbers of cattle available were still very low after the decline. It was evident that quality animals found a ready sale, but the amount buyers paid was restrained as their final product was continuing to decline in price particularly in the dairy sector, and to pay too much for the stock would mean bankruptcy. The judge at the spring Chelford event was Tom Osborne whose family had one of the largest herds in the south west; it was run on very commercial lines in recent years with little showing and low labour and food costs.

The **Goodwick** herd, founded in 1929 by Gilbert Osborne, and later taken over by his son Ken in 1961, built up to around 200 milkers at one time; had obviously used a number of bulls including Holmhurst Sharon Emperor, Streetly Wild Command, Collingham Main Darlington 2nd, interspersed as well with their own sires, G. Charming Prince, G. Oxford Emperor, G. Joyous Lad, G. Winsome Lad 2nd. The herd had a number of 100,000lb cows and the Osbornes were fortunate in the longevity of their cattle. In the earlier days, during the '50s and '60s, they gained a quantity of awards including championships at regional shows and herd competitions. Ken Osborne used to pay tribute for these achievements as well as for the running of the herd to Basil Palmer their herdsman who was with them until his retirement, but for a while more recently there was no time for much showing until Tom Osborne became involved.

To return to the Chelford event, the top price was for Broadlane Sunlight 8th from a young herd, **Broadlane,** owned by the Norbury family that was making rapid progress. She realised 940 guineas and the sale was marked by the number of new buyers. The Champion was Drisgol Belladonna 122nd, sired by another USA bull, Merrivale Peerless, another sire that was to have quite an influence. Thankfully the BSE problem continued to decline, incidence being over 60% less than in 1996, lending further credence to the scientists' findings as to the cause, but there was another worrying health problem – the continued increase in tuberculosis in cattle. A number of herds were being affected that had been clear for years; some said this was caused by cross infection from badgers but there still was no conclusive evidence on this; worryingly the problem was to get worse. Broadlane Shorthorns had been building up since around 1979 when the Norbury family found their Friesians were not yielding as they should, so, not fancying Holsteins because of their size, they had purchased Shorthorns gradually at Crewe, buying a Tonelea and a Dunham female to start with, then adding from dispersal sales. They found at one stage they could not obtain semen locally so by chance they started blending and gradually built up with judicious choice of sires including Meadowhaven Pride's Starr, Hauxwell Barrington Duke, Fletching Baronet, Dunham Choirboy and Orchardhome Lord Walton 3rd as well as some of their own breeding, such as B. Historian as well as others on the Bull Scheme. Gary Norbury, who took over from his father, is one of those a little sceptical about the value of PIN and prefers to make his own assessments. His stockmanship has proved this very successful.

During the year there were some three dispersals: **Goldstraw** for the Housemans was bought about by ill health, sadly for a recently established herd in West Wales, and although they had made considerable progress this had struck the low price time, but their top was for Goldstraw Rosie Belle, a winner of many prizes by a very successful sire Drisgol Superblend, who reached 1,000 guineas. The other sale was of the long-established **Thornthwaite** herd of Mrs Marriot, which also reached a similar top price for T. Lady Rosedale 69 but both suffered a low average of around £460, but this was not to be so for the very old **Wreay** herd that over the years had experienced two incredible sales in previous years. But this was a retirement sale, as 'Billy' and Margaret Jackson had decided to disperse owing to their son going to New Zealand. In recent times as well as bulls from the scheme, Winbrook Firecracker and Drisgol Mabel's Prospect had been used to good effect. The herd had been milking three times a day for some time when they achieved an average yield of 6,935kg at 3.95% B fat but more in recent times they had changed back to twice daily milking. The herd had been pure-bred for many years but had gone toward the blended principle; the Wreay lines had become so well appreciated that this attracted a huge crowd from the UK and Ireland where the breeding had nicked in very well. The top price was 2,300 guineas for W. Princess Foggathorpe 25th and the second did go to Ireland at 1,500 guineas for one of the famed Wild Eyes, this time 407, again demonstrating the constancy of such families. The average for 70 cows was £744 and heifers £488. Several went to Ireland, where there was another favourable coloured breed sale with an Amber heifer, Lovely Diana 10th, selling at 1,100 guineas; she had been the breed Champion as well, helping the Hole brothers' consignment considerably! As did their Amber Barrington Iris 61st that was reserve Champion, sold very close to calving, at 800 guineas. Their stock and that of the other consignees from England including Maxton were always well received. The **Amber** herd completed a very successful year by winning the gold cup for the UK that year with A. Barrington Iris 46th. The same herd also achieved the reserve with A. Starling 3rd.

Towards the end of 1998 Her Majesty the Queen was advised to delegate some of her responsibilities, and one of these were some of her Patronages. Her **Royal Highness The Princess Anne accepted the invitation to replace her as Patron of the Shorthorn Society of Great Britain and Ireland**.

1999 in the beef sector thankfully started with an air of optimism in Perth and it was also a great start for Chapelton as they achieved senior Champion, reserve supreme and reserve Champion as well as the team awards for bulls with their C. Majestic, and C. Masterkey respectively, adding C. Mercedes to make up the three for that group; Masterkey gained the top bid of 3,500 guineas but they left the supreme Championship to the junior Champion Adhor Merlin, bred by Rhoda Mclaren and owned by Alan Wass, and he also reached 3,500 guineas. The female award went to Uppermill Rothes Moira making it three in a row and thereby they had won the Dunmore trophy outright; Moira reached 850 guineas but it was Moncreiffe White Lady that achieved the top price female at 900 guineas: all setting an average very similar to the previous spring event.

This year the Beef Shorthorns tested two new outlets, the first was actually a revamped show and sale at Thirsk that had been launched and organised by the north of England beef members the year before, as there had been a lot of interest shown in that area. Some 42 females went through the ring before a large crowd and an average of 531 guineas was achieved and the top price of 1,000 guineas went to the Champion Tugby Tessa 11th, an interesting animal as she was the result of a mating between 2 Royal Show Champions, Balmyle Crackle and Balmyle Tessa, and so should prove an interesting breeder. A junior heifer class winner, Tugby Irania, sold to the same buyer at 955 guineas. The second event was the addition of a beef section at the Chelford autumn dairy event and here again there was a reasonable entry headed by Tugby Firethorn that sold for 1,320 guineas with an average similar to Thirsk. The autumn Perth event had a very few entries for bulls and 8 averaged 2,178 guineas with a top of 2,800 guineas for the reserve Champion Loch Awe Mephistophiles who had been reserve Junior Champion at the Royal Highland. The Championship was awarded to a young herd founded in 1993 that was growing fast – **Croxton Park** for their Croxton Endeavour. It was another young herd with the prefix Cragie that captured the supreme interbreed beef single animal competition at the Royal Show, the National Westminster Trophy, from Mr and Mrs Russell from Aberdeen with Uppermill Loch Alsha, a five-year-old sire that they had bought around three years before. Two weeks before this event they had stood reserve supreme interbreed at the Royal Highland with the same bull. The female Championship at the Highland went to Chapelton Broadhooks J18 and they repeated the success at the Royal when another Chapelton animal, Chapelton Kiwi, was reserve to Loch Alsh.

The Amber herd continued their run of success in the dairy sector with the Championship at the Portadown sale in N. Ireland with Amber Merry Maid 51st; she also sold at the top price of 1,250 guineas and 4 of their entry of 9 achieved 1,000 guineas and over. Continuing their winning streak they gained the top prices at the Chelford Spring event their A. Princess Alida and A. Barrington Iris 72, both of the blended type, sold at 710 and 810 guineas respectively; the next, at 650 guineas, went to the pure-bred Newpark Mandy 5th from H.S. Craig and Sons from Bishops Auckland, the long established herd that were much involved with the Northern Dairy strains in the earlier days and that suited their conditions admirably. Champion of the event was Dunham Claribel 101. A further event at Chelford was the dispersal of the long established Ockley herd for M.J. and S.M. Calvert. This herd had been trucked up from Surrey following the decision to cease dairying on their estate and had for a long time been a winning one in herd competitions in the South East although they had not shown for many years. They had been involved with the blended scheme almost from the start and the consignment in fact included a number of Holstein cows but unfortunately it was not EBL tested so limiting the sale possibilities. However the top price was 750 guineas for Ockley Pilgrim 41st and the Shorthorns' average exceeded that of the Holsteins. The autumn show and sale was again held in difficult times but it reached a reasonable average of 551 guineas. The Champion was Maxton Lady Darling 36th, who also gained the top price of 910 guineas. The event was judged by Neil Madeley, owner of the up and coming **Nejay** herd whose Nejay Charming 5th had won the breed Championship at the recent European Dairy Event both on inspection and also the Total Performance Evaluation. That was a new development that included the CGI and production as well as inspection, so all credit to them. Foundation stock came from Shorthorn Society Sales and reduction or dispersal sales, one of the best being Churchill Foggy 27th purchased in 1988 with many of her descendants in the herd, another being Valentine Dainty Princess. Mainly blended sires are used. Their current average is 7934kg at 3.81%bfat and 3.16% protein.

Two other sales also struck this difficult period: one the dispersal of the old established **Greaves** herd that contained a number of valuable bloodlines and so drew an excellent crowd despite the fact that the numbers were greatly reduced. The Cynthia family was the best represented and were eagerly sought after and the top of the sale was purchased by the Haywards for Hooton at 920 guineas for G. Cynthia 126th, a great purchase as she had had many records of over 7,400kg. Another such prospect was another Cynthia, the 123rd, who had just yielded 8,000kgs with her 2nd calf and was purchased at 740 guineas by G.Madeley of **Rodway** who later in the season held a reduction of his interesting herd that included several breed champions. At this sale one of these, R. Butterbur 21st reached 1,450 guineas having been a dairy event Champion as well as having given 7,500kg as a heifer. Other high calls at the sale were R. Marie 26th at 880 guineas, R. Topsy at 800 guineas and R. Primrose 10th at 780 guineas; just as at the Greaves sale there was much interest from N. Ireland and R. Sonnschein 4th was sold to G. Booth from Co. Tyrone.

The Royal Show was marked for me by the high quality and number of the exhibits (over one hundred) with beef and dairy, and my official retirement but I suspect the two were not connected! More so because of the judge, who was over from Canada but was so well known and respected throughout this country and Canada alike for his Hauxwell prefix. He was most complimentary about the turnout and the progress the breed had made, eventually selecting Cotley Melody 38th as his Champion and the very well known Hooton Lily Fair 111th, who had been Champion in 1995 but still lasting well, as reserve.

M. Taggart took over officially as Society Secretary at this event but my 20 years' stewardship, which seemed to have gone so quickly, was almost an apprenticeship compared with the 43 years served by Jim Norton for the Irish Shorthorn Association; he had been so helpful to me, and had also decided to retire this year. We would miss our many friends but we were relieved as there had been so many changes to the breed and it was well on the way to recovery. The other administrative decision was the appointment of Frank Milnes as the Society Field Officer who had also carried out the classification work since the retirement of Edward Evans. One other administrative change was made: from time immemorial the Annual General Meeting had been held during the Royal Show with the consequent disruption; now the council had thankfully decided it could be incorporated in an open day and that it should be peripatetic so that each region would be able to be more involved.

One of the first developments in **2000** was that Her Royal Highness the Princess Anne consented to become the **Patron of the Beef Shorthorns as well as the parent Society**. The second was the decision of their council that the **beef section of Coates's Herd Book would be closed as from January 1st, 2001, to any outside influence** although breeders could still use the breed's Dairy, Northern Dairy, Whitebred or Lincoln Red bloodlines; also any imported Shorthorns or breeding should carry that country's designation e.g. Imp Aus (for Australia) or Imp Ca (for Canada).

In their registration the February Perth Show and Sale showed a healthy increase in the breed averages at 2,860 guineas for 21 bulls and an excellent top price at 6,000 guineas when the senior Champion Chapelton Nimrod, another fine son of Tofts Romany, was purchased by Uppermill; this seemed to be a perfect way to greet the new century, especially as their bull Uppermill Remit was the reserve Champion. Chapelton Norseman, the supreme Champion, sold to a very healthy 4,500 guineas.

A further Chapelton bull C. Neptune by Romany, went at 4,500 guineas to C.J.S. Marler who was going add to founding or re-founding the **Wavendon** herd that many years before, in the late '30s and '40s, had been a well known Dairy Shorthorn herd. Major L. Marler had purchased the Basildon herd in the '60s but owing to business commitments it had to be sold. C. Marler had become internationally known for his Belted and Dun Galloways with the Bolbec prefix, having won some 10 Royal Shows and 4 Highland Shows. He had recently dispersed these at his renowned wildlife centre near Buckingham and was gathering females from Calrossie Uppermill and Chapelton including Flossie, Secret, Lovely, Rothes, Broadhooks and Blythsome lines as well as a number of embryos from Australia, and was quickly to become a major success at events while the breed was coming back to prominence. The young herd built up to some 70 head at the time of writing selling his first offering of males at Perth at 6,000 guineas each for W. High Finance and W. War Emblem.

The autumn event was another success for Uppermill as they had both the supreme Champion, and the reserve Champion, also the highest price with the Champion being U. Firby selling at 2,800 guineas and the reserve, U. Forden, making 4,600 guineas. The next highest price for Groveland Puccini was paid by C. Coombs of Loch Alsh and

J. Playfair Hannay of Tofts at 3,200 guineas. The Champion female came from Chapelton: a full sister to their Broadhooks, the 1985 Royal Highland winner by Tofts Romany, she made the top price female at 3,400 guineas. The sale average was £2,468, well up on the previous October event.

Here perhaps I should point out belatedly and with no relevance to the above report, to students or others new to the breed, that the price paid does not necessarily reflect the quality of the bull as the purchaser has to assess what assets that particular animal has that can correct or improve their own stock. One bull that has many correct points may be totally the wrong sire for your particular herd requirements.

The Regional Thirsk Show and sale produced their first record with the very young Champion Newfield Plum Blossom, a winner of the Great Yorkshire classes and sired by one of Australia's current best bulls, Spry's Pakaraka Quarterback, selling at 1,225 guineas. The average for cows was 643 guineas and heifers in calf 469 guineas. A similar average was obtained at the later Chelford event although there were only a few entries: Tugby Firestar sold at 1,000 guineas to go to the Spalton's beef herd at Maxton (they had just sold a dairy bull Maxton Invader to N. Ireland). Dairy Champion in this sector went to the Dent's Winbrook Jill 113rd and the reserve Dunham Jill 17th, with the male award going to Broadlane Premier Gwynne. The outstanding aspect of this sale had been the number of 7/8,000kg yields in the pedigrees that had probably been one of the main factors attracting the large crowds present. It was always a shame that the dairy stock could not attain the prices of the beef sector, but the dairy industry was yielding such a poor return it was not surprising. It was also the case that many dairy units were turning over to beef although the returns were not much better but the overheads were less.

One of the good things affecting the livestock industry was the re-opening of the export situation in Europe, albeit at a low level, after the horrors of the BSE problems.

But it was not this that bought large attendance at the **Greystones** dispersal in Lampeter, S. Wales, for Sally Willis. She had been a passionate advocate of pure breeding and built up a choice herd from a variety of sources to great effect and her array of championship and first awards confirmed this. It was one of these that raised huge interest when Greystones Joy sold at 1,800 guineas to another renowned pure herd, Rantonall of the Winningtons in Stafford. Her daughter, G. Joy 2nd, stayed in the principality, selling at 1,000 guineas to the Davies Elkington herd in St Clear. A number of cattle were sold locally to commercial buyers but a major consignment buyer was from Devon, I. Samuel, who was expanding his recently founded herd. He had finally purchased 13 and another volume buyer came from N. Ireland, C. Elkin, who took 17. The averages really did not reflect the interest, rather the current trade, as there were a number of senior cows and also young stock; cows averaged 411 guineas; calved heifers 529 guineas; maiden heifers 207 guineas.

A herd ceasing milk production, the **Pewterhouse** of Marshall Kelsall, was also dispersed. This unit had been one that had returned to the breed from Friesians in the early '80s and again had bred mainly on pure lines; again there was major interest from N. Ireland with a number going there and also Scotland. This herd averaged £476 and maiden heifers £254.

In the principal shows and dairy events the Cotley herd had a field day, or several, as they were Champion at the Royal Show with C. Anne 40th, this time before a N. Irish Judge, Ken Workman of the Whitefalls herd. Reserve to her on this occasion was Rodway Butterbur, and Anne 40th then went on to win the South West Dairy Event with the reserve to her this time being her herd mate Cotley Fairy 104th. Cotley had also been placed Champion and reserve at the earlier Bath and West show with two other animals C. Melody 98 and C. Anne 35th; what a year for them. They did however leave the European Dairy event to others and here the ribbon went to Nejay Princess; that herd also pulled off a great treble as her dam Valentine Dainty Princess won the total performance evaluation Championship and Nejay Princess went on to gain reserve interbreed Champion. The breed reserve at this event was Marleycote Waterloo 57. It had become the custom to present the NMR trophy for the highest national average in the UK at this event and on this occasion it was awarded to John Reader for his **Wenvoe** herd down in Wales with a remarkable yield average of 9,003kg per animal. This herd is part of a 180 cow unit that includes Holsteins with around 40 Shorthorns, milked three times a day. Their principal families in this breed are Briars and Rosalind, several of whom are in their 10th or 11th lactation. Some of the bulls used are Winbrook King Henry, Maxton Top Hat, Meadowhaven Prides Starr, and their own W. Briars Man and W. Briars Master that are also available in A I.

A remarkable year for the breed as well, but towards the end M. Taggart had decided to leave the organisation and **Frank Milnes** was appointed as Acting Secretary in the short term, and then at the start of **2001** he was appointed as **Secretary of whole Society, both Beef and Dairy as well as the World Council.** This was to be one of the few good things to occur in this year. One other was the negotiation by one of the previous Beef Society presidents, Cary Coombs, **of a contract for the breed to supply Marks and Spencer** with Shorthorn beef through Scotbeef Ltd, an independent company that would co-ordinate and supply traditional premium beef to that supermarket company following trials during January and February. This was to be delayed, but the Perth Show and sale was another plus marker as there was tremendous interest in the Beef Shorthorns reported as one of the most spectacular sales of recent times with the top price reaching 6,800 guineas for a second prize bull Proud Landmark of Quoiggs. He already had several prize cards to his name, and went to J. Cambell Graham at Drymen who also bought Pode Hole Power House, from a very recently founded herd with the prefix Pode Hole of C. and H. Horrell near Peterborough (the H is for Harry, the 13 year old enthusiast) for 3,400 guineas. Champion on the day was Uppermill Birse selling at 3,800 guineas; he was followed by Chapelton Publican, another by Tofts Romany, as reserve Champion selling at 6,500 guineas going to another new herd. Loch Awe North Easter, a second prize prospect, sold at 5,000 guineas. The female Championship went Fingask Petula Crocus from W. McGowan who sold to the top of that section at 1,300 guineas, all contributing to an average of £2,648 for 24 bulls. The President J. Playfair Hannay made the pertinent comment that 'it was a great show of commercial bulls that was reflected in the price and it was pleasing to note that commercial beef producers were outbidding the pedigree men on a number of occasions'.

The sale was on February 5th and on **February 20th foot and mouth was confirmed in the country.** This was to start the most horrific outbreak the UK had known for many years. All movement of stock was halted and all sales and showing were later cancelled. The first outbreaks were in pigs where it was considered they had been fed either uncooked or insufficiently cooked household waste that included meat. Owing also to the long distances that stock had to be transported because of the Government's policy on abattoirs, also the large supermarket companies' slaughter policies where they preferred to have all or most of their animals slaughtered where they had some control, the disease spread like wildfire. The south west and the north west were the worst affected initially and then the whole of Britain. As a consequence of the number of outbreaks the normal methods of control were totally unable to cope with the outbreak. The total inadequacy of the Government policies fuelled the situation, until the army was called in with a disciplined approach, but again this should have been done weeks before; although it is easy to say with hindsight, the enquiries came to the same view.

Every business, not just those in the countryside, was affected to a greater or lesser degree by the knock-on effects. Farms and villages became isolated; the holiday trade was closed and overseas tourists stayed away with a consequent huge loss of income. Food and machinery companies suffered huge losses and winter fodder could not be conserved. Thousands of farmers were ruined, as even if they did not have the disease they were unable to sell their stock and many had insufficient fodder to feed the stock they had. The stress caused even if your farm was not infected was incredible, families were isolated and the strains on relationships were horrendous. Rents or mortgages were unable to be paid, and thousands of animals were unnecessarily slaughtered, owing again to the cohort or contact policy. When the disease was eventually conquered there were huge tracts of land that were barren of stock for months to come, some still are, and the palls of smoke in the early days as one went through these areas emphasised the terrible experience. There was some discussion concerning vaccination as some countries such as Denmark had been fairly successful in this approach during the major European outbreak of 1952; but there are at least three different types of the problem and at present the vaccination would have to done annually, so even now, no decision has been taken in this respect and still there are insufficient precautions being taken on imported meat, legal or otherwise. We are informed that more meat is entering the country illegally than legally; the Audit Commission has quoted an incredible figure of 12,000 tons; so we are still in considerable danger. We are far behind countries like Australia in respect of curbing illegal trade or import. Thank God, the breed was extraordinarily fortunate in the fact that relatively few were lost but of course the loss of those was catastrophic. The Society were notified of most of them; they are listed with their prefixes: Biggar of Chappelton; Brown of Easthele; Emerson of Wheatside; Goaman of Fordlands; Ritson of Ireby; Hewson of Parton; Dent of Winbrook; Prince of Huxley; Jackson of Wreay; Grange of Alveston; Richardson of Copley; Bailley of Roadway; Evans of Whitehouse; Coulthard of Briscoll; Teasdale of Brafell.

The wait to see if your herd is affected is bad enough, but then, if it is affected, the stress of losing your life's work and the actual disposal must be more than most can bear. Then you have the financial stress, and the emotional stress. In, I think, every case, those affected have started up again. Their courage and fortitude was phenomenal. Some, like Chapelton, obtained embryos from overseas, thus bringing in new as well as old bloodlines; their Canadian embryos traced back to many of the best cattle exported and several traced to the much-mentioned Irish stock. Dairy replacements came from many sources, from members who had been more fortunate, such as the Spencers of Courtover, who had hoped to disperse before the problem. Others, like Parton, were able to locate some of their old breeding from other sources and, like Brafell, were able to re-stock partially from herds in Wales that had been going to disperse, like Mrs Thomas, widow of the late Glynn Thomas, of Penycoed, and others that had stock to sell.

But all those whose herds had been infected had been kept busy as John Teasdale of Brafell had said with the horrors of keeping up the pyres and then the emptiness and the cleaning and sterilising of their premises that partially kept their minds employed. The **Courtover** herd had originally been founded in 1934 as a flying herd, but later was graded up to pedigree status with bulls such as Uplands Lord Troilus 2nd and Uplands Foggathorpe Diplomat and later Stockwood Gay Lad 5th and Courtover Supreme as well as bulls from the Young Bull Proving Scheme; their recent policy had been toward the blended cattle but the time had come for retirement that of course had to be delayed by the problem. Donald Spencer had been on the Society council for many years, including being President in 1989 and 1990, as well as his farming and a leading member of Monmouth County Council. Like so many, he combined many interests with work for the Society.

Thankfully Ireland was not so badly affected by the foot and mouth problem but most events were cancelled as a precaution until towards the end of the year. The Shannonside club held a show and sale at Kilfenora with a good entry. Tonore Silver 4th, bred by Pat Casey, was the eventual young Champion but the top price was for Ovaun Ita, bred by M. Gunn at £790; other events were the Strokestown show and the show and sale at Nenagh, when cattle sold up to £1,040 for Mizen Belle from P. Salter, with calves reaching £440, and in-calf heifers to £840. Champion on the day was Knockagarry Primrose 28th who went back to Maxton breeding. However the sale of the year was the dispersal of the Ballingarrane herd that had achieved so much, so understandably there was a large attendance with a large number of cattle selling over IR£1,000, the top of the day being B. Belle 269th that went at IR£ 2,100 to J. and N. Faulkner from Co. Cavan; animals went throughout the whole of Ireland as buyers eagerly snapped up the breeding, recently served heifers selling to IR£1,700 and young calves to IR£ 700; the Jennie Dean, Belle, Lottie, Daphne and Grayling lines were eagerly sought by old and new buyers alike. This year the Irish Shorthorn Breeders Association requested a further register in the Herd Book. The Irish Register and the Shorthorn Council agreed to join the Irish Cattle Breeders Federation. Further administrative decisions were that in future the red and white register would become the Supplementary Register and the Journal would only be an annual publication but improved in design again.

The only Perth consignment at the end of this year was that of the customary Glenisla heifers on the 27th of October which, quite apart from their ready demand, was yet another step back to normality in a horrendous year for all livestock farmers. There were 31 heifers available both to their usual buyers and also to some who were re-stocking after their losses, but even some of those would have to await delivery as their areas were not yet clear of restrictions. Top bids were 1,500 guineas for Glenisla Margo R33 and also for Glenisla Foxglove

Tansy R47. Maiden heifers sold to 1,450 guineas for Glenisla Mercenary to go to Chapleton for the Biggars, who had already secured embryos. The sentiments expressed by the late James Biggar, not long after losing his life's work and at the age of ninety, epitomised the spirit and fortitude of all those affected: 'We are starting again for the sake of Donald (his son) and the Grandchildren, I am looking forward to the next ten years.'

2002 was obviously a difficult time for many, but amidst all the worries there was a definite air of relief. Many whose stock had not suffered the disease were in severe financial difficulties as stock had not been able to be moved or sold as restrictions remained in force for some time, added to which those so affected had insufficient fodder and little or no cash to buy any; despite all this trade was good as farmers endeavoured to put the problems behind them. There were also a number who were revising their systems and in some cases there was evidence that a number were returning to the Shorthorns. There were many enquiries for Shorthorn stock with some also changing from dairy to beef. The February Perth show and sale saw immense interest in the breed: 24 bulls drew an average of 2,662 guineas with the top of 8,000 guineas, the best for 40 years, being paid by D. Bull at Croxton Park, for Harry Horrell's Podehole Rambo the junior and supreme Champion by Loch Awe Lucky Jim.

This was remarkable as Harry from Thorney near Peterborough was only 13 years old and, as mentioned, a passionate follower with his family of the breed; even more remarkable was the fact that as well as this he also had the female Champion Podehole Rhapsody by the same sire who gained the top female price of 4,200 guineas, selling to Glenrinnes Farms (again the best price for many years). The reserve Champion Richard of Quoiggs from Blackford Farms, who was also senior male Champion, reached 5,000 guineas, going to I. and N. Girvan from Kelso. Following him closely, Bonaccord Ramstoorie from the Aberdeen City Council reached 4,500 guineas going down to Romsey, Hampshire. Almost exported! The reserve Champion female D.A. Mcleod's GlenGloy Flossy sold at 2,400 guineas.

Although the prices were lower in the autumn there was still strong commercial interest when 11 bulls sold at £2,148. Glenisla Rhum, a Royal Highland show winner, received the Championship and sold at 4,200 guineas to Glen Rinnes Estate; following him as at the Highland was the Durno's Uppermill Rue at 3,800 guineas and his herd mate U. Ringleader realised 3,000 guineas. In the female ring Tessa of Craigeassie for Lord and Lady Glendyne gained the Champion trophy but the top price was a Northern Ireland cow with her calf, Glenbrae Augusta from J. Nelson, for 4,000 guineas to J.Cambell Graham of Drymen. In the unled section Major J.Gibb's 18-month-old heifer

Glenisla Foxglove Tansy sold at 3,500 guineas and, as usual, his consignment was well received as G. Una Clipper made 2,800 guineas and G. Rosebud 1,600 guineas being his top bids. The two Chelford beef section shows and sales met similar interest when buyers were seeking females but Champion male at the June event was Hallsford Anthracite sold at 1,890 guineas. In the female H.M. Prison Wymott sold Colonywymott Flossy Bess at 880 guineas and her herd mate C.Lavenda Damsel for the same figure; both had calves at foot. Cows due to calve in the autumn from P. Wood of Winchester averaged £689 and up to 850 guineas for Newfield Nutmeg. Strong trade again in the autumn, this time Colonywymott gained the Championship with C. Lightening who made 990 guineas and stock was sold to as far away as Cornwall and Scotland. Averages were: cows with calves £802; cows in-calf £525; heifers in-calf £868

The Thirsk event was judged this year by Robert Grearson, head herdsman from Chapelton, and he gave the Championship to Derryage Rhyme from Harry Horrell; he had an extraordinary year selling at 1,350 guineas but the top price went to J.Playfair Hannay for their heifer Tofts Princess Royal selling at 1,650 guineas to create a record at this event. Another curious record was also broken when Glenbrae Banner, bred by James Nelson, sold from Northern Ireland to the West Country, being the first bull to be sold for breeding to England for 40 years and carrying both English and Irish bloodlines.

The show season had got back to normal and the Royal Highland saw a Chapelton sire at the top of the breed again: Chapelton Nimrod owned by the Durnos of Uppermill gained the trophy and ribbon and Uppermill also took the female award with their Rothes Morna. Down at the Royal Chapelton breeding was again to the fore: owned and exhibited by the Horrells, Chapelton Promoter, reserve to him was Glenariff Lancaster Krystal that was the female winner.

The **Glenariff** herd is owned by the Barrett family near Kings Lynn who have a number of other interests among which is a very unusual one for cattle breeders – they are world famous canary breeders. Maybe their appreciation of good stock gives them an eye for cattle as well, as their herd, founded in 1989, is rapidly becoming successful in the UK. They have secured a number of Championships at major shows including the Royal Norfolk Interbreed and the Great Yorkshire Interbreed and the Royal Welsh breed to name a few. Their stock bulls, Uppermill Lister and Beggar and Chapelton Legend left them some excellent stock. One of the very pleasing things is the number of promising herds that are coming along to bring the reputation back to the breed in all parts of the country as well as in Ireland.

This is also true on the dairy side but the industry is so reduced and has many more restraints it is much harder to make inroads; however their share of the market is growing as breeders recognise the breed's potential and productive longevity and temperament. This is demonstrated by the number of both pedigree and commercial breeders that are at sales; having said that, pedigree has to be commercial as well. The term is to differentiate between those that are interested in the breeding aspect or not. On the dairy side the full Chelford buyers' gallery also demonstrated the returning interest. The June event was won by Amber Princess Anne 39th for the Hole family and the reserve was Weaverdale Foggy 6th from the Pattinsons, who continue to bring forward very genuine correct cattle from their farm on the top of the Derbyshire hills. Many black and white buyers were seen to emphasise the genetic improvement and appeal that has been achieved and catalogue entries showed several entries with yields up to 9,000kg lactations, an aspect never seen before.

The top price of 900 guineas was gained by the W.D. and B.P. Norbury partnership with their Broadlane Greenleaf 5th who went to one of those re-stocking, A.H. Ritson of Ireby. There was also an entry from Messers Long with their very low cost production regime where heifers sold to 480 guineas but the average for the main sale was £588 for heifers and £612 for cows. The October event saw Ian Collins of the Churchroyd herd select Rodway Wildmaid 17th as his Champion with Hooton Fair Achievement as reserve; here again there was a flying trade with Dunham Duchess 41st reaching the highest price at 990 guineas. Champion went to the long established Wallhope herd of Messrs Pugh at 900 guineas; the averages on the day were: calved cows £801; in-calf cows £740; calved heifers £787; served heifers £609, with the one bull, Hooton Achievement, reaching £850.

The Doggrells had decided to change to a Beef Shorthorn herd and so put their Chicklade milking section on the market but unfortunately their sale was the week after a sale of 500 head commercial Shorthorn herd nearby that even included some of their breeding, so the prices were low for excellent cattle as quotas were full, but their top was 1,020 guineas for Chicklade Strawberry 241 going to the Whittles in the next county.

In the show and event season the Royal Show was another success for Hooton with their H. Fairy Duchess 25th this time heading the winners and her reserve was Cotley Anne 40th, Champion in 2000. At the European Dairy Event Fairy Duchess did it again when she was Champion as she was at the Great Yorkshire; runner up to her at the Dairy Event was Ellerghyll Lady Marigold and at Harrogate it was Marleycote Pamela 9th. Exhibitors this year were still very handicapped by severe movement restraints, so all credit to them all. Over the water in Ireland the President John Teasdale reported he was unprepared for what he found at the national ploughing match. Anyone who has not

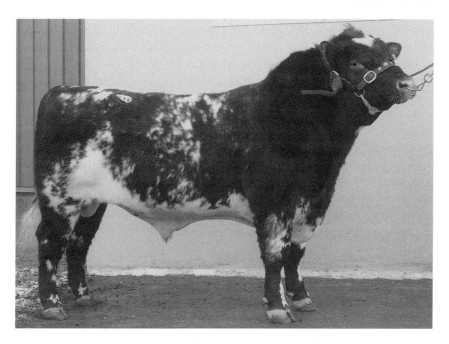

Fearn Scotsman

attended this event has missed the experience of a lifetime and will be surprised! Spread over 500 acres this peripatetic event is attended by, I swear, the whole of Ireland! Every organisation remotely connected to agriculture is there and that naturally includes the Irish Shorthorn breeders, but it is normally the south-eastern club that is responsible for their stand. How they do it I have no idea but year after year they obtain and man a sponsored Dutch Barn at a cost of around IR£3,000 for the period of the event and for that period it is packed with interest and enthusiasm. The highlight and part of the method of repaying the sponsor is a raffled calf or the equivalent funds with ticket buyers there from morning to night, as well as interested enquiries. Quite how it is so successful I don't know as they are not alone in such activity at the event but their effort and enthusiasm is fine to witness. All credit to them.

Mention of enthusiasm reminds me of the calf shows with the young breeders; this year was the first all breed calf show with tremendous competition and enthusiasm in the various breeds; in the Shorthorn ring, most of the competitors come from the Midlands and North. On this occasion David Dent of Winbrook was the judge, picking Marleycote Thorndale Bates 77th as his Champion from G.G. Baynes and Son out of an entry of 36 calves, and Twemlows Baroness from R.W. Barnett as reserve. The **Marleycote** herd, founded in 1932 at Slaley,

Hexham, had bred on traditional lines developing their well known families of Peerless Rose, Thorndale Bates, Petal and Waterloo with a series of excellent bulls that knitted in using Histon Premier, Feathercome Marksman and Premier, Eathorpe Bellringer, Orchardhome Nelstar, Meadowhaven Prides Starr and Amber Duke, Maxton High Society and their own Marleycote Cragsman and Waterloo Cragsman. Surplus heifers were sold and their bull calves run on for bull beef. Their current herd of 120 head of cows contains a few Ayrshires as at one time they were unable to find sufficient Shorthorns and they have moved to blending, but stressing that they return to the pure-bred so that the beneficial traits are retained by the dominant Shorthorn genes. Both the two sons, Paul and Richard, trained with Holsteins but have no wish to move the herd across to that breed. Since the boys have been able to help, the herd has increased its showing as it is considered an excellent form of advertising. Their current average is 6530kg at nearly 4% fat and 3.48% protein all lifted from about 1990 when it was around 5,500kg.One of the refreshing developments in recent years has also been the return of younger members as well as their enthusiasm which is all important as they will be the breeders of the future and the future of the breed.

Enthusiasm is not necessarily the prerogative of the young and that was demonstrated at the surprise Cotley retirement dispersal when some 270 head came under the hammer. Over 70 years of breeding was on offer. The herd had been successful over so many years that it

Osbornes team Cotley: C. Melody 98, C. Anne 40 and C. Anne 35: the Champion Interbreed Group at the Bath and West 1999.

was not surprising to see the ring absolutely packed with buyers and supporters as well as new faces; especially in recent years the consistent success of the breeding policy had been evident to all at the Royal, at dairy events and regional shows. Top price of the day was 2,000 guineas achieved almost at the end of the sale when C. Pathfinder 2nd by C. Sundowner out of C. Anne 35, the Royal Show reserve Champion winner and twice Bath and West Show Champion, was purchased by Simeon Thomas of Drysgol. C. Pathfinder, his brother, went at 1,700 guineas to the Ritsons of Ireby. As well as being a winner in the ring, C. Anne 35 was a winner in production as well as she had yields up to 9,867kg with her 5th calf at an amazing 5.16%butterfat and 3.75% protein. She herself, at 9 years of age, was purchased for 1,000 guineas. A daughter, C. Anne 46th, in-calf to Winbrook Henry and by Sequa Barra Shorty, was the top price female at 1,700 guineas. There were in fact 22 lots exceeding £1,000 and averages were for 118 cows and heifers £732; calved heifers £720; autumn in-calf heifers £850; spring in-calf heifers £724; bulling and young heifers £522; bulls £1,855.

Although the book is drawing to a close it is true to say that the enthusiasm continues as during the next years the demand for both sectors continued with records in the beef sector at Perth with a bull **Fearn Scotsman selling to a recent herd owned by Bill and Jane Landers of Newton Stewart for the highest price for 50 years – 11,000 guineas**. They had just won the Championship with their own Cairnsmore Sam who sold at 6,500 guineas to the Glenrinnes herd, while in the autumn sale Christopher Marler of Wavendon sold a cow and calf, Blythsome Jut with Wavendon Empire Maker, for another record at Perth at 4,800 guineas. Then they sold Wavendon Flossy Fiat privately for 6,500 guineas a little later. As I write in 2004, 5,500 guineas was bid for Glengloy Lovely Tapaidah from D. MacLeod of Glen Gloy at Perth setting yet another record there. All demonstrating the return of public confidence. On the dairy side there are economical yields that would have been considered a mirage a few years ago both on the mainland and in Ireland and buyers have returned from other breeds.

A few years ago buyers had started to return to the breed as they were so much cheaper than the competition. They were then surprised how well they performed, and they learned that the old values had been retained, but the cattle had size, were cleaner, smoother fleshed and more in line with modern requirements and so they came back again and brought their friends with them. David Baynes, when President, said, 'We no longer have the milk industry built on sentimentality. Black and white breeders are buying Shorthorns as replacements proving we must be breeding the right sort of cattle.' The whole cattle-breeding industry can no longer afford sentiment; the stock, whether it be beef or dairy, has to pay its way and there have to be good reasons to buy what one does. One has to be prepared for change, so one must retain a variety of types. **The genes of the breed provide the benefits of dominance, structural soundness giving excellent trouble-free feet and legs, thus lowering veterinary costs; good temperament giving ease of handling; maternal attributes, ease of calving providing less stress to dam and calf, as well as less labour and supervision; best protein value, giving better returns; marbling, providing better tasting and better cutting meat, and good growth on low cost foods if required.** With the returning interest there is a great danger of the increased popularity resulting in indiscriminate rearing. Any breed that expands rapidly runs the risk of falling into the trap of popularity bringing increased prices, and that may bring decreased selection and culling, it has happened before in other breeds and this breed cannot afford that to happen.

Today the scene is so very different from that of even one hundred years ago, let alone two hundred years when the breed was established. Today's market is such that the price of the final product is being driven down, so that the farmers in their turn have had to reduce their costs and overheads. In dairying and in beef the animal required is one that converts low cost products into meat, milk, or cheese or by-products. The same applies to beef products. The beast must also be the one that thrives. The other main consideration is how long that animal can remain economically productive and this is an essential point as if the animal's surplus progeny can be sold, either as a producer, as meat, or as a replacement, there is a distinct cash advantage in having more to sell. Some breeds today with the pressures put on them require a 25% replacement rate, whereas the Shorthorn can be 16% or less, depending on the system. Today the farmer generally has to achieve absolutely maximum production from his investment; the pressure on him, or his staff if he can afford them, is more than ever before and the pressure on his land is the same, land costs are so high that he has to obtain maximum economic production from all three – man, beast and land.

When you look at the photographs it is plain to see the changes in type in both beef and dairy; despite in some cases having the straw up to their bellies, supposed to exaggerate their closeness to the ground, it is still easy to notice the shortness and compactness particularly when compared with their handlers.

Today's Shorthorn has been re-modelled in both the dairy and beef sectors to convert low-cost fodder with low-cost methods, to a product that is acceptable to the public, while at the same time, because of its structure, providing economic longevity with as few problems as possible. Today's aims, which are being achieved, are to produce as much as possible from as few animals as possible at the lowest input and costs; the combination is an extremely important balance. Today's cattle produce many times more than their ancestors with as little veterinary involvement as possible, so the noted proven docility, ease of calving and lack of foot problems coupled with good mobility assists low labour involvement. The farmer today *has* to handle a large number of stock to survive so it has to be as trouble-free as possible. The saying of Bates all those years ago holds as well today as it did then: 'The only test of excellence is the comparison of the food they consume with the improvement they make.' The breed can thrive under any climate and management system. In the beef market the breed can utilise the upland if required, to the maximum ability converting low quality grazing; it can also convert the predominating mediocre Holstein type beast, or poor quality suckler that has developed, to be a reasonable meat producer. The Dairy Shorthorn today can produce the products required with lower labour input and overhead costs, so the swing back to the breed must, and will continue, but its future remains with our current breeders who are charged with ensuring that the Shorthorn meets the current needs, what ever they will be, and also maintain a variety of types to cope with future trends. The auctioneer John Thornborrow once stated, 'The breed has an illustrious past and it can have a bright future but it will be no less than the breeders choose to make it.' So true and at present it is steadily regaining its rightful place in this highly competitive market.

12. Sales, Shippers and Sellers

Much has been written about breeders and cattle so it is now appropriate that some space is devoted to the other side of the business and those who contributed to its success: the sale venues, the auctioneers and the exporters.

Over the years there have been a number of markets involved and throughout the book many resulting prices and sales have been recorded. The importance of Perth in the beef sales has been shown and how the world came there in the good times; but around the United Kingdom and Eire there have been many venues, some that have come and gone and some that were mainly regional. The early days in Scotland did not revolve around Perth as my chapters may have intimated: Aberdeen, Inverness and to a lesser extent Edinburgh, Elgin and Oban all played a part. The first three all had shows and sales as well as collective sales.

In Ireland, Belfast and Dublin were undoubtedly the main centres but there were also many others such as Cork, Cookstown, Carrick-on-Shannon, Limerick, Munster, Londonderry to name a few with Dublin and Belfast holding very large store sales as well.

In England Kingham, Penrith and Birmingham were early venues and of course Smithfield, although the latter was specialised.

The other sites developed in the main for dairy type events although to start with both types were catered for. The sales developed as and when the associations considered there would be demand and some of these developed into national venues. Reading had been originally a regional event and took over in 1926 as a major southern centre for the society following the perceived falling off of demand at Birmingham. A similar situation arose in Penrith; right in the dairy area, it started selling both types, then fell back with great success to the dairy type as demand increased. The situation here was no doubt helped by the dedication of the Thornborrow family. York, Bristol, Chippenham, Peterborough, Leicester, Preston, Gloucester, Shrewsbury, Carmarthen, Banbury, Stratford upon Avon, Taunton, Castle Cary, Yeovil, and others all played their part. Yeovil became the main centre for the south west and Crewe took over from Penrith as the north west centre, and more recently Chelford in the Midlands. Carlisle has had several sales over the years and is the regular venue for the Whitebred Shorthorns.

Glenariff Maisie Gina

The Glenisla herd, down off the hills for water.

Rodway Foggathorpe Primrose 19, Champion of the 2004 Royal Show

1905: selling in the street in Banbury before the huge market complex was built.

In the early days very large numbers of stock were involved: Birmingham over 400; Aberdeen 350; Perth up to, I believe, 580; Penrith 250; Dublin 300; Belfast up to 400. All such numbers of entries were quite common. There were also sales tacked on to shows for some years like the Royal Show, but they were normally specially selected stock. Other such sales have for some reason not proved successful. There were also a few so called Elite Sales at the National Agricultural Centre with special entry requirements but they did not last very long as the dairy herds in the area had shrunk to a minimum.

Naturally among all of these there were and are reduction and dispersal sales, mainly on site, although some are moved to the centres either for the convenience of the buyer or seller. The latter are often sad events as they mean a death or changing of farming practice by the vendor although they can be looked upon as an occasion where that herd's genes and possibly the work of generations are spread to strengthen established herds or attract new buyers who may well start herds (especially if they buy quality).

The other large demand in the past has been the export trade, which has involved a number of companies or individuals in this very specialised trade. In the very early days exporting was carried out by boat and entailled huge amouts of care and feeding: originally done by people like Francis Torrome, J.W. Nash, J. Sharples, Donald McLennon, Humphrey Smith from Ireland, who were followed by men like Walter Biggar who was followed by his son James A. J. Marshall, James Nelson and Son, Alexander Bruce, William Candry, Alexander and Addis, James Taylor, L.P. Duncan and more recently people like Hugh Black or companies like British Livestock Exports whose director was Col. D. Kennedy and then Neil Stanford. To a lesser degree Anglo Scottish Cattle Co., whose directors included Lord Lovat, and Donald Maclean with Edward Trotter, and last, but not by any means least, the expert James Schofield who also had a herd at Appleby. Among exporter/importers were families like the larger than life characters,the Duggans, Bernardo, Emilio and Carlos, who had some of the Collynie herd among their large Shorthorn herd. This was on the huge estancias where they also had enormous Hereford and Angus herds; Frank Harding from USA and a host of others.

James Schofield consistently warned about following the extreme types to the ultimate and stressed the need for uniformity. 'What you should be looking for are stock which can produce 9 or 10 cwt steers at 24-30 months of age as this would give the shipper the maximum carcass capacity in the truck or boat hold. Too much length in the quarter would mean it would not fit the hold as the cubic capacity was standard and too short would mean that the available space was not filled. The Shorthorn is the obvious dual purpose beast to rectify the cross breed pollutions seen too often in the commercial trade.'

Gerry Rankin had been with his uncle A. J. Marshall for about 16 years and out in Argentina for many years before managing the Boots company Westdrums herd. A man of great humour and wisdom who said, 'Too often when a change of type is desired by the market, breeders go too far, stay in the middle there is no future for the bull that starts to look good at three years of age or the one who is maturing at twelve months. The ultra short legs have fooled more people than is good for the breed and furthermore we don't promote the breed as we should.' These words summed up where the breed was from the beef point of view; things were still going well however the signs were there.

Auctioneers over the years have been such men as Henry Wetherell, Henry Strafford, also J.B. and W. H. Lythall at Birmingham; Gavin Low and John Robson in Belfast;. Ganly and Sons in Dublin, whose huge regular sale of store cattle attracted tremendous interest having 1,200 to 2,000 head in their market since 1847. They had got the organisation to a fine art, checking and sorting 450 per hour for identity and paperwork before sale. Johnson and Co were more recent Irish auctioneers of the breed. Then Macdonald Fraser in Scotland who also sold in Ireland on occasions. Their history and those of J. Thornton and Co. and John Thornborrow follow here.

Macdonald Fraser and Co. Ltd

Much reference is made to Perth in this history and synonymous with this is of course Macdonald Fraser and Co. This company has played a very important part in the development of the breed so I feel a short history will be of interest.

In 1864 Macdonald and McCullum Donald Maclennan, as the firm was known then, were in a modest way of business; no one would have guessed what was to come – world renown, with people from all over the world converging on the Caledonian Road and more recently to the Livestock Centre outside the City of Perth, Scotland.

The company was joined in 1862 by John M. Fraser as a young man of sixteen and he eventually became a partner in 1872. The firm became Macdonald Fraser in 1897, with John M. determined even then to make Perth a world market, although at that time the market was at the bottom of Mill St in Perth at what is known as The Horse Cross and in a very small way of business. The first bull sale was in 1865 and enjoyed the support of Col. Williamson of Lawers and Mr White of Muirhead; fourteen Shorthorns sold to a top of 39 guineas and an average of 14 guineas. In 1869 a second prize bull sold at 51 guineas. As the numbers were small, the bull sale did not warrant a separate day from the normal Friday market but by 1872 the numbers were increasing so the bull sale was held on a Wednesday in mid March; this was recorded as having 75, selling for a total of £1,964.

Around the same date Aberdeen Angus were becoming a part of the spring Sale and in 1880 the sale book refers to '10th March Annual Show and Sale of Shorthorn and Angus bulls, cows and heifers. This sale confined to pedigree stock'. In 1892 the two breeds had separate sale dates with 286 Angus on February 24th and Shorthorns having 242 on March 2nd.

The market was becoming too small and by this time a friendship had developed between the company and William Duthie and discussions between him and others led to the idea of a larger site in around 1871. By 1875 the new Caledonian Road market was opened with the object of expansion for the company and the market to act for the Scottish region of the Shorthorn Society. It was in 1876 that an Argentinean came as a visitor and was so impressed by the stock on offer during this visit that a golden trail was opened.

In 1879 the sale was visited by several overseas visitors and from then on buyers regularly began to come from Canada, USA,

No spare spaces at the Perth sales.

Australia,Argentina, Germany and South Africa.

Naturally the company was also concerned with sales on farms, selling at dispersals and also reduction sales for men like Duthie and others mentioned elsewhere. In 1887 J.M. Fraser sold his first £100 bull but by 1900 bulls were fetching 660 guineas and in 1920 6,600 guineas was reached; much later, in 1946, they set more records selling two bulls in one day, among many others, for 14,500 guineasand then almost immediately after one for 14,000 guineas which record still stands today.

As the numbers grew the old market became so full that the Shorthorns had to be judged in the street for quite a few years. There was a unique atmosphere in the premises with its central sale ring, subsidiary rings and the cattle being even then on two levels.

It was almost a foregone conclusion that even if you did not see your friends at all in the interim, your contacts, whether from overseas or this country, would be at the next event; if not, one was worried. So the company, the city,d its hotels and shops, as well as the railway, all benefited; all buyers, sellers and those whose interest and life it was could be found at this Mecca.

Cattle, and of course other stock, filled the market week in and week out and J.M. Fraser continued to be a figurehead until he was eighty, confirming my original thoughts that to be with Shorthorns is an aid to longevity! His sons, W. Lovat Fraser and Harry J. Fraser, joined the firm in 1902 and 1905 respectively and, like their father and his clients, had to contend with the slump years.

The peaks for the breed before World War I were years like 1910 when the firm sold 1,734 to average £46 and the top average was the Collynie herd of £378 with a top of £1,100. By now sales were held at Perth, Aberdeen, Inverness and Darlington, with most of these having spring and autumn events. They were so popular they were even held on successive days, i.e. Aberdeen on Oct 8th, Inverness Oct 9th and Perth on Oct 10th, in 1947.

One of the remarkable things was that in some years the bull sales were regarded by the directors as loss-making so on some occasions John M. Fraser financed them himself as they were undoubtedly a means of maintaining contacts and a variety of business. After World War I there came a boom time and prices took off again. In 1920 the spring sale of Shorthorns numbered 486 and they averaged £302, with a top of 6,600 guineas; the overall bull average that year was £270 for 2,061 head. By 1933 the average had fallen to 50 guineas and fortunes stayed low till after the post war boom of 1946 when the firm sold the bulls, Pittodrie Uprise and his brother Upright, as mentioned elsewhere for 14,000 and 14,500 guineas respectively.

In 1952 the Highland market in Perth was the venue for the renowned sale of the world famous host Cruggleton herd over two days, involving 224 lots. It averaged 524 guineas with a top of 2,400 guineas and was attended by buyers and supporters from all over the world.

During the following decades many changes took place with Macdonald Fraser becoming a part of United Auctions in 1962 with Lovat Fraser as chairman. He had joined the firm in 1902. John M. Fraser remained as head of the firm until 1938, when he retired at the amazing age of 92 having devoted 70 years of his life to the all absorbing livestock industry. Harry died in 1976 and Lovat's son Roley joined the firm in 1951 and retired as chairman of the United Auctions group in 1992.

With the coming of the continental breeds the market sales and bull weeks became multi-breed affairs and this coincided with the temporary decline of the Shorthorn and Angus but as we go into the next century the wheel is turning with both coming back with a new place and type with averages of several thousand pounds.

In 1990 the company took a major decision to move from the atmosphere of the city site with its proximity to the rail head, where it had been since 1875.The new site was the Perth agricultural centre, outside the city but alongside the motorway, in a way a similar site. It was a very brave move, and the first bull sale took place there in the February of that year.

This was a difficult decision which at the time was very unpopular but has now stabilised and hopefully will continue for many years to come and acquire its own atmosphere.

As shown in the other chapters the fashionable aspect of the breed meant that it was the breed preferred by many estates and landowners and the firm dispersed many of these during the troubled times of the 1930s. Lovat Fraser dispersed many famous herds of the time as far south as the Isle of Sheppy.

After the war the Angus were the 'in beef breed' and it fell to Roley Fraser to disperse as far down as the Wych cross herd in Littlehampton,Sussex.

Today this historic group, United Auctions Ltd, has outlets at several other centres in Scotland and carries on under the chairmanship, at the time of writing, of Mr DavidLeggat; but the beef centre of the U K remains in Perth as visualised so long ago by J. M. Fraser.

John Thornton & Co.

John Thornton was the founder of this company, which had very long associations with the Shorthorn. He had joined the Great Western Railway at 13, but he was not happy, so he followed up an enquiry and met Mr Strafford, the principal auctioneer of the time, and joined him at 17 as his clerk. Through this he met William Torr, referred to elsewhere, and it was he who loaned Thornton £200 to set up offices in Langham Place, London, in 1868 where he began by compiling a circular of stock for sale.

This grew into *Thornton's Shorthorn Circular*, which continued as 'Bible' of sales, etc. It was published till 1928 when the company assigned the copyright to the Shorthorn Society. From his first issue he received an offer from USA for £40,000 worth of stock, no mean start. Then, in another piece of good fortune, he was offered the sale of the herd of Rev. John Storer, who was a well known breeder and author of the time. Thornton made good that day 'being of fluent tongue and able to make the bidders mind up for him!' He hit the ground running as the demand was tremendous, so he gained the description of 'a herd book in trousers'!

In a few years he gained most of the herd sales and excelled in creating a record selling for the Earl of Dunsmore, a sale that made an average of £672 for 39 head. This included the bull the Duke of Connaught at 4,500 guineas. This record stood for many years, but not content with this the following week he sold, for W. Torr, 84 head which averaged £511; all this was in 1875. Mainly as a result of this performance, in 1877 he received a shipment of 32 head from Mr Cochrane in USA when prices were low over there. They averaged £510, a figure far in excess of that expected. While doing all this he also compiled the Jersey Herd Book and was their Secretary till his death.

In 1884 he was on the jury of the Amsterdam International Exhibition and received a gold medal for his services; he also was involved with the huge French Exhibition. In recognition of his services at this he was awarded the Ordre of Merite Agricole, seldom conferred on an Englishman. In 1904 a circular was sent round the world as many felt he should receive a testimonial and over 900 people from Britain, Australia, Canada, France, South Africa, Argentina and USA wished to contribute. In 1908 King Edward was going to confer a Knighthood but sadly John Thornton died before it was bestowed.

Frank Mathews had joined the staff in 1887 and quickly took on the preparation of the circular and catalogues; as the son of a breeder, A. T. Matthews, he knew what was required. His first sale was one at Kingham collective sale and then he too was launched.

The company traded as John Thornton, Hobson and Co. in the '40s until Alec Hobson went off with his own company.

The firm went on to be a stronghold of Matthews, as later Neville Matthews took over the firm with his brother Cecil, whose two sons, F. A. N. Matthews and John, joined later and it was F. A. N. Matthews who was Secretary of the South Eastern Shorthorn Region for many years.

Thornborrow & Company

As the regions developed the various auctioneers in those regions became favoured, so the attachment grew. First there was Thornborrow & Company, founded in 1863, in the north east by Thomas Thornborrow who had worked with Harrison and Hetherington in Carlisle. He was joined in 1886 by his son John Thornborrow and later by his son, J. T. Thornborrow, who had got some of his practical farming knowledge at the well known herd of Mr Toppin at Skelton. As Managing Director of Penrith Farmers, he started sales at Penrith in 1907; they were mainly Beef Shorthorns at the time but there was a general swing to dairy over a period of years. In 1910 the Northern Counties Association of Shorthorn Breeders was formed and very shortly changed to Penrith Association of Shorthorn Breeders! Also in 1917 they started sales at Crewe. In 1919, following a presentation to John T. Thornborrow for his services to the breed, he characteristically sold Gatley Lancer for the record price for Great Britain of 4,750 guineas. J.T. was a very busy man as he was also Secretary to the Penrith Association and the York Shorthorn Association as well as the now extinct Cumberland Pig Association and the Large Black Pig Association, to say nothing of the Northumberland Shorthorn Association, as well as being on the Shorthorn Society Council, all of which must have given him very little time for any thing else! In 1922 Thomas Jefferson Thornborrow joined the firm and it was he who expanded the firm to take on sales all over Britain.

In 1951 John D. Thornborrow(son of J.T.) joined the company, having had a grounding of Shorthorn practical work with the famous Oxton herd of then G. R. H. Smith. He made a stylish start on the rostrum while on leave from National Service at the dispersal of the old established herd of Kaberfold for W. J. Dent. What a way to start! It must have been quite awesome, as there were over 1,000 people present but he evidently passed with flying colours selling the 2nd top heifer for 350 guineas.

He became a partner in 1957 and in 1964 the company became the official Shorthorn Society Auctioneers. In 1969 John D. decided that rather than general auctioneering he would specialise in livestock and he formed his own company moving to Leamington Spa to become one of the only two livestock specialist organisations at the time. He was joined initially by Clive Rhodes and then in 1986 by Edward Wheaton from a well known auctioneering family.

In 1979 John had been joined by his wife June as a partner in the company; she also acted as regional secretary to the mid west region for many years. The company certainly did not specialise in one breed or livestock type. John sold everything except his family: Holsteins, where he sold his record price of 21,000 guineas; miniature horses, Jerseys, Herefords, red deer, llamas, alpacas, pigeons, zoo animals, poultry, water fowl, Angora goats, sheep, books, plants, also rare breeds in multitudes, as he was the auctioneer for the Rare Breed Survival Trust as well as several other breed societies. He built a huge reputation for his photographic memory for pedigrees, his unique style and his clarity. He was created an Honorary Life Vice President of the Shorthorn Society, one of only three, in the long history of the society at that time.

Just prior to his retirement the livestock industry went into decline and without a market he decided first to join the Banbury Market company for a less demanding life and then he returned to Harrison and Hetherington in Penrith, so a circle had been completed for the Thornborrow Family before his retirement.

Greenslade, Taylor, Hunt

As mentioned in a previous chapter, the south west region was in fact one of the largest at the height of the Society, with around 807 members and in later years was the largest geographic one as well, as it stretches from Wiltshire to Lands End, although for many years Devon and Cornwall were not included. Although there was a club, the official region was founded in 1946 when the Society regularized the member groups and supplied an advised constitution. This region's first chairman was a Mr D.C. Dare, who farmed the Curry herd and was followed by Major Aldridge of the Stourhead herd prefix. Their original auctioneers were **Taylor, Hunt and Co**, founded by R. B. Taylor and Mr Hunt, each of whom had two sons; all four wanted to be in the company, so to relieve the problem the Hunts went to Langport and Bridgewater and the Taylors remained in Yeovil. A. R. Taylor (Dick) took responsibility for the livestock and the market sales and eventually became Secretary of the region; he was also secretary of the British Friesian Society region and that of the Guernsey Society as well, all covering the counties of Dorset, Wiltshire and Somerset. R. B. Taylor remained as senior partner until he was 82 and died in 1954.The Dare family farmed around Crewkerne and, as there were seven children, H. M. Dare was *told* he was to be articled to **R.B.Taylor and Sons,** as it had now become, as his father could not afford to put all his sons in farms. He started on the property and farm sale side of the business. Sadly Mr Dick Taylor was killed in a car accident in 1952 so Mr Dare became responsible for the livestock and as Mr R.B.Taylor retired he became the senior partner, later to be joined by his son Martin who had been articled to the well known West Country estate agents Woolley and Wallace of Salisbury.

The various societies staff were allocated ther own staff, and Shorthorns were allocated Arthur R. Bartlett who held the position for 28 years until he was 80 in 1980. As the region members thought highly of his services they subscribed to a carriage clock on his retirement. He was one of a family of 11 who could field a full cricket team for their family alone in the Castle Cary district! A further long-standing partner well known in the firm was Henry Simons who sold dairy stock in the company for over 28 years, which is believed to be a record for any team of auctioneers selling in partnership; he retired as a result of the cutbacks enforced during the foot and mouth epidemic of 2001. H.M. Dare had died in 1971 and Martin Dare then became the senior partner. The company, still known as R.B. Taylor and Sons, owned their own market in Yeovil but this was sold 25 years ago to the local council and thereafter they shared another market in the town with Palmer and Snell and Co and this is where most regular sales have been held, although in the 1950s sales were also developed in Exeter. In 1999 R.B.

Taylor joined forces with Greenslade and Hunt and so the firms then became Greenslade Taylor Hunt as it is today, thus the circle was completed from the original Taylor Hunt Company.

Thus sales are also held in Taunton and these are mainly looked after by Derek Biss who became involved as a result of the merger which was to give the combined forces of the new company access and facilities over a large area; but it also meant that R.B. Taylor in its several forms has worked with the industry for over 100 years. There have been sales in the region at such other places as Castle Cary, Chippenham and Gloucester, but other auctioneers mainly hold these. This region is the largest and would have had quite an influence on council as the representation was by a number of delegates elected according to the number of members in any region. As long ago as 1951, when their membership was 807 a resolution was prepared to the effect that 'consideration should be given to the unsatisfactory position of the Dairy Shorthorn in relation to its competitors'; following debate it was modified 'to consider what steps should be taken to further improve the Shorthorn' they considered 'that members throughout the country all had differing objectives and in the South breeders needed milk production as they were losing out to other breeds'.

Frank R. Marshall and Co.

In November 1990 the Society decided to move their sales from Crewe to Chelford, in Cheshire. This centre had already become well known as a venue for pedigree livestock sales patronized by the Belgian Blue, Holstein, and Texel societies as well as various other breed clubs, and had built up a reputation as a major centre for calf and store cattle sales. In addition it had become one of the most diverse auction centres in the UK with the largest weekly horticultural sales in the country, which had evolved from the sale of just a few plants. It grew into vegetables, potatoes, flowers, plants and shrubs as well as livestock and poultry. The partners, Frank R. Marshall and Co., always held the view that they should diversify and developed having sales at least four days a week as well as nowadays a very large Sunday market. Initially the Shorthorn sales were held in spring and autumn by John Thornborrow and Co. using the market facilities of Frank R. Marshall until his retirement in 1997, when **Marshalls**, as they were then to become, were appointed as the official auctioneers to the society. Gwyn Williams joined John Thornborrow on the rostrum during the change over period and the sales began to increase later to include a section for the Beef Shorthorns in 1999 as their popularity increased. By this time the market had grown and in 1997 the company had built new buildings to accommodate the expansion with better facilities so that by 2004 the Shorthorn entry had increased to 161 with buyers coming from all over the UK and Ireland, as the market was so conveniently situated just off the M6 motorway.

Conclusion

To draw comparisons with the past is impossible as the circumstances are so very different, but one can say that the breed had sunk almost to its lowest possible state before the breeders accepted the situation. Then in effect they emulated what their forefathers had done so many years ago, by blending the existing stock with what was available to improve it. Purists might differ with that view, but they must recall the use of the Holderness with the Teeswater and the European or Dutch cattle which produced a breed that was so unique it changed the world of cattle breeding. Our modern breeders also started with what they had, but it did not suit the market so they used breeds or bloodlines that improved what they had but they did not lose the good points of what they inherited from their forefathers. So that was the success of today's breeders and their skill, which was assisted by the modern breeding aides to identify the traits required, just as the 'pure' breeders used bloodlines from other countries to improve their stock. But their creation also had to suit the modern requirements for production.

Today the scene is so very different to even one hundred years ago let alone two hundred years ago when the breed was established. Today's market is such that the price of the final commodity is being driven down; farmers in their turn have had to reduce their costs and overheads. In dairying and in beef the animal required is the one that converts low cost products into meat, milk or cheese or by-products and the same applies to the beef products. The beast required must also be one that thrives. The other main consideration is how long that animal can remain economically productive; this is essential as if that animal's surplus progeny can be sold, either as a producer, as meat or as a replacement, there is a distinct cash advantage. Some breeds today with the pressures that are put upon them require a 25% replacement rate or more, whereas the Shorthorn replacement rate can be 16% or less depending on the system. Today the farmer generally has to achieve absolutely maximum production from his investment, as always, but the pressure on him, or his staff if he can afford them, is more than ever before. The pressure on his land is the same, but land costs are so high that he has to obtain maximum economic production from all three – man, beast and land.

To summarise: public confidence has returned to the breed. This has also been demonstrated by the semen company Red Cattle Genetics that now regularly stocks around 20 sires that are demanded by farmers of all breeds, not just Shorthorns. To draw comparisons with the past would be impossible as the circumstances are so very different, but one can say that the breed had sunk almost to its lowest possible state, as can be seen from the graphs, before the breeders accepted the situation. Then in effect they emulated what their forefathers had done so many years ago, by blending the existing stock with what was available to improve it. Purists might disagree with that interpretation but they must recall the use of the Holderness with the Teeswater and the European or Dutch cattle, so arriving at a breed that was so unique it changed the world of cattle breeding. Our modern breeders also started with what they had, but it did not suit the changing market, so they used breeds or bloodlines that improved what they had *but they did not lose the good points of what they inherited from their forefathers*. So that has been the success of today's breeders, and their skill was assisted by the modern breeding aides, to identify the traits required, just as the pure breeders used bloodlines to improve their stock.

Today's Shorthorn has been remodelled in both the dairy and beef sectors to convert low-cost fodder with low-cost methods to a product that is acceptable to the public while at the same time, because of its structure, providing economic longevity with as few problems as possible. Today's aims that are being achieved, but have to be balanced, are to produce as much as possible from as few animals as possible at the lowest input and cost. Today's cattle produce many times more than their ancestors with as little veterinary involvement as possible so the noted proven docility, ease of calving and lack of foot problems, coupled with good mobility, assist low labour involvement. The farmer today has to handle large numbers of stock to survive so it has to be as trouble-free as possible. The saying of Bates all those years ago holds as well today as it did then: *'the only test of excellence is the comparison of the food they consume with the improvement they make'*. The Breed can thrive under any climate and management system. In the beef market the breed can utilise the upland if required, to the maximum ability converting low quality grazing;, it can also convert the predominating mediocre Holstein type beast, or poor quality suckler that has developed, to be a reasonable meat producer. The Dairy Shorthorn today can produce the products required with lower labour input and overhead costs so the swing back to the breed must and will continue, but its future remains with our current breeders who are charged with ensuring that the Shorthorn meets the current needs, whatever they be, and also maintain a variety of types to cope with future trends. The auctioneer John Thornborrow once stated, **'The breed has an illustrious**

past and it can have a bright future, but it will be no less than the breeders choose to make it.' At present it is steadily regaining its rightful place in this highly competitive market.

Appendix I
IMPORTANT CHRONOLOGICAL EVENTS IN THE DEVELOPMENT OF THE SHORTHORN SOCIETY

1822	First herd book by George Coates.
1846	Herd book taken over by Henry Strafford.
1874	Shorthorn Society of Great Britain and Ireland formed.
1875	Society incorporated and took over the herd book..
1895	Lincoln Red Association formed and register their own.
1904	Prefix registration made official.
1905	Dairy Shorthorn Association formed.
1907	Irish Shorthorn Breeders Association set up.
1909	British Holstein Society founded (name changed in 1914,1919,1946)
1918	Grading register started.
1918	Tattoo system made obligatory.
1918	Geographic representation on council introduced.
1920	Dual Shorthorn Association founded.
1924	Dual Shorthorn Association closed.
1929	Bull register of merit set up.
1932	Dairy Shorthorn journal started.
1935	Lincoln Red Association registrations into Coates herd book.
1936	Dairy Shorthorn Assoc amalgamated with Shorthorn Society.
1936	Office moved to Victoria House London from Hanover Square N London.
1937	Dairy Shorthorn Journal became Shorthorn Journal (1st time).
1940	Staff moved to Westfield, Medmenham, Marlow, for duration.
1943	Lincoln Red went alone again.
1944	MMB started A I stations and scheme.
1944	Advance register for females and improved register of merit or bulls started.
1944	Northern Dairy Shorthorn Association founded.
1946	Regional associations established.
1947	Advance register for females started.
1950	Poll Shorthorns Society started.
1952	Dehorning of females accepted at shows (bulls in 1960).
1958	Beef Shorthorn Association decided to have their own herd book section.
1959	Beef Association changed to Beef Shorthorn Cattle Society.
1962	Hybrid experimental register started.
1962	Whitebred Association started.
1962	Poll Shorthorn and Beef Society amalgamate.

1965	N. Dairy Shorthorn Association re amalgamated with Shorthorn Society.
1967	Classification scheme started.
1968	Society moved to Green Lodge from London.
1970	Blended scheme official.
1970	Irish improvement scheme started.
1970	Cattle Breed Improvement Services Ltd set up.
1971	Dairy Shorthorn Breeders Ltd set up.
1974	First world conference series started.
1976	Beef society agreed to introduction of Maine Anjou blood.
1978	Beef Shorthorn Society requested autonomy.
1978	Society moved to Leamington Spa.
1979	Building of Stoneleigh office started.
1980	Building officially opened by Her Royal Highness Princess Anne.
1989	World conference held in the UK.
1989	Red and white register opened.
1990	Society sales moved to Chelford.
1992	Beef Society administration moved to Stoneleigh.
1994	Milk Marketing Board wound up.
1994	Red Cattle Genetics (Stoneleigh) Ltd founded.
1998	Her Majesty the Queen retired as patron and Princess Anne replaced her.
2000	Society annual general meeting peripatetic.
2001	Red and white register changed to supplementary register.

Appendix II
BREEDS OR TYPES THAT HAVE EVOLVED FROM SHORTHORNS

name of breed	foundation of breed
UNITED KINGDOM	
Lincoln Red	Local Shorthorn Type
Luing	Beef Shorthorn 50% Highland 50%
Blue Grey	Shorthorn / Galloway
Blue Albion	Shorthorn / Welsh Black
Beevbilde	Shorthorn 35% / Lincoln Red 55% / Angus 10%
BRW	Shorthorn / Red Friesian or Meuse - Rhine-Isle or Danish Red or Red Holstein(see detail in book)

name of breed	foundation of breed
Whitebred	Shorthorn Type
Northern Dairy	Shorthorn Type

AUSTRALIA

Murray Grey	Angus / Shorthorn
Illawarra	Shorthorn / Ayrshire / Devon
Droughtmaster	Shorthorn / Brahman
Belmont Red	Shorthorn / Africander on Africander / Hereford
Quasah	Shorthorn / Sahiwal
Mandalong	Poll Shorthorn / Charolais / Chianina / British White / Brahman (Stabalised @25%British.58% Continental17%Brahman)
Weebollabolla	Shorthorn Type

BELGIUM

Belgian Blue	Dutch black or Red Pied / Shorthorn

CHINA

Chinese Red Steppe	Shorthorn / Mongolian

COLOMBIA

Hawaii Lucerna	Shorthorn 30% Harton Criollo 30% Friesian 40%

DENMARK

Danish Red	German Red / Meuse-Rhine Isle / Shorthorn

FRANCE

Maine-Anjou	Mancelle / Shorthorn
Amorican	Breton / Shorthorn

GERMANY

German Shorthorn	German Red / Shorthorn

name of breed	foundation of breed
HUNGARY	
Pankota Red	Hungarian Pied/80% Lincoln Red Shorthorn
INDIA	
Taylor	Zebu/Shorthorn/Jersey
JAPAN	
Japanese Shorthorn	Mishima and Wagu/Shorthorn
RUSSIA	
Bestuzhev	Shorthorn/Simmental/Friesian
Kurgan	Siberian Red/Shorthorn
SOUTH AFRICA	
Bonsmara	Africander $^5/_8$ Hereford $^3/_{16}$ Shorthorn $^3/_{16}$
UNITED STATES OF AMERICA	
Beefmaster	Brahman 50% Hereford 25% Shorthorn 25%
Brahorn	Brahman /Shorthorn 1st cross
Beefmaker	Shorthorn/Charolais/Hereford/Angus/ Brahman/Brown Swiss
American	Brahman 50%/Charolais 25%/Bison 1/ 8 Hereford and Shorthorn $^1/_{16}$
Santa Gertrudis	Brahman 5/8.Shorthorn $^3/_8$
Hash Cross	Red Angus /Highland/Hereford/ Shorthorn

SOME BREEDS THAT INTRODUCED SHORTHORN BLOOD FOR IMPROVEMENT

Senepol	Jamaica
Belgian Red	Belgium
Charolais	France
Rouge De La Oeust	"
Breton Black	France "
Aubrac	"
Normande	"
Saler	"
Norwegian Red	Norway
Swedish Red	Sweden
Red Poll	U K
British White	"
Ayrshire	"and Finland
Burlina	Italy
Tagil	Russia
Red Steppe	"
Doran	South America and Costa Rica
Criollo	"
Meusse-Rhine-Isle	Holland
Hatton	India/Sri Lanka
Makawell	Hawaii
Galican Blonde	Spain
Sanhe	Mongolia

SOME SHORTHORN TRIBE /FAMILY BLOODLINES AND THEIR ORIGINS

A number of enquiries are received asking the origins of bloodlines despite their probable dilution over the years.

It will also be noticed that some crop up in more than one column and this is due to the time when they were started, numbers were short and our forefathers worked very closely together so several families were established in the other's herds. A very good thing too as this partly accounts for why the beef sectors of the breed have always been known for the milk they were able to provide and also the dairy lines could provide excellent beef carcasses

Examples of these are SECRETS and MOSS ROSES

BATES	BOOTH		COLLING AND CRUIKSHANK
BARONESS	AVERNE	PRINCESS ROYAL	CHERRY
BARRINGTON	AUGUSTA	QUEEN OF ROTHES	ELIZA
CAMBRIDGE ROSE	AVALANCHE	RAMSDEN	LADY
COUNTESS	BLYTHSOME	ROSE	LADY MAYNARD
DUCHESS	BRACELET	SECRET	NONPAREIL
FLETCHER	BRIGHT	SECRET CLIPPER	
			PHOENIX
FOGGATHORPE	BRAWITH BUD	STRAWBERRY	PRINCESS
FURBELLOW	BROADHOOKS	SYMPATHY	RED ROSE
GREENLEAF	BRIGHT	URY MAID	ROSE
KIRKLEVINGTON	CHERRY	VENUS	SECRET
MILLICENT	CLIPPER	VICTORIA	WILDAIR
MOSS ROSE	CROCUS	VIOLET	
OXFORD	DAIRYMAID	WHIMPLE	
PRINCESS	DUCHESS OF GLOSTER		
RED ROSE	FLOSSY		
SECRET	JEALOUSY		
SERAPHINA	JILT		
WATERLOO	LADY DOROTHY		
WILD EYES	LANCASTER		
	LAVENDER		
	LOVELY		
	LOVELY BRIGHT		
	MATCHLESS		
	MOSS ROSE		
	MAUDE		
	NONPAREIL		
	PAULINE		

Several prominent breeders in more modern times have started their own continuous families very satisfactorily but those above are some of the originals.

An example of later families are those of the Marr breeding:- Beauty, Clara, Emma, Goldie,Maude,Marigold, Missie and Princess Royal.

Appendix III
SOME SHORTHORN RECORDS

YIELDS

1945 Pedigree. Winton Gentle 2nd owned and bred by J. R .& J. H. Burge, Winchester, Hampshire.
223,917lb Milk in 15 lactations

1956 Pedigree. Clanville Lady Butterfly 8th 27,703 lb in 305 days, 33,902lb in 497 days 3xday milking in the herd of D. Weston.

1954 Pedigree. Boxgrove Barbara 4th owned by S. M. Roberts.Crouch House, Edenbridge. Bred by Boxgrove School Ltd. Highest fat yield in lactation 21,470lb milk 4.86% 104lb fat in 305 days. Peak yield 119lb in 24 hours. Complete lactation 454 days 25, 810lb 4.86% 1,254lb fat 6th lactation.

Grade Register. 1965 Wall Flower 2nd owned and bred by A. Pickford, Wincanton, Wiltshire.15 calves 266,644lb milk and 7,536 lb butterfat.

Pedigree.1963 Theale Maude 12th,owned by H. Haldin of Hinxhill, bred by W. Cumber and Son,Theale, Berkshire: 12 calves 203,875lb milk.

Pedigree. Kingsley Musical 3rd1975, bred and owned by G. BlakeKings Seymour Clevedon. Somerset. 201,875lb 12 calves.

1986 Pedigre. Eathorpe Anne 21st,owned by A. Orsler, Leighton Buzzard, Bedford. Bred by G. Robson, Marton, Rugby. 15Calves 215,246 lb milk 7,708lbs butterfat 6578lbprotein.

World Recordfor any Breed. **SINGLE YIELD** 1939 Cherry. Grade Register. Owned MessersWort &Way. Amesbury, Wiltshire. 41644lb milk 365 days.

Grade Register. Biggarmaid, owned and bred by Fielding Johnson. Compton Basset, Wilts. 33,240lb in 365 days.

Pedigree. Whateley Musical 13th, bred and owned by G. Snape and Sons, Alcester, Warwick. 1972 35,293 Lb milk 305 days.

Pedigree .Aldenham Kirklevington 20th, owned and bred by J. Piers Morgan, Watford. 1937 .16,964lb in 315 days(305 days yield not known) 19,424 in 365 days.

Pedigree. Northease Waterloo Rose 27th, bred and owned by J. H. Robinson, Lewes, Sussex . 195716857 lb in 305 days 1st calf 2xday milking

YOUNGEST 100,000 lb.Pedigree. Densford Darlington Cran 14th, bred by L.C. Denza, Ford Fm, Wiveliscombe, Somerset. 8 years old in 5 lactations 8198 lb fat.

BUTTERFAT YIELD 1953 Grade register. Dorothy, bred and owned by Messers Robarts. Northwood, Middx. 6th lact 23,713lb with 4.51% fat or 1058lb of fat. She gave 156.599lb in 9 lactations with 5366lb of fat and still producing.

1983 Hinxhill Duchess 82nd, 8,727lb fat in $11^1/_2$ lactations. Milk yield 203,885lb. C. Epps, Ledbury,Hereford.

OVERSEAS RECORD.1923 IllawarraMelba 15th Darbalara. 32,522 lb milk in 365 days. 1,614lb butterfat or 5%.

HIGH PRICES - DAIRY
Eaton Earl Foggathorpe 3,000 guineas 1943 Reading to Mr Morris. Groby Revelex Dairy Premier 3,000 guineas 1950 Reading to Mrs Mills, New York, U S A.
Friarstown Wild Seraph 3,000 guineas 1960 Reading to Ballyclough A I Centre.

BEEF at Auction
1946 Pittodrie Upright 14,500 guineas 1946 Perth Bull sales to Ralph Smith,U S A.
1946 Pittodrie Uprise 14,000 guineas 1946 Perth Bull Sales to Col. Hardie, Balathie.

Private sale
Bapton Constructor 15,000 guineas to Louda Stud. Ontario,Canada

HIGHEST DAIRY AVERAGE AND DISPERSAL SALE PRICES
2,800 guineas Lenborough Dubbie 218 at Lenborough Dispersal.
3,150 guineas Orchardhome Maude 6th and 3 month old calf.
1993 Show and Sale June 42 lots averaged over 1,000 guineas and 47 lots averaged £1,302.
3,000 guineas 1994. Drisgol Reduction for Drisgol Mabel 13th.

OVERSEAS SALE RECORDS

NEW YORK MILLS SALE FOR S.CAMPBELL U S A 1873.109 head averaged £734.10 shillings.
15 Duchesses £3,679.18 shillings. Top 8120 guineas for Eighth Duchess of Geneva.
1980 Illinois USA Sale of Irish cattleHighfield Rathcannon bred by John Malloney,County Clare. $48,000 for a $^2/_3$ share.

Averages females selling to $9,200 Avg $5,297.
Males avg $ 23,925.
U K Early sale 1875 The Earl of Dunmore Sale. Stirlingshire averaged £672.8 shillings for 39head(30 Cows and 9 Bulls).
Top Duke of Conaught 4,500 guineas, 3rd Duke of Hillhurst 3,000 guineas Top females. Marchioness of Oxford 3rd 1800 guineasRed Rose of Balmoral 1280. guineas.This sale is recorded here, as if the dollars were adjusted, it was the highest of its era as the New York Sale would have been £626 by comparison.

LIST OF MOST OF THE COUNTRIES TO WHICH SHORTHORNS HAVE BEEN EXPORTED
(SOME WILL BE DUPLICATED OWING TO NAME CHANGES BUT THESE APPLIED AT THE TIME OF EXPORT)

Abyssinia	Cuba	Luxembourg	Swaziland
Argentina	Cyprus	Mexico	Sweden
Australia	Denmark	Nigeria	St Helena
Austria	Egypt	Norway	Spain
Azores	East africa	Palestine	West africa
Belgium	Ecuador	Pakistan	Tasmania
Bolivia	France	Poland	Tanganyika
Brazil	Germany	Port Sudan	Transvaal
British Columbia	Gold Coast	Peru	Uganda
British Guyana	India	Portugal	Uruguay
Canada	Israel	Rhodesia	United States
China	Italy	Romania	Venezuela
Chile	Jamaica	Russia	West Indies
Columbia	Japan	Serbia	Yugoslavia
Central Asia	Kenya	South Africa	

Appendix IV
SHORTHORN SOCIETY PAST PRESIDENTS

1875-6	The Duke of Devonshire.KG.
1876-7	Lord Penrhyn.
1877-8	Lord Skelmersdale.
1878-9	Earl Of Dunmore.
1879-80	Col. Nigel Kingscote. CB. MP. (later Sir Nigel Kingscote. KCB)
1880-81	The Duke of Manchester.
1881-2	The Earl of Bective. MP.
1882-3	H. Chandos Pole-Gel.

1883-4	The Earl of Feversham.
1884-5	H. W. Beauford.
1885-6	Lord Moreton. MP.
1886-7	F. J. Saville FolJambe.
	(later The Rt Hon F. J. S. Foljambe.)
1887-8	Andrew Mitchell.
1888-89	Col. Robert Gunter. MP (Later Sir Robert Gunter. BT.)
1889-90	W. T. Talbot Crosbie.
1890-91	The Duke Of Richmond And Gordon.
1891-2	H. J. Sheldon.
1892-3	Sir Jacob Wilson.
1893-4	Philo Mills.
1894-5	St John Ackers.
1895-6	Richard Stratton.
1896-7	Lord Brougham and Vaux.
1897-8	William Booth.
1898-9	H. Denis De Vitre.
1899-1900	Lord Rathdonnel.
1900-1	Herbert Leney.
1901-2	Col. Sir Nigel Kingscote. KCB.
1902-3	The Rt. Hon. Victor C. W. Cavendish. MP.(later The Duke of Devonshire)
1903-4	Viscount Baring (Later The Earl Of Northbrook.)
1904-5	Sir Oswald Moseley.
1905-6	E. W. Stanyforth (Later Col. E. W. Staniforth. CB.)
1906-7	Lord Moreton.
1907-8	Lord Midleton.
1908-9	Joseph Harris.
1909-10	A. M. Gordon.
1910-11	C .H. Joliffe.
1911-12	George Taylor.
1912-13	Earl Manvers.
1913-14	William Duthrie.
1914-15	Sir Walpole -Greenwell. BT.
1915-16	H. Parkin -Moore.
1916-17	The Rt. Hon. Frederick S. Wrench.
1917-18	The Rev. C. H. Brocklebank.
1918-19	Dr. Vaughan Harley.
1919-20	Sir. Gilbert Green. BT. CVO (later Lord Daresbury.CVO.)
1920-21	Lord Merthyr.
1921-2	Marquess of Crewe. KG.
1922-3	The Hon C B Portman(Later Viscount Portman)
1923-4	Lord Desborough.
1924-5	F. L .Wallace.
1925-6	Col H. T. Fenwick. CMG. MVO. DSO.
1926-7	Col. Joseph Griffiths. CMG.

1927-8	Capt The Rt. Hon. E. A. Fitzroy. PC.MP.
1928-9	William Hunter.
1929-30	Lord Harlech. CB.
1930-31	Major Clive Behrens.
1931-2	Duthie Webster.
1932-3	Sir Edward Mann. BT.
1933-4	Hugh Baker.
1934-5	Lord Daresbury. CVO.
1935-6	Major S. P. Yates.
1936-7	Col. S. E .Ashton.OBE. MP.
1937-8	Capt John MacGillivray. OBE.
1938-9	Robert Hobbs.
1939-46	Norman J. Lee.(all War)
1946-7	Major Miller Mundy.
1947-8	Major Robert Mowbray
1948-9	Capt N. Milne Harrop MBE
1949-50	E. C. J. Allday
1950-51	Capt John MacGillivray OBE
1951-2	Col S. E. Ashton OBE MP
1952-3	J. Stanley Chivers
1953-4	W. J. Cumber
1954-5	Sir Peter Greenwell Bt
1955-6	James Holme
1956-7	R. H. Watherston
1957-8	R. L. Jones
1958-9	John G. W. Woodman
1959-60	James Biggar
1960-1	J. D. Webb
1961-2	G. R. H. Smith
1962-3	Brig. P. B. E. Acland. MC.
1963-4	H. N. Halden.
1964-5	G. J. Wooster. MBE.
1965-6	William Woof.
1966-7	Robert D. Best.
1967-8	G. R. Maundrell.
1968-9	R. T. Rose.
1969-70	Capt. Sir John Armytage. Bt.
1970-1	Capt. G. G. Rutherford
1971-2	R. M. Kimber.
1972-3	Lt Col. H. L. Dewhurst.
1973-4	J. Hill.
1974-5	E. K. Robarts.
1975-6	J. D. Spalton.
1976-7	R. G. Osborne.
1977-8	R. G. Osborne.
1978-9	L. V. B. Thomas.

1979-80	L. V. B. Thomas.
1980-1	H. W. S. Teverson.
1981-2	H. W. S Teverson.
1982-3	Col S.J Watson. MBE .
1983-4	Col S. J. Watson. MBE.
1993-4	T. H.. Lancaster
1984-5	B .W. Howe.
1985-6	J. D. Spalton .
1986-7	J. D. Spalton.
1987-8	Mrs E. R. Wheatley -Hubbard. OBE .
1988-9	Mrs E. R. Wheatley - Hubbard. OBE.
1989-90	H. D. Spencer.
1990-1	H. D. Spencer.
1991-2	J. C. Hayward.
1992-3	J. C. Hayward.
1994-5	T. H. Lancaster.
1995-6	G. A. Madeley.
1996-7	G. A. Madeley.
1997-8	R. G. Whittle.
1998-9	R. G. Whittle.
1999-00	Dr A. A. Mescal.
2001-02	Dr A. A. Mescal.

PAST SECRETARIES

1874-1888	H. J. Hine.
1888-1920	E.J. Powell.
1921-1936	V. H. Seymour.
1936- 1949	Leonard Bull.
1950- 1960	Arthur Furneaux.
1961 -1977	Arthur Greenhaugh.
1978- 1979	K. V. Cousins.
1979 -1999	J.H. Wood-Roberts.
1999-2000	M.J. Taggart.
2000-	F. Milnes

BEEF SOCIETY PRESIDENTS FROM 1960

1960	Capt G C Rutherford
1961	Alex Anderson
1962-3	Lt Col H L Dewhurst
1964	Donald P MacGillivray
1965	W. L. Anderson
1966	Major P. H .Henderson D F C
1967	P. H. Dickson
1968	R. H. Watherston
1969	Capt G. C. Rutherford
1970-71	Wm Anderson

1972-73	James Biggar
1974-76	R. Henderson
1977-80	Capt. G C Rutherford
1981-82	Wm McGowan
1983-84	J. H. Dewhurst
1985	Wm Anderson
1986-88	Major J. P. O .Gibb
1989-91	J. Campbell Graham
1992-93	Mrs E. Lang
1994-95	D. Biggar
1996-97	C. Coombs
1998-2000	R. Howard
2001-02	J. Playfair Hannay

BEEF SHORTHORN SOCIETY SECRETARIES

1959	D. G. Noble
1960 (Act)	Miss M. .P Ramsey
1961-63	J. M. Jardine
1964-67	Miss M. P. Ramsey
1968-83	T. M. O. Lang
1984-91	Mrs B. McDonald
1992-99	J. H. Wood-Roberts
1999-2000	M. J. Taggart
2000-	F. Milnes

NB. In 1959 The Scottish Shorthorn Breeders Association changed to The Beef Shorthorn Society but remained within the frame work of the parent Society and after 1978 they obtained independence but maintained a close association. However they retained the same Secretary and administration from 1991 on.

Appendix V
LIST OF BOOKSWHICH COVERTHE YEARS OFTHE SHORTHORN

A SELECTION
The History of Shorthorn Cattle. by James Sinclair. Covers the origins to 1900 in great detail.
Thomas Bates And The Kirklevington Shorthorns. By J. Cadwallader Bates.
*Shorthorns Of Scotland.*By T B Marson.
Sittyton Letters. By T.T Marson. Letters of Cruikshank1873-1891 (Limited edition)
Scotch Shorthorns. By T.T Marson. A study of all the beef herds in 1945-46
Thornton's Circulars. Commencing 1866. An annual record of Shorthorn sales shows and events in great detail and became *The Shorthorn Record.* in 1919.

Sirloin and Saddle. and *Field And Fern.* By the Druid(H.Dixon)
History Of Improved Shorthorns. By Thomas Bell.
The History Of Killerby,Studley And Warlaby. By William Carr.
Red White And Roan. By Alvin Saunders About American Shorthorns.
Leading Tribes. By Holt Beaver
Shorthorn Herds In England. 1880 By R.W. Ashburner.
Shorthorn Experiences . By R.W. Ashburner.
History Of Dairy Shorthorns. By George T. Burrows. Shorthorns in the UK
around 1950 and before.(Vinton & Co, London, 1907)
The History Of Aberdeenshire Shorthorns. By Isobella Bruce. A detailed study
in 1923 of the early Aberdeen beef type of Shorthorn and its blood lines.
Shorthorn Record, Took over from *The Thornton Circular* in 1919.

MORE RECENT PUBLICATIONS
Shorthorn Breeders Guide. Later became *Shorthorn Breeders Review.*
Dairy Shorthorn Journal. 1932 on.
Beef Shorthorn Record.
Shorthorn *Journal.*

MEMORABILIA AND DOCUMENTS
Beamish Museum, Durham.
Museum of Rural Life, Reading University.

INDEX

with prefix where appropriate in *italics* and pictures in **bold**